DREAMLAND

GRADED MATHEMATICS

PART - 7

TIRTH RAAJ BHANOT
Hons. (Maths), MA (English), B. Ed.
Formerly Sr. Teacher
Air Force Central School,
Subroto Park, New Delhi

SUSHMA NAYAR
M.Sc. I (D.U.), B. Ed.
H.O.D Mathematics
Delhi Public School,
Mathura Road, New Delhi-3

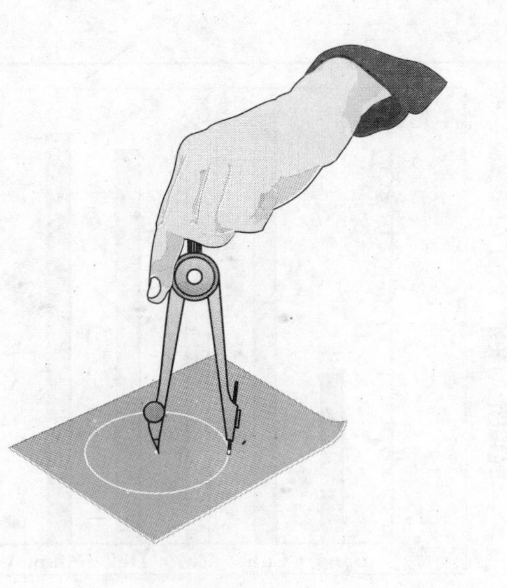

Published by

DREAMLAND PUBLICATIONS
J-128, KIRTI NAGAR, NEW DELHI - 110 015, (INDIA).
Tel : 011-2510 6050, Fax : 011-2543 8283
E-mail: dreamland@vsnl.com
www.dreamlandpublications.com

First published in 2014 by

DREAMLAND PUBLICATIONS

J-128, Kirti Nagar, New Delhi - 110 015 (India)

Fax : 011-2543 8283, Tel : 011-2510 6050

ISBN 978-93-5089-256-5

Printed at :

Shalini Offset Press Pvt. Ltd.

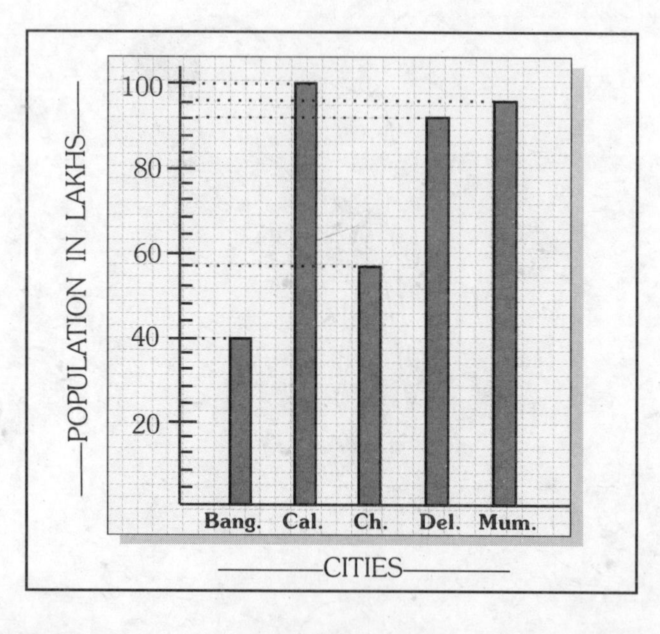

PREFACE

The present series—**GRADED MATHEMATICS**—has been brought out to meet the needs of the students of Middle Classes in the subject of mathematics. Till recently, this subject was considered to be a bug-bear by students only because of the stereo-typed methods of its teaching. But our treatment of the subject is altogether different and so the present series is certainly a series *with a difference.*

The series has been brought out in conformity with the latest syllabus issued in 2002. It encourages the student to develop a mathematical, *i.e.* logical thinking which is so useful in day-to-day life. Liberal use of *diagrams* as well as *illustrations* and the choice of *sums from day-to-day life* are some salient features of the book.

The present volume is meant for class VII. Topics in this book have been given an easy-to-difficult order while exercises contain numerous sums with a view to giving ample practice and generating self-confidence in the pupils. Two chief features of the book are a **miscellaneous exercise** at the end of each unit followed by a list of **memorable facts** studied in the unit.

We feel highly delighted to place the series in the hands of the teachers and the pupils hoping positively that it will admirably meet their approval from every angle. Still improvement has its scope in every human effort. So, constructive suggestions for the betterment of the series are highly welcome.

—T. RAAJ BHANOT

LATEST SYLLABUS 2002

CLASS-VII

(Periods 180)

UNIT-I NUMBER SYSTEM *(Periods 40)*

Rational Numbers

Recall of fractions. Definition of a retional number (Need for rational numbers may be explained through suitable illustrations). Representation of rational numbers such as $\frac{1}{4}, -\frac{1}{4}, \frac{1}{2} - \frac{1}{2}, \frac{2}{1}, -\frac{2}{1}$ etc. on the number line. Equality and order relations in rational numbers ('Order Realtion' may be explained by converting rational numbers into fractions with the same denominator). Absolute value of a rational number (Without using x, y, etc.).

Operations on Rational Numbers

Addition and subtraction of rational numbers. Multiplication of rational numbers. Properties of the above operations (*Addition* and *Subtraction* should be first explained with rational numbers with common denominator. Names of the properties may not be mentioned). Reciprocal of a non-zero rational number. Division by a (non-zero) rational number as multiplication by the reciprocal of the divisor. Existence of a rational number between any two rational numbers (Students may be made to understand that between any two rational numbers, we may obtain as many rational numbers as we like).

Decimal Representation of Rational Numbers

Termination and non-termination repeating decimals (conversion of non-terminating repeating decimals to the form $\frac{p}{q}$ should be excluded). Computations with rational numbers in the form of terminating decimals (simple cases only. Decimal numbers should not be of more than 3 decimal places for the purpose of computation).

Exponents

Laws of Exponents. Extension to positive integral powers of rational numbers. Meaning of a negative exponent and zero exponent. Use of exponential notation in expressing large numbers and small numbers.

UNIT-II COMMERCIAL MATHEMATICS *(Periods 25)*

Direct and Inverse Variations

Direct and Inverse variations and their applications to problems on *Time and Work*, *Time and Distance* (only simple and direct problems should be included).

Application of Percentage

Some more problems on *Percentage*, *Profit and Loss* (C.P. may include overhead charges. Profit and Loss questions should not include more than two transactions). *Simple Interest* formula and its application.

Finding S.I., P, T, R and A (Notations are Standard). (S.I.=Simple Interest, P=Principal, T=Time in years, R%=Rate and A=Amount).

UNIT-III ALGEBRA *(Periods 40)*

Multiplication of Algebraic Expressions

Multiplication of : *a monomial by a monomial, a binomial by a monomial, a binomial by a binomial, a trinomial by a binomial* (*exponents* of the variables should be only natural numbers).

Standard Identities

$(a+b)^2 = a^2+2ab+b^2$

$(a-b)^2 = a^2-2ab+b^2$

$(a+b)(a-b) = a^2-b^2$ and their applications (All the three identities may also be verified by cardboard models).

Factorisation of Algebraic Expressions

(i) By *taking out a common factor* in two or three or more terms. *(ii)* By *taking out a common factor* from a *group of terms* (grouping method). (The degree not to exceed 4 or 5). *(iii)* By *using the above three standard identities.*

Equations in one Variable

Solving a *linear equation* in one variable (solution can be *integral* or *rational*).

Word problems based on linear equations (Simple problems only).

UNIT-IV GEOMETRY *(Periods 50)*

More About Triangles

(a) Construction of a **triangle**, given *(i)* its *three sides* *(ii)* its *two sides and the included angle.* *(iii)* its *two angles and the included side.* *(b)* Construction of a *right triangle* given its *hypotenuse* and *a side*. Verification of the following properties : 1. Angles *opposite equal sides* of a triangle are equal. 2. Sides *opposite equal angles* of a triangle are equal. *Pythagoras theorem* and its converse (This should be verified experimentally by taking sides of the triangles such as 3, 4, 5; 5, 12, 13 etc). *altitudes, medians, perpendicular bisectors* of the *sides* and *angle bisectors* of a triangle (concepts identification only). *Orthocentre, centroid, circumcentre* and *incentre* of a triangle (concepts identification only).

Congruent Triangles

Concepts of **congruent figures**. Recall of constructions of triangles with different given conditions. Construction of two triangles with the same measurements and verifying the following : *(i)* SSS Congruence Rule. (ii) SAS Congruence Rule. (iii) ASA Congruence Rule. (iv) RHS Congruence Rule (All the Congruency Rules (conditions) should be verified *using tracing paper* and *superposition*. Simple problems based on these congruence rules involving one or two logical steps).

Quadrilaterals

Vertices, sides, angles, diagonals, adjacent sides and *opposite sides* of a quadrilateral (Only convex quadrilaterals are to be discussed). *Interior* and *exterior* of a quadrilateral; *quadrilateral region*. Verification of the following property : The sum of *the angles of a quadrilateral is 360°*.

Circle

Segment of a circle, *Semicircular region, Angle in a semicircle, Angles in the same segment*. Verification of the following properties :

1. Angles in the same segment are equal.
2. Angle in a semicircle is a right angle (Simple problems based on these properties involving one or two logical steps).

UNIT-V MENSURATION *(Periods 15)*

Area

Area of *rectangular paths*.

Volume and Surface Area

Faces, edges and *vertices* of a **cuboid** and **cube**. *Surface area* of a **cuboid** and a *cube*. Idea of *unit of volume*. *Volumes* of a **cuboid** and of a **cube** (simple problems from daily-life).

UNIT-VI STATISTICS *(Periods 10)*

Bar Graph

Reading and *interpretation* of a given *bar graph* (Simple cases only. display bar charts from newspapers, magazines, etc.) For a given data, drawing of bar graphs on graph sheets (Only one bar to be included at a time).

CONTENTS

REVISION OF WHAT WE HAVE LEARNT

A. Answer :

1. Which is the lowest counting number ? ....
2. Which is the lowest whole number ? ....
3. Which is the largest natural number ? ....
4. Is 0 a natural number or whole number ? ....
5. Which is the smallest 4-digit number ? ....
6. Which is the consecutive predecessor of 0 ? ....
7. Which is the consecutive successor of 0 ? ....
8. How many thousands make a million ? ....
9. What is the place value of zero ? ....
10. How many factors has a prime number got ? ....
11. Is 1 a composite or prime number ? ....
12. Which number is the only even prime number ? ....
13. Which is the common factor between two co-primes ? ....
14. What is the L.C.M. of two co-primes ? ....
15. What is the H.C.F. of two co-primes ? ....
16. p is a factor of q. What is the H.C.F. of p and q ? ....
17. p is a factor of q. What is the L.C.M. of p and q ? ....
18. Which is the greater –7 or –17 ? ....
19. Which is solved earlier : a *vinculum* or *simple brackets* ? ....
20. What is the second term of a ratio called ? ....

B. Explain the difference between :

21. (a) *a number* and *a numeral* (b) *face value* and *place value*
22. (a) *a minuend* and *a subtrahend* (b) *a multiplicand* and *a multiplier*
23. (a) *a multiple* and *a factor* (b) *prime* and *composite numbers*
24. (a) *H.C.F* and *L.C.M.* (b) *co-primes* and *twin-primes*
    (c) *a consecutive predecessor* and *a consecutive successor*

25. (*a*) *a positive integer* and *a negative integer*
(*b*) *a quotient, a dividend* and *a divisor*
(*c*) *a ratio* and *a proportion* (*d*) *extremes* and *means*

26. (*a*) *fourth proportional, third proportional* and *mean proportional*
(*b*) *direct variation* and *indirect variation*

27. (*a*) *numerator* and *denominator* (*b*) *a term* and *an expression*

28. (*a*) *principal, interest* and *amount* (*b*) *a line* and *a line-segment*

29. (*a*) *interior* of a triangle and *exterior of a triangle*
(*b*) *supplementary* and *complementary angles*

30. (*a*) *area* and *perimeter* (*b*) *a parallelogram* and *a rectangle*

C. 31. What is the face value and the place value of the digit 7 in the numeral 581732. Find their difference also.

32. Write the smallest number of six digits having 3 different digits.

33. How many three-digit numerals are there in all ?

34. Write the numeral 943720695 as a number-name in the *Indian* as well as in the *international* notation.

35. Find the sum of 103, 217, 186 and 276 orally

36. Replace each * by the correct digit :

(*a*)
```
  9 2 6
- * 9 *
-------
  3 * 9
```

(*b*)
```
  6 4 7
+ * 8 *
-------
  9 * 6
```

(*c*)
```
        9 8 3 7
      ×   3 * 8
      ---------
      * 8 6 * 6
  2 9 * 1 1
  -------------
  * * * 9 7 * 6
```

(*d*)
```
715 ) 1 5 3 7 2 5 ( **5
      1 4 * 0
      -------
        1 * 7 *
          7 1 5
        -------
        3 5 7 5
        3 5 7 5
        -------
              0
```

37. The ratio of gold and copper in a ring is 24 : 1. If the ring weighs 5·5 grams, how much copper has been mixed in its gold ?

38. A quantity x was added to both the terms of a ratio 8 : 5. As a result, a new ratio 7 : 5 was obtained. Find the value of x.

39. The *first, third* and *fourth* terms of a proportion are 6, 10 and 25 respectively. Find its *second* term.

40. Find the mean proportional between 16 and 25.

41. 35 men can do a job in 6 days. In how many days will 15 men do it ?

42. A shopkeeper announced a discount of 25% on the prices of all his wares. Find the discounted price of a bicycle whose previous price was Rs. 2240.

43. Sandeep bought a stereo for Rs. 5548. As some defect developed in it, he had to spend Rs. 152 on its repairs. Sandeep sold it for Rs. 5510. What was his loss % ?

44. Eggs were bought at Rs. 9·60 per dozen and sold at Rs. 85 per hundred. Find the gain or loss %.

45. A person sells 10 oranges at the same price as he had bought 11 oranges. Find his gain per cent.

46. A man puts Rs. 610 in a bank that pays interest at the rate of 5% per annum He takes his interest when it becomes Rs. 20. After how many days does he take the interest if the year is leap ?

D. 47. Find the sum of $4x^2 - 5xy + 3y^2$; $-6x^2 - 4xy + 2y^2$ and $-3x^2 - 2xy - 4y^2$

48. If $P = 3x^2 - 7x - 8$, $Q = x^2 + 8x - 3$ and $R = -5x^2 - 3x + 2$, find the value of $P - Q + R$.

49. If $a = 3$, $b = 2$, $c = 5$, find the value of $2a^3b^2 - 5b^2c - c^2$

50. Solve the equation : $5(3x + 4) - 8(6x - 7) = 9x - 8$

51. There are two numbers one of which is twice the other. If their sum is 123, find the numbers.

52. Write the names of :

(a) four *basic operations* :

....

(b) four *aggregation signs* :

....

53. The lengths of two poles differ by 20 cm. Had the longer pole been longer by 10 cm., its length would have been four times the length of the other pole. Find their lengths.

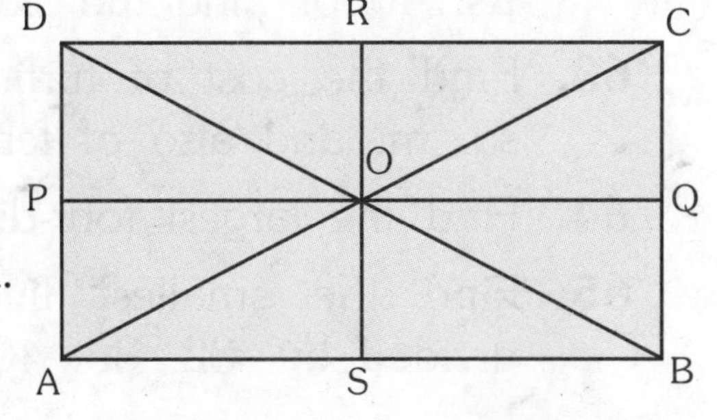

54. In the figure given in front, name—

(a) concurrent lines at O

(b) which lines pass through the points D, R.

(c) eight sets of collinear points.

55. Name the *type* of each angle :

56.

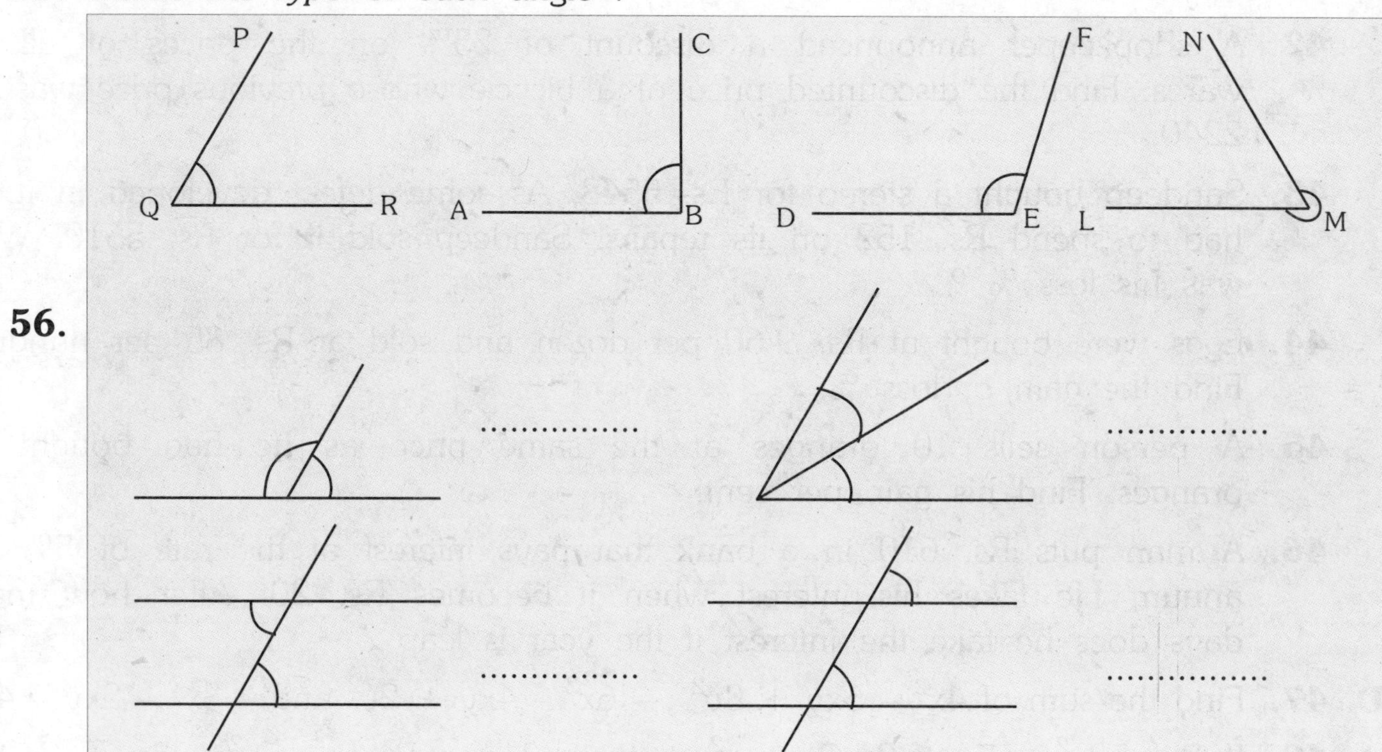

57. Name the type of each triangle in terms of angles :

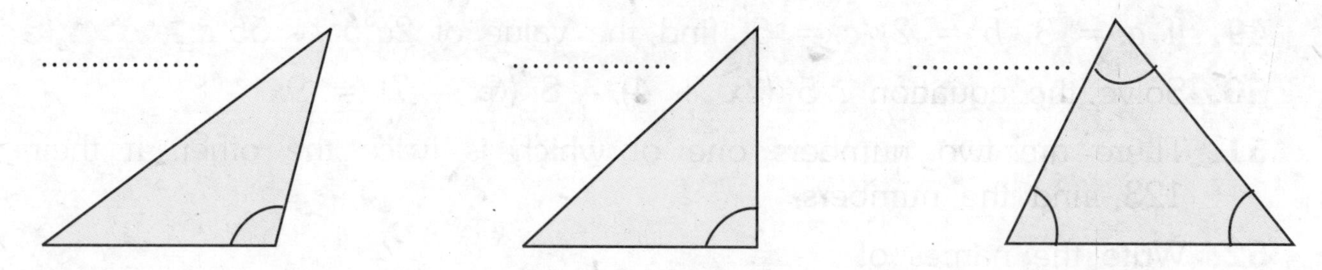

58. In a triangle ABC, $2\angle A = 3\angle B = 6\angle C$. Find the measure of each angle.

59. Draw angles of 60°, 90°, 120°, 45° using a *scale* and *compasses*.

60. Take a line-segment AB and draw its right bisector.

61. A square room has its side equal to 7 metres in length. Its floor has been tiled with square tiles of 35 cm. × 35 cm. Find the cost of tiling it if each tile cost 50 paise.

62. The cost of paving the floor of a square bed-room at Rs. 10 per sq. m is Rs. 4000. Find the side of the room.

63. Find the cost of turfing a field 30m long and 15m wide at Rs 3·00 per sq. m. and also of fencing it at Rs 1·50 per metre.

64. Find the largest four-digit number exactly divisible by 135.

65. Find the smallest five-digit number that leaves 7 as remainder when divided by 32, 36, 40, 45 and 48 respectively.

UNIT I

ARITHMETIC

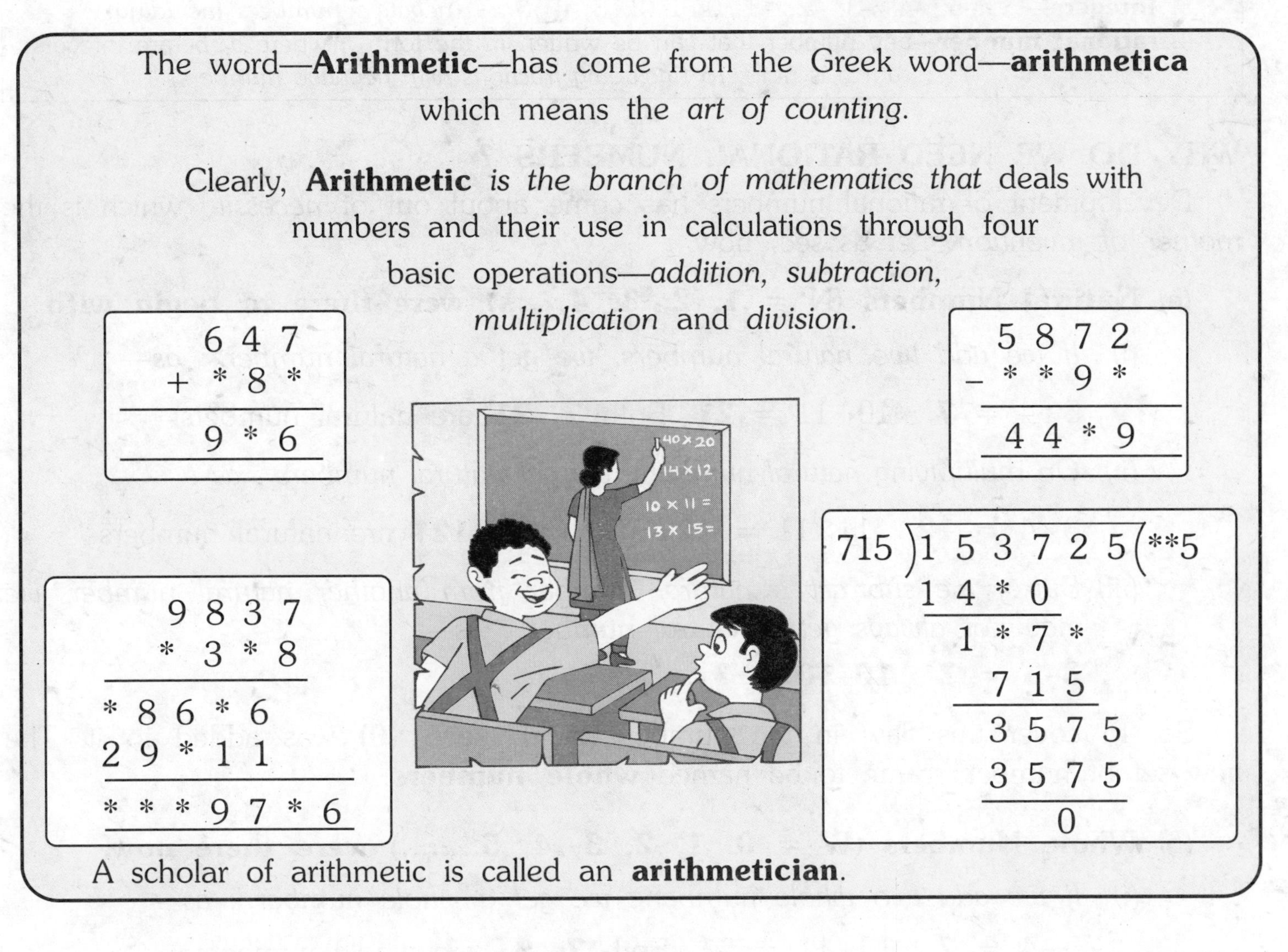

The word—**Arithmetic**—has come from the Greek word—**arithmetica** which means the *art of counting*.

Clearly, **Arithmetic** *is the branch of mathematics that* deals with numbers and their use in calculations through four basic operations—*addition, subtraction, multiplication* and *division*.

A scholar of arithmetic is called an **arithmetician**.

IN THIS UNIT—

1. Rational Numbers—I
2. Rational Numbers—II
3. Rational Numbers : Addition and Subtraction
4. Rational Numbers : Multiplication and Division
5. Rational Numbers : Absolute Value and Density
6. Rational Numbers : Decimal Form
7. Rational Numbers : Exponents

1 RATIONAL NUMBERS—I

KNOW THESE TERMS :

1. **natural numbers**—numbers 1, 2, 3, 4, 5....... *(0 excluding)*
2. **whole numbers**—numbers 0, 1, 2, 3, 4, 5.... *(0 including)*
3. **integers**—......–5, –4, –3, –2, –1, 0, 1, 2, 3, 4, 5.......*(negative numbers including)*
4. **rational number**—any number that can be written in the form $\frac{a}{b}$ where *a*, *b* are integers but *b* is not zero *(including fractions with negative numbers)*

WHY DO WE NEED RATIONAL NUMBERS ?

Development of rational numbers has come about out of *necessity* which is the *mother of invention*. Let us see, how.

(a) **Natural Numbers (N = 1, 2, 3, 4, ...) were there to begin with.**

(i) *If we add two natural numbers, we get a natural number ; as—*

3+4 = **7** ; 10+11 = **21**. Both **7, 21** are natural numbers.

(ii) *On multiplying natural numbers, we get natural numbers ; as—*

3×4 = **12** ; 11×11 = **121**. Both **12, 121** are natural numbers.

(iii) *But if we subtract a natural number from another natural number, we may not always get a natural number ; as—*

3–3 = ? ; 10–10 = ?

So, to cover this flaw in the number-system, **zero (0)** was added to it. The new set of numbers came to be named **whole numbers**.

(b) **Whole Numbers (W = 0, 1, 2, 3, 4, 5........) were there now.**

(i) *If we add two whole numbers, we get a whole number ; as—*

3+4 = **7** ; 10+11 = **21**. Both **7, 21** are whole numbers.

(ii) *If we multiply two whole numbers, we get a whole number ; as—*

3×4 = **12** ; 11×11 = **121**. Both **12, 121** are whole numbers.

(iii) *But when we subtract a whole number from another whole number, the result is not always a whole number ; as—*

3–7 = ? ; 10–11 = ?

So, to cover this flaw in the number-system, **negative numbers** were added to it. The new set of numbers came to be named **integers**.

(c) **Integers (I = –3, –2, –1, 0, 1, 2, 3.......) were there now.**

But even *integers* could not do all the jobs as required.

If we add two integers, we get an integer ; as—

$3+(-1) = \mathbf{2}$ which is an integer. *(addition)*

If we subtract an integer from another integer, we get an integer ; as—

$3-(-1) = 3+1 = \mathbf{4}$ which is also an integer. *(subtraction)*

If we multiply an integer by another integer, we get an integer ; as—

$3\times(-5) = \mathbf{-15}$ which is an integer too. *(multiplication)*

But when we divide an integer by another integer, we may not get an integer as quotient ; as—

$\mathbf{3 \div 2 = ?\ ;\ 9 \div 11 = ?}$

So, to cover this flaw in the number-system, **rational numbers** were invented. Rational numbers are denoted by the letter ***Q*** because they can solve the problem of finding a **quotient**.

WHAT ARE RATIONAL NUMBERS ?

A rational number is a number that can be expressed in the form $\frac{a}{b}$ where *a* **and** *b* **are both integers but** *b* **is not zero** ; as—

$\frac{5}{7}, \frac{-5}{7}, \frac{-7}{-8}, \frac{8}{-9}$ etc.

In a rational number $\frac{a}{b}$, *a* is the **numerator** and *b* is the **denominator**

IRRATIONAL NUMBERS

It is quite clear that inexact divisions led to the invention of *fractions* which we call **rational numbers**. So, we can define an irrational number as under :

An *irrational number* **is a number that cannot be expressed as a fraction,** *i.e.* **in the form** $\frac{a}{b}$.

For example, *pi* (π) has its value 3·141559. This value is only approximate. The decimal places in it continue indefinitely but they do not *recur (repeat)*. So, this value cannot be expressed as a fraction. Therefore *pi* (π) is an irrational number.

Similarly $\frac{3}{0}$ cannot be a rational number as it cannot be defined in any manner.

+VE and –VE RATIONAL NUMBERS

(a) **A rational number is said to be** *positive* **if its** *numerator* **and** *denominator* **have** *similar signs* **before them** ; as—

$\frac{5}{8}, \frac{17}{19}, \frac{36}{47}$ are positive rational numbers as the numerator and the denominator of each of them have the sign + **(plus)** before them.

$\frac{-5}{-8}, \frac{-17}{-19}, \frac{-36}{-47}$ are also positive numbers as the numerator and the denominator of each of them have the sign – **(minus)** before them.

(b) **A rational number is said to be** *negative* **if its** *numerator* **and** *denominator* ***have different signs*** **before them** ; as—

$\frac{-5}{8}, \frac{17}{-19}, \frac{-36}{47}$ are negative rational numbers as the numerator and the denominator of each of them have different signs before them.

SOME PROPERTIES OF RATIONAL NUMBERS

PROPERTY 1

We know that $\frac{-3}{-5}$ is a positive rational number, because

$$\frac{-3}{-5} = \frac{(-3) \times (-1)}{(-5) \times (-1)} = \mathbf{\frac{3}{5}}$$

So if $\frac{a}{b}$ be a rational number and both a and b are negative integers, then $\frac{-a}{-b} = \frac{a}{b}$

PROPERTY 2

We know that $\frac{3}{-5}$ and $\frac{-3}{5}$ are both rational numbers.

But $\frac{3}{-5} = \frac{3 \times (-1)}{(-5) \times (-1)} = \mathbf{\frac{-3}{5}}$

So, if $\frac{a}{b}$ be a negative rational number with its b negative, we can write it in the form such that b is positive, *i.e.* $\frac{a}{-b} = \frac{-a}{b}$

PROPERTY 3

We know that $\frac{3}{5}$ is a rational number and—

$$\frac{3 \times 2}{5 \times 2} = \mathbf{\frac{6}{10}} = \frac{6 \times 5}{10 \times 5} = \mathbf{\frac{30}{50}} = \frac{30 \times 3}{50 \times 3} = \mathbf{\frac{90}{150}}$$

Clearly, the rational numbers $\frac{3}{5}, \frac{6}{10}, \frac{30}{50}$ and $\frac{90}{150}$ are equal.

So, if $\frac{a}{b}$ be a rational number and m be an integer other than zero, then $\frac{a}{b} = \frac{a \times m}{b \times m}$

PROPERTY 4

We know that $\frac{90}{100}$ is a rational number but its *numerator* and *denominator* are both divisible by 10.

So, $\frac{90}{100} = \frac{90 \div 10}{100 \div 10} = \mathbf{\frac{9}{10}}$

So, if the numerator and the denominator of a rational number are divided by a common divisor, the value of the rational number does not change, *i.e.* $\frac{a}{b} = \frac{a \div m}{b \div m}$

RATIONAL NUMBER 0

As 0 is an integer, so it is a rational number too.

We can write it as $\frac{0}{1}$ or $\frac{0}{-1}$ as a rational number.

But we can write it $\frac{0}{2}$, $\frac{0}{-2}$, $\frac{0}{3}$, $\frac{0}{-3}$ ...... also.

The reason is that **0 divided by any divisor is equal to 0.**

So, $\frac{0}{1} = \frac{0}{-1} = \frac{0}{2} = \frac{0}{-2} = \frac{0}{3} = \frac{0}{-3} =$ ...... In other words, all these rational numbers represent the same rational number 0.

REMEMBER :

1. 0 is not a natural number. *1 is the lowest natural number.*
2. *0 is the lowest whole number.*
3. 0 was added before 1 to natural numbers so that a numeral may be subtracted from itself. Thus we got the set of *whole numbers.*
4. *Negative numbers* were added before 0 to the set of whole numbers so that larger numerals may be subtracted from smaller ones. Thus we got the set of *integers.*
5. *Rational numbers* were added to the number-system of integers so that each integer may be divided by any other integer except zero.
6. The word—**rational**—means *based on reasoning.*
7. A *rational number* is a number that can be expressed in the form $\frac{a}{b}$ where both *a, b* are integers but *b* is not zero.
8. A rational number is said to be *positive* if its numerator and denominator both have *similar signs* before them.
9. A rational number is said to be *negative* if its numerator and denominator both have *different signs* before them.
10. *(a)* $\frac{-a}{-b} = \frac{a}{b}$ *(b)* $\frac{a}{-b} = \frac{-a}{b}$ *(c)* $\frac{a}{b} = \frac{a \times m}{b \times m}$ *(d)* $\frac{a}{b} = \frac{a \div m}{b \div m}$
11. *(a)* Any integer can be expressed as a rational number by writing it as the numerator and putting 1 as its denominator.

    (b) But to express the integer 0 as a rational number, we write it as the numerator and any other integer as its denominator. The reason is that 0 divided by any integer is equal to 0. But it is not true in the case of any other integer.

Let us solve some examples :

Example 1 : Write down the *numerator* **of each of the following rational numbers :**

(a) $\frac{12}{9}$ (b) $\frac{9}{11}$ (c) $\frac{-6}{7}$ (d) $\frac{17}{-19}$

Solution : Numerators are as under :

(a) 12 (b) 9 (c) –6 (d) 17

Example 2 : Write down the *denominator* **of each of the following rational numbers :**

(a) $\frac{-7}{11}$ (b) $\frac{8}{-9}$ (c) $\frac{-11}{15}$ (d) $\frac{-8}{-9}$

Solution : Denominators are as under :

(a) 11 (b) –9 (c) 15 (d) –9

Example 3 : Write down a rational number with its numerator = –3 × (–2) and denominator = 2 – 9.

Solution : Reqd. Numerator $= -3 \times (-2) = \mathbf{6}$

Reqd. Denominator $= 2 - 9 = \mathbf{-7}$

∴ Reqd. Rational No. $= \frac{6}{-7}$ *Ans.*

Example 4 : Write down the following rational numbers as integers :

(a) $\frac{8}{1}$ (b) $\frac{0}{3}$ (c) $\frac{-9}{1}$ (d) $\frac{0}{1}$

Solution : (a) $\frac{8}{1} = \mathbf{8}$ (b) $\frac{0}{3} = \mathbf{0}$ (c) $\frac{-9}{1} = \mathbf{-9}$ (d) $\frac{0}{1} = \mathbf{0}$

Example 5 : Write down the following integers as rational numbers :

(a) **0** (b) **–11** (c) **23** (d) **–19**

Solution : (a) $0 = \frac{0}{1}$ (b) $-11 = \frac{-11}{1}$ (c) $23 = \frac{23}{1}$ (d) $-19 = \frac{19}{1}$

Example 6 : Here is a rational number $\frac{-7}{8}$. Express it with—

(a) **numerator 14** (b) **denominator –24**

Solution : (a) Given Rational Number $= \frac{-7}{8}$

Required numerator $= 14$

Clearly, we can get 14 from –7, if we multiply it by –2

∴ $\frac{-7}{8} = \frac{-7 \times (-2)}{8 \times (-2)} = \frac{\mathbf{14}}{\mathbf{-16}}$ *Ans.* $\left[\frac{a}{b} = \frac{a \times m}{b \times m}\right]$

(b) Given Rational Number = $\frac{-7}{8}$

Required denominator = -24

Clearly, we can get -24 from 8, if we multiply it by -3

$\therefore \frac{-7}{8} = \frac{(-7)\times(-3)}{8\times(-3)} = \frac{\mathbf{21}}{\mathbf{-24}}$ *Ans.* $\left[\frac{a}{b} = \frac{a \times m}{b \times m}\right]$

Example 7 : Express : (a) $\frac{7}{-6}$ **with denominator 6**

(b) $\frac{-8}{-9}$ **with denominator 9**

Solution : (a) Given Rational Number = $\frac{7}{-6}$

To get 6 from -6, we shall multiply it by -1

$\therefore \frac{7}{-6} = \frac{7\times(-1)}{(-6)\times(-1)} = \frac{\mathbf{-7}}{\mathbf{6}}$ *Ans.* $\left[\frac{a}{b} = \frac{a \times m}{b \times m}\right]$

(b) Given Rational Number = $\frac{-8}{-9}$

To get 9 from -9, we shall multiply them by -1

$\therefore \frac{-8}{-9} = \frac{(-8)\times(-1)}{(-9)\times(-1)} = \frac{\mathbf{8}}{\mathbf{9}}$ *Ans.* $\left[\frac{a}{b} = \frac{a \times m}{b \times m}\right]$

Example 8 : Express in standard form :

(a) $\frac{-9}{36}$ (b) $\frac{-7}{-35}$

Solution : (a) Given Rational Number = $\frac{-9}{36}$

The denominator is already positive,

The numerator and the denominator have 9 as their highest common divisor

$\therefore \frac{-9}{36} = \frac{(-9)\div 9}{36\div 9} = \frac{-1}{4}$ $\left[\frac{a}{b} = \frac{a \div m}{b \div m}\right]$

$\therefore$ Standard form of $\frac{-9}{36} = \frac{\mathbf{-1}}{\mathbf{4}}$ *Ans.*

(b) Given Rational Number = $\frac{-7}{-35}$

The denominator and the numerator have similar signs.

$\therefore \frac{-7}{-35} = \frac{7}{35}$ $\left[\frac{-a}{-b} = \frac{a}{b}\right]$

Now, the numerator 7 and denominator 35 have 7 as their highest common divisor

$\therefore \frac{7}{35} = \frac{7\div 7}{35\div 7} = \frac{\mathbf{1}}{\mathbf{5}}$ *Ans.* $\left[\frac{a}{b} = \frac{a \div m}{b \div m}\right]$

PRACTICE EXERCISES 1

A. Answer :

1. What does the word—*rational*—mean ? ....
2. In which basic operation did natural numbers fail ? ....
3. Which number was added to natural numbers ? ....
4. Which number-system followed the natural numbers ? ....
5. In which basic operation did whole numbers fail ? ....
6. Which number-system followed whole numbers ? ....
7. In which basic operation did integers fail ? ....
8. Which number-system followed the integers ? ....
9. Which is a rational number $\frac{0}{1}$ or $\frac{1}{0}$? ....
10. Is $-1\frac{2}{3}$ a rational number ? Is it correct to write it as $-1 + \frac{2}{3}$? ....

B. Answer *yes* or *no* :

11. Is zero a natural number ? ....
12. Is zero a whole number ? ....
13. Is every natural number a whole number also ? ....
14. Is every whole number a natural number also ? ....
15. Is every natural number an integer also ? ....
16. Is every integer a natural number too ? ....
17. Is every whole number an integer as well ? ....
18. Is every integer a whole number as well ? ....
19. Is every integer a rational number too ? ....
20. Is every rational number an integer also ? ....
21. Is it correct to write 0 in its rational form as $\frac{0}{2}$? ....
22. Is it correct to write 5 in its rational form as $\frac{5}{2}$? If not, why ? .... Write its correct form also.

C. Write—

23. all the natural numbers between 0 and 3 : ....

24. all the whole numbers between 0 and 4 : ....

25. all the integers between –3 and 3 : ....

26. the integer which is neither +ve nor –ve : ....

27. the integer 3 in its rational form : ....

D. Sort out :

28. the denominators of the following rational numbers :

(a) $\frac{12}{-15}$ (b) $\frac{-3}{7}$ (c) $\frac{-1}{5}$ (d) $\frac{-2}{-9}$ (e) $\frac{3}{-8}$

29. the numerators of the following rational numbers :

(a) $\frac{5}{-6}$ (b) $\frac{7}{-8}$ (c) 5 (d) $\frac{-2}{-5}$ (e) $\frac{1}{3}$

30. the *positive* rational numbers :

(a) $\frac{3}{7}$ (b) $\frac{-11}{13}$ (c) $\frac{-8}{-7}$ (d) $\frac{0}{-3}$ (e) $\frac{-10}{-11}$

E. Express :

31. the rational number $\frac{5}{-6}$ with—

(a) numerator 15 (b) denominator 18 (c) numerator –25

32. the rational number $\frac{-11}{-13}$ with denominator 13.

33. each of the following rational numbers with a *positive denominator* :

(a) $\frac{7}{-9}$ (b) $\frac{-9}{-17}$ (c) $\frac{-4}{-9}$ (d) $\frac{6}{-1}$

34. in standard form :

(a) $\frac{-14}{-35}$ (b) $\frac{-36}{-60}$ (c) $\frac{51}{-34}$ (d) $\frac{-4}{6}$

F. Do as directed :

35. Fill up the blank to complete each equation :

(a) $\frac{-4}{7} = \frac{\ldots\ldots}{49}$ (b) $\frac{5}{-9} = \frac{-5}{\ldots\ldots} = \frac{25}{\ldots\ldots}$

(c) $\frac{-9}{-11} = \frac{\ldots\ldots}{44}$ (d) $\frac{-4}{\ldots\ldots} = \frac{8}{14} = \frac{\ldots\ldots}{-56}$

36. Solve :

(a) 14 + (–3) – (–4) (b) 18 + (–3) ÷ (–5)

(c) –5(–6) × 4 ÷ 6 (d) 19 (–7) ÷ (–8) + 3

G. Write True *(T)* or False *(F)* against each statement :

37. All natural numbers are rational numbers. ....

38. All whole numbers are rational numbers. ....

39. All integers are rational numbers. ....

40. All fractions with denominators other than 0 are rational numbers. ....

41. $\cdot\bar{3}$ is a recurring decimal and it is a rational number. ....

42. *pi* (π) is a rational number ....

43. A rational number has the form of a fraction. ....

44. The numerator of a rational number may be +ve or –ve. ....

45. The denominator of a rational number must be +ve only. ....

46. The denominator of a rational number may be zero. ....

47. The standard rational form of the rational number –5 is $\frac{-5}{-1}$ ....

48. The standard rational form of the rational fraction $\frac{-a}{-b}$ is $\frac{a}{b}$ ....

H. Define :

49. *(a)* a rational number :

....

....

(b) an irrational number :

....

....

50. *(a)* What is meant by *Arithmetic* ?

....

....

(b) What is the word for a *scholar* of *arithmetic* ?

....

2 RATIONAL NUMBERS—II

KNOW THESE TERMS :

1. **negative rational number**—rational number whose numerator and denominator have unlike signs before them
2. **positive rational number**—rational number whose numerator and denominator have like signs before them.
3. **mixed rational number**—a number made up of an integer and a rational number.

RATIONAL NUMBERS ON A LINE

We know how to represent integers on a line. For it, we draw a line and mark a point O on it. It stands for 0 which is neither +ve nor –ve. All *positive integers* (1, 2, 3, 4, 5.....) are represented on the line **to the right of 0**. All *negative integers* (–1, –2, –3, –4, –5......) are represented on the line **to the left of 0**. The entire process has been shown in the diagram given below.

(Negative integers) *(Positive integers)*

E´ D´ C´ B´ A´ **O** A B C D E

–5 –4 –3 –2 –1 **0** 1 2 3 4 5

Respective positive and negative numbers are opposites of each other. In fact, we can consider the point O as a mirror which shows the images of points A, B, C, D, E inside it. Point A´ is as behind the mirror as is A in front of it. Each point is represented by an integer. Points A, B, C, D, E are marked with positive integers, 1, 2, 3, 4, 5. The reflections of these points (A´, B´, C´, D´, E´) are marked with negative integers –1, –2, –3, –4, –5. In the same manner —

We can represent rational numbers on a line. A line is drawn and a point O is marked on it. This point stands for **zero**. The *positive rational numbers* are represented on the line **to the right of 0**. The *negative rational numbers* are represented on the line to **the left of 0**. But in the case of rational numbers, we have got to represent their fractions as well.

E´ D´ C´ B´ A´ Q **O** P A B C D E

–5, –4, –3, –2, –1 **⁻½ 0 ½** 1 2 3 4 5

Observe the diagram given above. OA is positive where A stands for the rational number 1. Now, if we want to mark the rational number $\frac{1}{2}$ on the line, we shall plot a point P just at the middle point of OA. Then OP = PA = number $\frac{1}{2}$. Similarly if we are to represent the rational number $\frac{-1}{2}$ on the line, we shall mark a point Q just at the middle point of OA´. Then OQ = QA´ = $\frac{-1}{2}$.

Now let us take some other examples. Suppose we want to represent the rational numbers $\left(\frac{3}{4}, \frac{-3}{4}\right)$ and $\left(\frac{5}{3}, \frac{-5}{3}\right)$ on a line. We will proceed as under :

To represent the rational number $\frac{3}{4}$, we shall draw a line and take a point O on it. Let this point stand for 0. As done earlier, mark the units OA and OA´ to the right and the left of O respectively. Now divide OA and OA´ each into four equal parts.

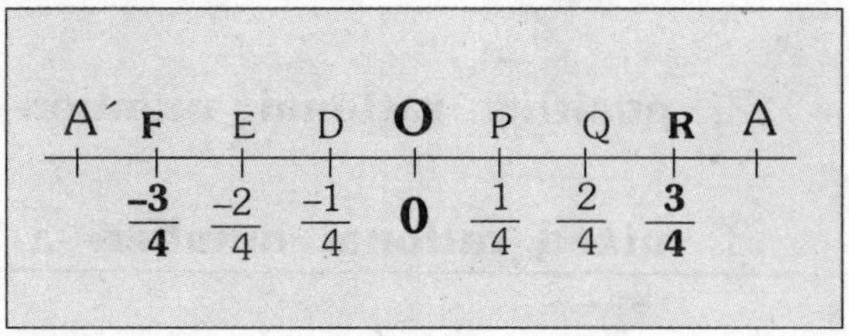

A´ F E D O P Q R A

$\frac{-3}{4}$ $\frac{-2}{4}$ $\frac{-1}{4}$ 0 $\frac{1}{4}$ $\frac{2}{4}$ $\frac{3}{4}$

Clearly, OP $= \frac{1}{4}$, OQ $= \frac{2}{4}$ and OR $= \frac{3}{4}$

And OD $= \frac{-1}{4}$, OE $= \frac{-2}{4}$ and OF $= \frac{-3}{4}$

As for the rational numbers $\frac{5}{3}$, $\frac{-5}{3}$, they are equal to $1\frac{2}{3}$ and $-(1\frac{2}{3})$

So, we shall take two units OA, AB to the right of O and units OA´, A´B´ to the left of O.

B´ T S A´ O A L M B

$\frac{-2}{3}$ $\frac{-1}{3}$ + -1 0 1 + $\frac{1}{3}$ $\frac{2}{3}$

As $\frac{5}{3} = 1\frac{2}{3}$, we shall let OA, OA´ represent the numerals 1, –1 respectively. Then we shall divide AB and A´B´ each in three equal parts. For $\frac{2}{3}$ and $\frac{-2}{3}$, we shall take the first two parts out of these three parts..

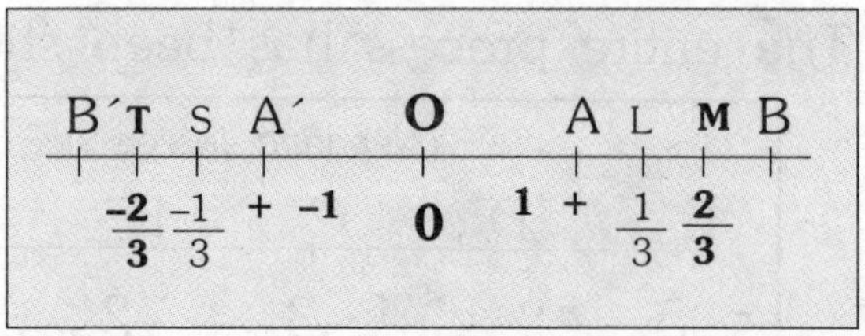

So, **OM** will represent $1\frac{2}{3}$ or $\frac{5}{3}$ and **OT** will stand for $-\left(1\frac{2}{3}\right)$ or $\frac{-5}{3}$

COMPARISON OF RATIONAL NUMBERS

As rational numbers are virtually fractions, they can be compared just as we **compare fractions**. Also, we have to take into account whether each of the given rational numbers is **negative** or **positive**.

(a) **As for integers, we know that—**

1. Every *positive integer* is **larger than 0**.
2. Every *negative integer* is **smaller than 0**.
3. Every *positive integer* is larger than every *negative integer*.
4. The *farther a* positive integer is from 0, the *larger* it will be.
5. The *nearer a* negative integer is to 0, the *larger* it will be.

(b) **As for fractions—**

In order to compare two fractions, we—

1. reduce them to the same denominator.
2. Then observe the numerators of the fractions to be compared.
3. The fraction with the larger numerator is the larger.

(c) Rational numbers are compared taking into consideration the methods of comparing both **integers** and **fractions**.

Example 1. Compare the rational numbers $\frac{5}{-8}$ and $\frac{-7}{12}$

Solution : Given rational numbers $= \frac{5}{-8}$ and $\frac{-7}{12}$

Finding the equivalent of $\frac{5}{-8}$ so that its denominator may be positive

$$\frac{5}{-8} = \frac{5 \times (-1)}{(-8) \times (-1)} = \frac{-5}{8}$$

Now we will compare $\frac{-5}{8}$ with $\frac{-7}{12}$

L. C. M. of the denominators 8, 12 = 24

$$\frac{-5}{8} = \frac{-5 \times 3}{8 \times 3} = \mathbf{\frac{-15}{24}} \text{ and } \frac{-7}{12} = \frac{-7 \times 2}{12 \times 2} = \mathbf{\frac{-14}{24}}$$

$\because$ the numerator –14> numerator –15

$\therefore$ $\frac{-14}{24}$ or $\mathbf{\frac{-7}{12}}$ **is the greater rational number** *Ans.*

Example 2. Arrange the rational numbers $\frac{-5}{11}, \frac{1}{-2}, \frac{-6}{7}, \frac{3}{-4}$ in ascending order.

Solution : Given rational numbers $= \frac{-5}{11}, \frac{1}{-2}, \frac{-6}{7}, \frac{3}{-4}$

First of all, we shall find equivalents of $\frac{1}{-2}$ and $\frac{3}{-4}$ with positive denominators.

$$\frac{1}{-2} = \frac{1 \times (-1)}{-2 \times (-1)} = \frac{-1}{2} \text{ and } \frac{3}{-4} = \frac{3 \times (-1)}{-4 \times (-1)} = \frac{-3}{4}$$

Now we shall compare $\frac{-5}{11}, \frac{-1}{2}, \frac{-6}{7}, \frac{-3}{4}$

L.C.M. of 11, 2, 7 and 4 is 308

$$\therefore \frac{-5}{11} = \frac{-5 \times 28}{11 \times 28} = \mathbf{\frac{-140}{308}} \text{ and } \frac{-1}{2} = \frac{-1 \times 154}{2 \times 154} = \mathbf{\frac{-154}{308}}$$

$$\frac{-6}{7} = \frac{-6 \times 44}{7 \times 44} = \mathbf{\frac{-264}{308}} \text{ and } \frac{-3}{4} = \frac{-3 \times 77}{4 \times 77} = \mathbf{\frac{-231}{308}}$$

The numerators are ; –140, –154, –264, –231

In the ascending order they are ; –264, –231, –154, –140

$\therefore$ Rational numbers in the ascending order are :

$\frac{-264}{308}, \frac{-231}{308}, \frac{-154}{308}, \frac{-140}{308}$, *i.e.* $\mathbf{\frac{-6}{7}, \frac{3}{-4}, \frac{1}{-2}, \frac{-5}{11}}$ *Ans.*

Example 3. Write the rational numbers $\frac{-3}{10}, \frac{7}{-15}, \frac{-11}{20}, \frac{17}{-30}$ in the descending order.

Solution : First of all, we shall find equivalents of $\frac{7}{-15}$ and $\frac{17}{-30}$ so that they may have positive denominators.

$$\frac{7}{-15} = \frac{7 \times (-1)}{(-15) \times (-1)} = \frac{-7}{15} \text{ and } \frac{17}{-30} = \frac{17 \times (-1)}{(-30) \times (-1)} = \frac{-17}{30}$$

Now we shall compare the rational numbers $\frac{-3}{10}, \frac{-7}{15}, \frac{-11}{20}, \frac{-17}{30}$

L.C.M. of the denominators 10, 15, 20, 30 = 60

$$\therefore \frac{-3}{10} = \frac{(-3) \times 6}{10 \times 6} = \mathbf{\frac{-18}{60}} \text{ and } \frac{-7}{15} = \frac{(-7) \times 4}{15 \times 4} = \mathbf{\frac{-28}{60}}$$

$$\frac{-11}{20} = \frac{(-11) \times 3}{20 \times 3} = \mathbf{\frac{-33}{60}} \text{ and } \frac{-17}{30} = \frac{(-17) \times 2}{30 \times 2} = \mathbf{\frac{-34}{60}}$$

Numerators are –18, –33, –28, –34

In the descending order, they are –18, –28, –33, –34

$\therefore$ Rational numbers in the descending order are

$$\frac{-18}{60}, \frac{-28}{60}, \frac{-33}{60}, \frac{-34}{60}, \textit{ i.e. } \mathbf{\frac{-3}{10}, \frac{7}{-15}, \frac{-11}{20}, \frac{17}{-30}} \textit{ Ans.}$$

RATIONAL NUMBERS BETWEEN TWO GIVEN NUMBERS

We know that 0 lies between 1 and –1

Similarly $\frac{2}{5}$ lies between $\frac{1}{5}$ and $\frac{3}{5}$

Let us learn how to find rational numbers between two given numbers.

Example 4. Write any two rational numbers that lie between $\frac{-6}{11}$ and $\frac{5}{6}$.

Solution : Given rational numbers = $\frac{-6}{11}$ and $\frac{5}{6}$

L.C.M. of the denominators 11, 6 = 66

$$\therefore \frac{-6}{11} = \frac{6 \times 6}{11 \times 6} = \mathbf{\frac{-36}{66}} \text{ and } \frac{5}{6} = \frac{5 \times 11}{6 \times 11} = \mathbf{\frac{55}{66}}$$

There are as many rational numbers between $\frac{-36}{66}$ and $\frac{55}{66}$ as there are integers between –36 and 55. For example :

$$\frac{-35}{66}, \frac{-34}{66}, \frac{-33}{66}, \ldots\ldots\ldots\ldots \frac{-1}{66}, \frac{1}{66}, \frac{53}{66}, \frac{54}{66}$$

We can write any two of them as the answer.

They can be $\frac{1}{66}$ and $\frac{39}{66}$

PRACTICE EXERCISES 2

A. Answer *yes* **or** *no* :

1. Every positive rational number is larger than zero. ....

2. Every negative rational number is smaller than zero. ....

3. A negative rational number is larger than a positive number. ....

4. Numerically larger negative rational numbers have smaller values. ....

5. Larger positive rational numbers are farther from 0. ....

6. For comparison of two rational numbers, they are reduced to a common denominator. ....

B. Represent these rational numbers on the number-line in the box :

7. $\frac{1}{2}$ and $\frac{-1}{2}$ **8.** $\frac{2}{3}$ and $\frac{-2}{3}$ **9.** $\frac{13}{5}$ and $\frac{-13}{5}$

10. $\frac{9}{4}$ and $\frac{-9}{4}$ **11.** $\frac{-7}{4}$ and $\frac{7}{4}$ **12.** $\frac{-5}{4}$ and $\frac{5}{4}$

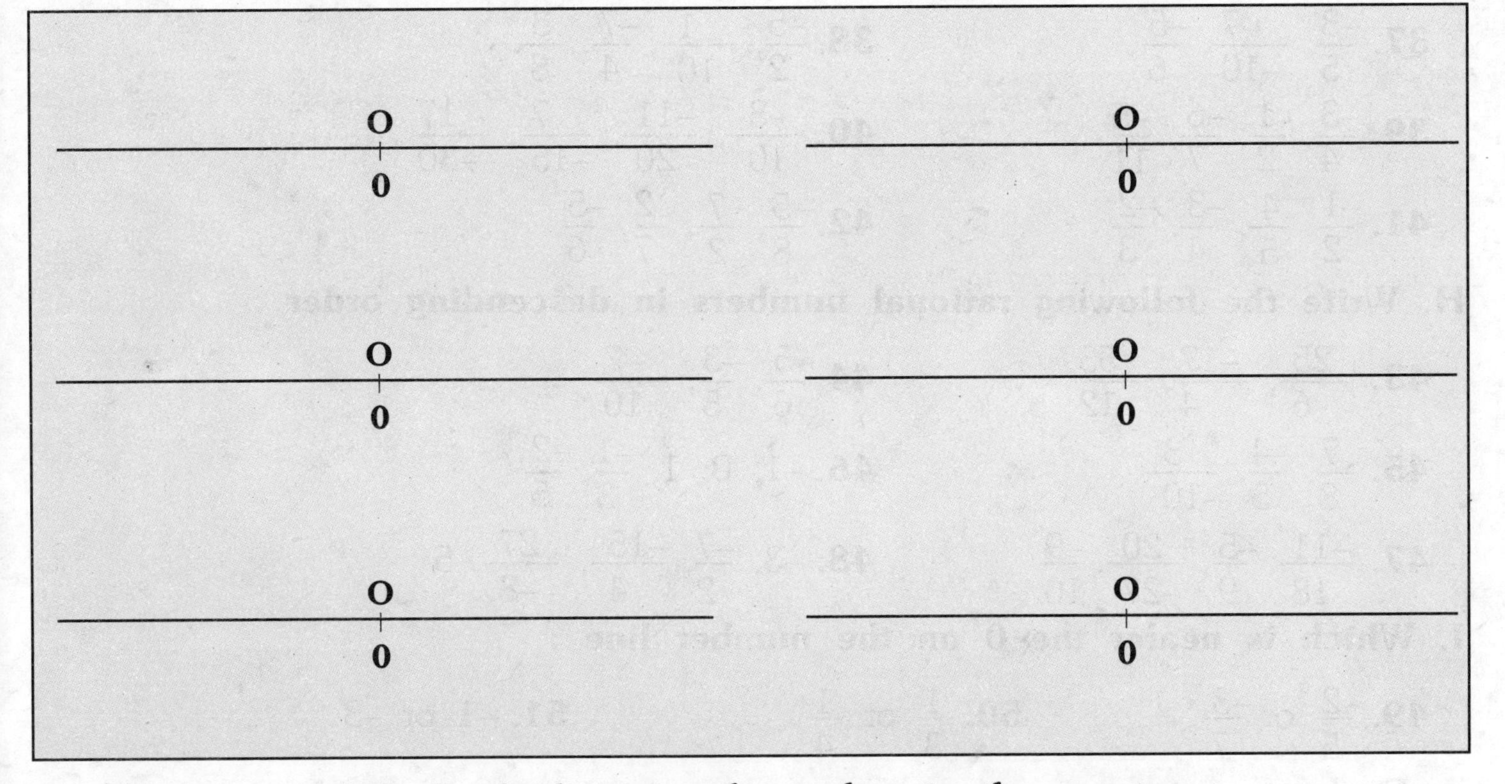

C. Compare and find which rational number is the greater :

13. $\frac{1}{2}$ or $\frac{7}{4}$ **14.** $\frac{-3}{4}$ or $\frac{-5}{2}$ **15.** $\frac{1}{3}$ or $\frac{2}{5}$

16. $\frac{3}{7}$ or 0

17. $\frac{-6}{13}$ or 0

18. $\frac{-4}{11}$ or $\frac{2}{-11}$

19. $\frac{2}{-3}$ or $\frac{-4}{5}$

20. $\frac{6}{-7}$ or $\frac{4}{5}$

21. $\frac{2}{3}$ or $\frac{-3}{-4}$

D. Write four equivalent rational numbers for each of the following :

22. $\frac{4}{5}$

23. $\frac{-2}{3}$

24. $\frac{5}{4}$

25. $\frac{3}{4}$

26. $\frac{-9}{7}$

27. $\frac{1}{3}$

E. Reduce the following rational numbers to their lowest terms :

28. $\frac{84}{112}$

29. $\frac{152}{209}$

30. $\frac{24}{66}$

F. Find the value of x :

31. $\frac{4}{9} = \frac{x}{27}$

32. $\frac{3}{11} = \frac{9}{x}$

33. $\frac{5}{9} = \frac{10}{x}$

34. $\frac{3}{5} = \frac{x}{10}$

35. $\frac{x}{7} = \frac{3}{7}$

36. $\frac{2}{5} = \frac{4}{x}$

G. Write the following rational numbers in ascending order :

37. $\frac{-3}{5}, \frac{7}{-10}, \frac{-5}{6}$

38. $\frac{-5}{2}, \frac{1}{10}, \frac{-7}{4}, \frac{3}{8}$

39. $\frac{-3}{4}, \frac{1}{2}, \frac{-6}{7}, \frac{-5}{11}$

40. $\frac{-3}{10}, \frac{-11}{20}, \frac{7}{-15}, \frac{17}{-30}$

41. $\frac{-1}{2}, \frac{4}{5}, \frac{-3}{4}, \frac{-2}{3}$

42. $\frac{-5}{8}, \frac{7}{2}, \frac{2}{7}, \frac{-5}{6}$

H. Write the following rational numbers in descending order :

43. $\frac{25}{6}, \frac{-17}{4}, \frac{53}{12}$

44. $\frac{-5}{6}, \frac{-3}{5}, \frac{-7}{10}$

45. $\frac{7}{8}, \frac{-4}{5}, \frac{3}{-10}$

46. $-1, 0, 1, \frac{-1}{3}, \frac{-2}{5}$

47. $\frac{-11}{18}, \frac{-5}{9}, \frac{20}{-27}, \frac{-9}{10}$

48. $-3, \frac{-7}{2}, \frac{-15}{4}, \frac{27}{-8}, 5$

I. Which is nearer the 0 on the number line :

49. $\frac{-2}{5}$ or $\frac{-3}{7}$

50. $\frac{1}{3}$ or $\frac{1}{4}$

51. -1 or -3

J. Find :

52. two rational numbers between -1 and 1.

3 RATIONAL NUMBERS (ADDITION AND SUBTRACTION)

KNOW THESE TERMS :

1. **addends**—quantities to be added to each other
2. **minuend**—quantity from which another quantity is subtracted
3. **subtrahend**—quantity which is subtracted from another quantity
4. **additive inverse**—rational number itself but with an opposite sign

Addition of rational numbers is carried out in a similar way to that in which we add fractions. The rational numbers to be added may have a common denominator or not. If they have a common denominator, the process of addition is very simple.

Suppose we are to add $\frac{p}{q}$ and $\frac{r}{q}$. The denominator q is the same. So, the sum is $\frac{p+r}{q}$, *i.e.* $\mathbf{\frac{p}{q} + \frac{r}{q} = \frac{p+r}{q}}$.

To add rational numbers with the same denominator, we simply *add their numerators* **to get the numerator of the sum** and we place the *common denominator* as the **denominator of the sum**.

Example 1. Add up $\frac{-3}{7}$ and $\frac{6}{7}$.

Solution : Given rational numbers $= \frac{-3}{7}$ and $\frac{6}{7}$

$\because$ both the rational numbers have the same denominator

$\therefore$ their sum $= \frac{-3+6}{7} = \mathbf{\frac{3}{7}}$ *Ans.*

Example 2. Find the sum of $\frac{8}{5}$ and $\frac{12}{-5}$.

Solution : Given rational numbers $= \frac{8}{5}$ and $\frac{12}{-5}$

First of all, we shall provide $\frac{12}{-5}$ with a +ve denominator

$$\frac{12}{-5} = \frac{12 \times (-1)}{-5 \times (-1)} = \frac{-12}{5}$$

Now $\frac{8}{5}$ and $\frac{-12}{5}$ have the same denominator.

$\therefore$ Their sum $= \frac{8+(-12)}{5} = \frac{8-12}{5} = \mathbf{\frac{-4}{5}}$ *Ans.*

If the denominators of the addends are different, we have to reduce them to the **same denominator**.

Example 3. Add up $\frac{-7}{9}$ and $\frac{3}{4}$

Solution : The denominators of both the rational numbers are different. They are 9 and 4.

L.C.M. of 9 and 4 = 36

We shall reduce both the given numbers to the denominator 36.

$$\frac{-7}{9} = \frac{(-7)\times 4}{9\times 4} = \mathbf{\frac{-28}{36}} \text{ and } \frac{3}{4} = \frac{3\times 9}{4\times 9} = \mathbf{\frac{27}{36}}$$

$$\text{Now} = \frac{-7}{9} + \frac{3}{4} = \frac{-28}{36} + \frac{27}{36} = \frac{-28+27}{36} = \mathbf{\frac{-1}{36}} \textit{ Ans.}$$

Example 4. Add up $\frac{-8}{15}$ and $\frac{2}{-3}$

Solution : First of all, we shall provide $\frac{2}{-3}$ with a +ve denominator.

$$\frac{2}{-3} = \frac{2\times(-1)}{-3\times(-1)} = \frac{-2}{3}$$

Now we are to add $\frac{-8}{15}$ and $\frac{-2}{3}$

As the denominators 15 and 3 are different

∴ Numbers must be reduced to the common denominator 15

$$\frac{-2}{3} = \frac{(-2)\times 5}{3\times 5} = \mathbf{\frac{-10}{15}}$$ and $\frac{-8}{15}$ already has its denominator 15.

$$\therefore \frac{-8}{15} + \frac{-10}{15} = \frac{-8+(-10)}{15} = \frac{-8-10}{15} = \frac{-18}{15}$$

The numerator and the denominator have 3 as their common factor

$$\therefore \frac{-18}{15} = \frac{-18\div 3}{15\div 3} = \mathbf{\frac{-6}{5}} \textit{ Ans.}$$

Example 5. Simplify : $\frac{-7}{10} + \frac{13}{-15} + \frac{21}{20}$

Solution : First of all, we shall provide $\frac{13}{-15}$ with a +ve denominator.

$$\frac{13}{-15} = \frac{13\times(-1)}{(-15)\times(-1)} = \mathbf{\frac{-13}{15}}$$

$$\text{Now } \frac{-7}{10} + \frac{13}{-15} + \frac{21}{20} = \frac{-7}{10} + \frac{-13}{15} + \frac{21}{20}$$

L.C.M. of the three different denominators 10, 15, 20 is 60.

$$\therefore \frac{-7}{10} = \frac{(-7)\times 6}{10\times 6} = \mathbf{\frac{-42}{60}} \text{ and } \frac{-13}{15} = \frac{(-13)\times 4}{15\times 4} = \mathbf{\frac{-52}{60}}$$

$$\text{While } \frac{21}{20} = \frac{21\times 3}{20\times 3} = \mathbf{\frac{63}{60}}$$

$$\therefore \frac{-7}{10} + \frac{-13}{15} + \frac{21}{20} = \frac{-42}{60} + \frac{-52}{60} + \frac{63}{60}$$

$$= \frac{-42 - 52 + 63}{60} = \frac{-94 + 63}{60}$$

$$= \mathbf{\frac{-31}{60}} \; Ans.$$

PRACTICE EXERCISES 3

A. Complete each statement :

1. Rational numbers are added just as we add ....

2. The basic step in addition of rational numbers is to reduce them to the same ....

3. $\frac{p}{\cdots\cdots} + \frac{\cdots\cdots}{q} = \frac{p + r}{q}$

4. All the rational numbers to be added must have positive.....................

5. The sum of two rational numbers with the same denominator is :

$$\frac{\text{.......................} + \text{.......................}}{\text{...................................}}$$

B. Add up :

6. $\frac{-2}{3}$ and $\frac{3}{4}$ **7.** $\frac{9}{-16}$ and $\frac{-5}{-12}$ **8.** $\frac{-3}{8}$ and $\frac{-5}{12}$

9. $\frac{6}{7}$ and $\frac{2}{-7}$ **10.** $\frac{5}{-8}$ and $\frac{3}{8}$ **11.** $\frac{8}{14}$ and $\frac{-5}{7}$

12. $\frac{-7}{8}$ and $\frac{25}{8}$ **13.** $\frac{3}{-5}$ and $\frac{-6}{5}$ **14.** $\frac{3}{5}$ and $\frac{2}{-3}$

15. $\frac{-4}{9}$ and $\frac{5}{6}$ **16.** $\frac{-3}{8}$ and $\frac{-7}{12}$ **17.** $\frac{-2}{3}$ and $\frac{5}{4}$

18. $\frac{3}{7}$ and $\frac{-4}{5}$ **19.** $\frac{-8}{15}$ and $\frac{2}{-3}$ **20.** $\frac{5}{9}$ and $\frac{-7}{18}$

C. Find the value of :

21. $\frac{-5}{9} + \frac{-7}{12} + \frac{11}{18}$ **22.** $\frac{5}{8} + \frac{-7}{18} + \frac{11}{12}$ **23.** $\frac{5}{9} + \frac{-7}{18} + \frac{11}{12}$

24. $\frac{-2}{3} + \frac{-5}{6} + \frac{1}{9}$ **25.** $\frac{-9}{10} + \frac{22}{15} + \frac{13}{-20}$ **26.** $\frac{7}{12} + \frac{13}{12} + \frac{-11}{24}$

D. Write each rational number as the sum of an integer and a rational number :

27. $\frac{15}{7}$ **28.** $\frac{-101}{20}$ **29.** $\frac{27}{-20}$ **30.** $\frac{-25}{7}$

31. Add up $\frac{2}{5}$ and $\frac{4}{5}$ on the number line

32. Which is the rational number whose additive inverse is the number itself ?

E. 33. I spend $\frac{1}{8}$ of my salary as my pocket-money while I give another $\frac{1}{8}$ of my salary to my sister. $\frac{2}{5}$ of my salary is spent on the family. How much of my salary do I spend in all ?

PROPERTIES OF ADDITION OF RATIONAL NUMBERS

PROPERTY 1

The sum of two rational numbers is always a rational number.

For example :

$\frac{1}{5} + \frac{3}{4} = \frac{4 + 15}{20} = \mathbf{\frac{19}{20}}$ which is a rational number.

$\frac{-2}{5} + \frac{2}{3} = \frac{-6 + 10}{15} = \mathbf{\frac{4}{15}}$ which is also a rational number.

So, we can generalise it as—

If $\frac{a}{b}$ and $\frac{c}{d}$ are two rational numbers, then $\frac{a}{b} + \frac{c}{d}$ is also a rational number.

PROPERTY 2

Two rational numbers can be added in any order.

For example :

$\frac{1}{4} + \frac{2}{3} = \frac{3 + 8}{12} = \mathbf{\frac{11}{12}}$ and $\frac{2}{3} + \frac{1}{4} = \frac{8 + 3}{12} = \mathbf{\frac{11}{12}}$

$\therefore \frac{1}{4} + \frac{2}{3} = \frac{2}{3} + \frac{1}{4}$

We can generalise it as—

If $\frac{a}{b}$ and $\frac{c}{d}$ are two rational numbers, then $\frac{a}{b} + \frac{c}{d} = \frac{c}{d} + \frac{a}{b}$.

PROPERTY 3

Three rational numbers to be added can be grouped in any order :

For example :

$\frac{-2}{3}, \frac{-5}{6}, \frac{1}{9}$ are three rational numbers to be added

(a) $\left(\frac{-2}{3} + \frac{-5}{6}\right) + \frac{1}{9} = \frac{-4 + (-5)}{6} + \frac{1}{9} = \frac{-9}{6} + \frac{1}{9} = \frac{-27 + 2}{18} = \mathbf{\frac{-25}{18}}$

(b) $\frac{-2}{3} + \left(\frac{-5}{6} + \frac{1}{9}\right) = \frac{-2}{3} + \frac{-15 + 2}{18} = \frac{-2}{3} + \frac{-13}{18} = \frac{-12 - 13}{18} = \mathbf{\frac{-25}{18}}$

(c) $\left(\frac{1}{9} + \frac{-2}{3}\right) + \frac{-5}{6} = \frac{1 - 6}{9} + \frac{-5}{6} = \frac{-5}{9} + \frac{-5}{6} = \frac{-10 - 15}{18} = \mathbf{\frac{-25}{18}}$

Clearly $\left(\frac{-2}{3} + \frac{-5}{6}\right) + \frac{1}{9} = \frac{-2}{3} + \left(\frac{-5}{6} + \frac{1}{9}\right) = \left(\frac{1}{9} + \frac{-2}{3}\right) + \frac{-5}{6}$

If can be generalised as—

If $\frac{a}{b}, \frac{c}{d}$ and $\frac{e}{f}$ be any three rational numbers, then

$$\left(\frac{a}{b} + \frac{c}{d}\right) + \frac{e}{f} = \frac{a}{b} + \left(\frac{c}{d} + \frac{e}{f}\right) = \left(\frac{e}{f} + \frac{a}{b}\right) + \frac{c}{d}.$$

PROPERTY 4

The sum of any rational number and zero is the rational number itself.

Examples : $0 + \frac{3}{4} = \frac{0}{4} + \frac{3}{4} = \frac{0 + 3}{4} = \mathbf{\frac{3}{4}}$

$\frac{-1}{6} + 0 = \frac{-1}{6} + \frac{0}{6} = \frac{-1 + 0}{6} = \mathbf{\frac{-1}{6}}$

So, we can generalize it as under :

If $\frac{a}{b}$ is any rational number, then $\frac{a}{b} + 0 = 0 + \frac{a}{b} = \frac{a}{b}$.

PROPERTY 5

The negative of a rational number added to it makes it 0. So, either of the +ve and –ve forms of a rational number is called the *additive inverse* **of the other.**

Examples : *(a)* The negative of $\frac{7}{8}$ is $\frac{-7}{8}$

$$\frac{7}{8} + \frac{-7}{8} = \frac{7 + (-7)}{8} = \frac{7 - 7}{8} = \mathbf{0}$$

(b) The negative of $\frac{5}{6}$ is $\frac{-5}{6}$

$$\frac{5}{6} + \frac{-5}{6} = \frac{5 + (-5)}{6} = \frac{5 - 5}{6} = \mathbf{0}$$

So, either of $\frac{7}{8}$ and $\frac{-7}{8}$ is the *additive inverse* of the other. We can generalise it as :

(a) If $\frac{a}{b}$ and $\frac{-a}{b}$ are added, the sum = 0.

(b) Either of $\frac{a}{b}$ and $\frac{-a}{b}$ is the *additive inverse* of the other.

SUBTRACTION OF RATIONAL NUMBERS

Subtraction is the process just inverse of the process of *addition*. So, it is clear that in order to subtract a rational number from another rational number, the *additive inverse* of the subtrahend should be **added** to the minuend.

TWO PROPERTIES OF SUBTRACTION

PROPERTY 1

The difference of two rational numbers is a rational number.

Examples : $\frac{1}{5} - \frac{1}{3} = \frac{1}{5} + \frac{-1}{3} = \frac{3 + (-5)}{15}$

$= \frac{3 - 5}{15} = \mathbf{\frac{-2}{15}}$ which is a rational number.

We can generalize it as—

If $\frac{a}{b}$ and $\frac{c}{d}$ are two rational numbers, then—

$$\frac{a}{b} - \frac{c}{d} = \frac{a}{b} + \frac{-c}{d}.$$

Example 1. Write the additive inverse of each of the following :

(a) $\frac{-3}{7}$ (b) $\frac{2}{5}$ (c) $\frac{-10}{31}$ (d) $\frac{-7}{25}$

Solution : (a) Additive inverse of $\frac{-3}{7}$ is $\frac{3}{7}$

(b) Additive inverse of $\frac{2}{5}$ is $\frac{-2}{5}$

(c) Additive inverse of $\frac{-10}{31}$ is $\frac{10}{31}$

(d) Additive inverse of $\frac{-7}{25}$ is $\frac{7}{25}$

Ans.

Example 2. Subtract $\mathbf{\frac{3}{4}}$ from $\mathbf{\frac{-7}{8}}$

Solution : We are to subtract $\frac{3}{4}$ from $\frac{-7}{8}$

$\frac{3}{4}$ is the subtrahend.

Additive inverse of the subtrahend $\frac{3}{4}$ is $\frac{-3}{4}$

$$\therefore \frac{-7}{8} - \frac{3}{4} = \frac{-7}{8} + \frac{-3}{4} = \frac{-7+(-6)}{8} = \frac{-7-6}{8} = \mathbf{\frac{-13}{8}} \textit{ Ans.}$$

PROPERTY 2

If 0 is subtracted from a rational number, the remainder is the rational number itself.

Example : $\frac{1}{5} - 0 = \frac{1}{5} - \frac{0}{5} = \frac{1-0}{5} = \mathbf{\frac{1}{5}}$

So, we can generalize it as—

If $\frac{a}{b}$ is a rational number, then

$$\frac{a}{b} - 0 = \frac{a}{b}.$$

Example 3. Subtract the sum of $\mathbf{\frac{3}{11}}$ and $\mathbf{\frac{5}{22}}$ from the difference of $\mathbf{\frac{16}{33}}$ and $\mathbf{\frac{5}{66}}$.

Solution : Sum of $\frac{3}{11}$ and $\frac{5}{22}$ $= \frac{3}{11} + \frac{5}{22}$

$$= \frac{6+5}{22} = \frac{11}{22} = \mathbf{\frac{1}{2}}$$

Difference of $\frac{16}{33}$ and $\frac{5}{66}$ $= \frac{16}{33} - \frac{5}{66}$

$$= \frac{32+(-5)}{66} = \frac{32-5}{66}$$

$$= \frac{27}{66} = \mathbf{\frac{9}{22}}$$

Now we are to subtract $\frac{1}{2}$ from $\frac{9}{22}$

$$\frac{9}{22} - \frac{1}{2} = \frac{9}{22} + \frac{-1}{2} = \frac{9+(-11)}{22}$$

$$\frac{9-11}{22} = \frac{-2}{22} = \mathbf{\frac{-1}{11}} \textit{ Ans.}$$

Example 4. **What should be added to $\frac{4}{9}$ to get $\frac{-7}{8}$?**

Solution : It is clear from the expression that

$\frac{-7}{8}$ is the sum of two numbers one of which is $\frac{4}{9}$

$\therefore$ Required No. $= \frac{-7}{8} - \frac{4}{9} = \frac{-7}{8} + \frac{-4}{9} = \frac{-63 + (-32)}{72}$

$= \frac{-63 - 32}{72} = \mathbf{\frac{-95}{72}}$ *Ans.*

Example 5. **The sum of three rational numbers is 1. If two of the numbers are $\frac{-4}{15}$ and $\frac{7}{10}$. Find the third number.**

Solution : Sum of the three numbers = 1

Two of the numbers are $\frac{-4}{15}$ and $\frac{7}{10}$

So, we shall subtract the sum of $\frac{-4}{15}$ and $\frac{7}{10}$ from 1

Sum of $\frac{-4}{15}$ and $\frac{7}{10} = \frac{-4}{15} + \frac{7}{10} = \frac{-8 + 21}{30} = \mathbf{\frac{13}{70}}$

$\therefore$ Required Number $= 1 - \frac{13}{70} = 1 + \frac{-13}{70} = \frac{70 + (-13)}{70}$

$= \frac{70 - 13}{70} = \mathbf{\frac{57}{70}}$ *Ans.*

PRACTICE EXERCISES 4

A. Write the *additive inverse* of each of these rational numbers :

1. $\frac{-5}{12}$ **2.** $\frac{4}{9}$ **3.** $\frac{-7}{11}$ **4.** $\frac{-3}{-8}$

5. $\frac{-10}{21}$ **6.** $\frac{-7}{8}$ **7.** $\frac{5}{9}$ **8.** $\frac{-15}{7}$

9. $\frac{8}{-13}$ **10.** $\frac{-12}{13}$ **11.** $\frac{4}{11}$ **12.** $\frac{-7}{20}$

B. Subtract :

13. $\frac{-5}{8}$ from $\frac{-3}{7}$ **14.** $\frac{3}{4}$ from $\frac{2}{3}$ **15.** $\frac{-11}{24}$ from $\frac{-5}{36}$

16. $\frac{-3}{4}$ from $\frac{5}{6}$ **17.** $\frac{3}{5}$ from $\frac{7}{20}$ **18.** $\frac{-8}{33}$ from $\frac{-7}{11}$

C. Solve the following :

19. $\frac{2}{5} + \frac{-3}{4} - \frac{5}{6}$

20. $\frac{-5}{7} + \frac{4}{28} - \frac{4}{7}$

21. $\frac{7}{8} - \frac{11}{12} + \frac{4}{15}$

22. $\frac{3}{10} - \frac{7}{2} + \frac{3}{4}$

23. $\frac{-6}{15} + \frac{7}{8} + \frac{-5}{9}$

24. $\frac{7}{-33} + \frac{8}{11} - \frac{-4}{22}$

25. $\frac{4}{9} + \frac{-5}{18} - \frac{-10}{27}$

26. $\frac{4}{21} + \frac{-5}{14} - \frac{-5}{7} + \frac{9}{28}$

D. 27. The sum of two rational numbers is –5. One of the rational numbers is $\frac{-13}{6}$. Find the other.

28. What should be added to $\frac{-7}{8}$ to make it $\frac{4}{9}$?

29. Two rational numbers together amount to –2. One of the numbers is $\frac{-12}{5}$. Find the other.

30. What number should be subtracted from $\frac{5}{7}$ to get –1 ?

31. Which number should be added to $\frac{5}{7}$ to make it –1 ?

32. What should be subtracted from $\left(\frac{-13}{8} + \frac{-3}{8}\right)$ to get 1 ?

E. Fill up each blank :

33. $\frac{-3}{26} - \frac{-4}{13} =$ ....

34. $\frac{-5}{11} +$ .... $= -1$

35. $\frac{-7}{23} +$ .... $= 3$

36. .... $+ \frac{7}{20} = -2$

F. Write *True* or *False* :

37. $1 - \frac{-9}{5} < \frac{12}{5} - 4$

38. $\frac{-5}{8} + \frac{-9}{13} = \frac{-5}{8} - \frac{-9}{13}$

39. 0 is its own additive inverse.

40. The difference between two rational numbers is a rational number.

41. The negative of a negative rational number is also negative.

42. If x and y are two rational numbers such that $x > y$, then $x - y$ is always a positive rational number.

43. If x and y are two rational numbers, then $x - y = x + (-y)$.

4 RATIONAL NUMBERS
(MULTIPLICATION AND DIVISION)

KNOW THESE TERMS :

1. **numerator**—integer above the line of division in a fraction or rational number
2. **denominator**—interger below the line of division in a fraction or rational number
3. **reciprocal**—the inverse of a fraction (rational number) got by changing the places of its numerator and the denominator

We know that in order to multiply two fractions :

1. *we multiply their numerators to get the* **numerator of the product**.
2. *we multiply their denominators to get the* **denominator of the product**.

This rule holds good for rational numbers as well, *i.e.*

Product of two rational numbers = $\dfrac{\textbf{product of their numerators}}{\textbf{product of their denominators}}$

In other words, **if $\frac{a}{b}$ and $\frac{c}{d}$ are two rational numbers, then**

$$\frac{a}{b} \times \frac{c}{d} = \frac{a \times c}{b \times d} = \frac{ac}{bd}$$

Examples : (a) $\frac{-2}{3} \times \frac{6}{7} = \frac{(-2) \times 6}{3 \times 7} = \frac{-12}{21} = \mathbf{\frac{-4}{7}}$

(b) $\frac{-13}{15} \times \frac{-25}{26} = \frac{(-13) \times (-25)}{15 \times 26} = \frac{13 \times 25}{15 \times 26} = \mathbf{\frac{5}{6}}$

PROPERTIES OF MULTIPLICATION

PROPERTY 1

The product of two rational numbers is always a rational number.

Examples : $\frac{5}{7} \times \frac{-3}{8} = \frac{5 \times (-3)}{7 \times 8} = \mathbf{\frac{-15}{56}}$ .... (a rational number)

$\frac{-3}{8} \times \frac{5}{-6} = \frac{-3}{8} \times \frac{-5}{6} = \frac{(-3) \times (-5)}{8 \times 6} = \mathbf{\frac{15}{48}}$..... (a rational number)

We can generalise it as—

If $\frac{a}{b}$ and $\frac{c}{d}$ are two rational numbers, then—

$\frac{a}{b} \times \frac{c}{d}$ or $\frac{ac}{bd}$ is also a rational number.

PROPERTY 2

Two rational numbers can be multiplied in any order.

Examples : $\frac{-3}{7} \times \frac{5}{11} = \frac{(-3) \times 5}{7 \times 11} = \mathbf{\frac{-15}{77}}$

and $\frac{5}{11} \times \frac{-3}{7} = \frac{5 \times (-3)}{11 \times 7} = \mathbf{\frac{-15}{77}}$

Clearly, $\frac{-3}{7} \times \frac{5}{11} = \frac{5}{11} \times \frac{-3}{7}$

We can generalise it as—

If $\frac{a}{b}$ and $\frac{c}{d}$ are two rational numbers, then $\frac{a}{b} \times \frac{c}{d} = \frac{c}{d} \times \frac{a}{b}$.

PROPERTY 3

The product of any rational number and 1 is the rational number itself.

Examples : $\frac{-5}{8} \times 1 = \frac{-5}{8} \times \frac{1}{1} = \frac{(-5) \times 1}{8 \times 1} = \mathbf{\frac{-5}{8}}$

$1 \times \frac{-3}{7} = \frac{-3}{7} \times \frac{1}{1} = \frac{-3 \times 1}{7 \times 1} = \mathbf{\frac{3}{7}}$

We can generalise it as—

If $\frac{a}{b}$ is a rational number, then $\frac{a}{b} \times 1 = 1 \times \frac{a}{b} = \frac{a}{b}$.

PROPERTY 4

Any rational number multiplied by 0 is equal to 0.

Examples : $\frac{-5}{8} \times 0 = \frac{-5}{8} \times \frac{0}{1} = \frac{(-5) \times 0}{8 \times 1} = \frac{0}{8} = \mathbf{0}$

$0 \times \frac{-3}{7} = \frac{-3}{7} \times \frac{0}{1} = \frac{0 \times (-3)}{7 \times 1} = \frac{0}{7} = \mathbf{0}$

We can generalise it as—

If $\frac{a}{b}$ is a rational number, then $\frac{a}{b} \times 0 = 0 \times \frac{a}{b} = 0$.

PROPERTY 5

Three or more rational numbers can be grouped in any order for multiplication.

Examples :

$\frac{3}{4} \times \frac{-5}{7} \times \frac{-6}{11} = \left(\frac{3}{4} \times \frac{-5}{7}\right) \times \frac{-6}{11} = \frac{-15}{28} \times \frac{-6}{11} = \mathbf{\frac{45}{154}}$......*(I grouping)*

$\frac{3}{4} \times \frac{-5}{7} \times \frac{-6}{11} = \frac{3}{4} \times \left(\frac{-5}{7} \times \frac{-6}{11}\right) = \frac{3}{4} \times \frac{30}{77} = \mathbf{\frac{45}{154}}$......*(II grouping)*

$\frac{-5}{7} \times \left(\frac{3}{4} \times \frac{-6}{11}\right) = \frac{-5}{7} \times \frac{-18}{44} = \frac{-5}{7} \times \frac{-9}{22} = \mathbf{\frac{45}{154}}$........*(III grouping)*

Clearly, $\left(\frac{3}{4} \times \frac{-5}{7}\right) \times \frac{-6}{11} = \frac{3}{4} \times \left(\frac{-5}{7} = \frac{-6}{11}\right) = \frac{-5}{7} \times \left(\frac{3}{4} \times \frac{-6}{11}\right)$

We can generalise it as—

If $\frac{a}{b}$, $\frac{c}{d}$ and $\frac{e}{f}$ are any three rational numbers, then—

$$\frac{a}{b} \times \left(\frac{c}{d} \times \frac{e}{f}\right) = \frac{c}{d}\left(\frac{a}{b} \times \frac{e}{f}\right) = \frac{e}{f}\left(\frac{a}{b} \times \frac{c}{d}\right).$$

PROPERTY 6

If a rational number is multiplied by the sum of two other rational numbers, the product is equal to the sum of the products of the rational number and either of the other numbers.

For example :

$$\frac{2}{3} \times \left(\frac{-4}{5} + \frac{-6}{7}\right) = \frac{2}{3} \times \frac{-28 -30}{35} = \frac{2}{3} \times \frac{-58}{35} = \mathbf{\frac{-116}{105}}$$

Also, $\frac{2}{3} \times \left(\frac{-4}{5} + \frac{-6}{7}\right) = \left(\frac{2}{3} \times \frac{-4}{5}\right) + \left(\frac{2}{3} \times \frac{-6}{7}\right)$

$$= \frac{-8}{15} + \frac{-12}{21} = \frac{-56 -60}{105} = \mathbf{\frac{-116}{105}}$$

Clearly, $\frac{2}{3}\left(\frac{-4}{5} + \frac{-6}{7}\right) = \left(\frac{2}{3} \times \frac{-4}{5}\right) + \left(\frac{2}{3} \times \frac{-6}{7}\right)$

We can generalise it as—

If $\frac{a}{b}$, $\frac{c}{d}$ and $\frac{e}{f}$ are three rational numbers, then

$$\frac{a}{b}\left(\frac{c}{d} + \frac{e}{f}\right) = \left(\frac{a}{b} \times \frac{c}{d}\right) + \left(\frac{a}{b} \times \frac{e}{f}\right).$$

RECIPROCAL OF A RATIONAL NUMBER

Suppose we have a rational number $\frac{7}{8}$

By what number should we multiply it to get 1 as the product ?

Clearly, it is $\frac{8}{7}$, as $\frac{7}{8} \times \frac{8}{7} = 1$

Similarly $\frac{2}{3} \times \frac{3}{2} = 1$ and $\frac{a}{b} \times \frac{b}{a} = 1$

What is the relation between the rational numbers of each pair ?

We say that $\frac{8}{7}$ is the **reciprocal** of $\frac{7}{8}$

$\frac{3}{2}$ is the **reciprocal** of $\frac{2}{3}$

and $\frac{b}{a}$ is the **reciprocal** of $\frac{a}{b}$

Another term for *reciprocal* is **multiplicative inverse.**

We can generalise it as—

(a) **We get the reciprocal of a rational number by changing the places of its numerator and denominator.**

(b) **Product of two mutually reciprocal rational numbers is equal to 1.**

Let us solve some examples now.

Example 1. Multiply (a) $\mathbf{3\frac{4}{17}}$ **and** $\mathbf{\frac{34}{77}}$ (b) $\mathbf{\frac{27}{55}}$ **and** $\mathbf{-1\frac{2}{9}}$

Solution : (a) $3\frac{4}{17} \times \frac{34}{77} = \frac{55}{17} \times \frac{34}{77} = \frac{10}{7} = \mathbf{1\frac{3}{7}}$ *Ans.*

(b) $\frac{27}{55} \times -1\frac{2}{9} = \frac{27}{55} \times \frac{-11}{9} = \frac{27 \times (-11)}{55 \times 9} = \mathbf{\frac{-3}{5}}$ *Ans.*

Example 2. Multiply $\mathbf{\frac{23}{5} \times \frac{-11}{69} \times \frac{17}{-22}}$

Solution : $\frac{23}{5} \times \frac{-11}{69} \times \frac{17}{-22} = \frac{23}{5} \times \frac{-11}{69} \times \frac{-17}{22}$

$= \frac{23 \times (-11) \times (-17)}{5 \times 69 \times 22}$

$= \frac{23 \times 11 \times 17}{5 \times 69 \times 22} = \mathbf{\frac{17}{30}}$ *Ans.*

Example 3. Prove that $\mathbf{\frac{-3}{11} \times \frac{5}{21} = \frac{5}{21} \times \frac{-3}{11}}$

Solution : L.H.S. $= \frac{-3}{11} \times \frac{5}{21} = \frac{-3 \times 5}{11 \times 21} = \mathbf{\frac{-15}{231}}$

R.H.S. $= \frac{5}{21} \times \frac{-3}{11} = \frac{5 \times -3}{21 \times 11} = \mathbf{\frac{-15}{231}}$

$\because$ L.H.S. = R.H.S.

$\therefore \mathbf{\frac{-3}{11} \times \frac{5}{21} = \frac{5}{21} \times \frac{-3}{11}}$ *Ans.*

Example 4. Write the reciprocals of the following :

(a) $\mathbf{\frac{3}{4}}$ (b) $\mathbf{\frac{p}{q}}$ (c) **−1** (d) $\mathbf{\frac{-3}{17}}$

Solution : Reciprocal of $\frac{3}{4} = \frac{4}{3}$ .... $\left(\because \frac{3}{4} \times \frac{4}{3} =\right)1$

Reciprocal of $\frac{p}{q} = \mathbf{\frac{q}{p}}$ .... $\left(\because \frac{p}{q} \times \frac{q}{p} = 1\right)$

Reciprocal of $-1 = \mathbf{\frac{1}{-1}}$ .... $\left(\because \frac{-1}{1} \times \frac{1}{-1} = 1\right)$

Reciprocal of $\frac{-3}{17} = \mathbf{\frac{17}{-3}}$ .... $\left(\because \frac{-3}{17} \times \frac{17}{-3} = 1\right)$

PRACTICE EXERCISES 5

A. Answer :

1. What is the product of a rational number and its reciprocal ? ....
2. What is the reciprocal of *zero* ? ....
3. What is the reciprocal of –17 ? ....
4. Which two numbers are their *own reciprocals* ? ....
5. What number is *zero* the reciprocal of ? ....

B. Answer *yes* **or** *no* **:**

6. The reciprocal of a positive number can be negative. ....
7. The reciprocal of a negative number is always negative. ....
8. The product of two rational numbers is also a rational number. ....
9. The other term for *reciprocal* is *multiplicative inverse*. ....
10. $a\,(b + c) = (a \times b) + (a \times c)$ ....
11. $p \times (q \times r) = r \times (p \times q) = q \times (p \times r)$ ....
12. A rational number multiplied by 1 is equal to itself. ....

C. Multiply :

13. $\frac{-91}{126} \times \frac{-36}{65}$
14. $\frac{-9}{11} \times \frac{77}{81}$
15. $\frac{-11}{18} \times \frac{-12}{33} \times \frac{6}{25}$
16. $\frac{2}{3} \times \frac{-5}{6} \times \frac{7}{15}$
17. $\frac{-4}{9} \times \frac{3}{20} \times \frac{-6}{8}$
18. $-5 \times \frac{9}{-10} \times \frac{-5}{18}$
19. $\frac{4}{5} \times \frac{-5}{13} \times \frac{26}{35}$
20. $\frac{7}{9} \times \frac{-45}{56} \times \frac{64}{75}$
21. $\frac{-3}{19} \times \frac{38}{45} \times 0$
22. $\frac{15}{27} \times \frac{2}{3} \times \frac{-26}{45}$
23. $\frac{-3}{8} \times \frac{5}{-7} \times \frac{7}{10}$
24. $\frac{a}{b} \times \frac{-b}{c} \times \frac{-c}{-a}$

D. Simplify :

25. $\left(\frac{3}{4} + \frac{-7}{8}\right) \times \left(\frac{11}{13} \times \frac{-5}{26}\right)$
26. $\left(\frac{-7}{3} \times \frac{26}{7}\right) - \left(2\frac{8}{11} \times 9\frac{1}{6}\right)$
27. $1 - \left(1\frac{17}{25} \times \frac{-15}{28} \times \frac{2}{-3}\right)$
28. $\left(\frac{-7}{5} \times \frac{-13}{15}\right) - \left(\frac{5}{12} \times \frac{-7}{18}\right)$
29. $\frac{-15}{7} \times \frac{21}{10} \times \frac{-5}{6} \times 1$
30. $\frac{-17}{23} \times \frac{19}{-34} \times \frac{-46}{57} \times 0$
31. $\left(\frac{-3}{4} + \frac{2}{15}\right) + \left(\frac{9}{10} \times \frac{-5}{18}\right)$
32. $\left(\frac{-14}{25} \times \frac{20}{-28}\right) - \left(\frac{13}{15} \times \frac{-15}{-26}\right)$

E. Verify the following :

33. $\frac{1}{2} \times \left(\frac{-3}{4} \times \frac{8}{9}\right) = \left(\frac{-3}{4} \times \frac{8}{9} \times \frac{1}{2}\right)$

34. $\frac{2}{3} \times \left(\frac{-3}{4} + \frac{-4}{5}\right) = \left(\frac{2}{3} \times \frac{-3}{4}\right) + \left(\frac{2}{3} \times \frac{-4}{5}\right)$

35. $\frac{-3}{16} \times \frac{8}{-21} = \frac{8}{-21} \times \frac{-3}{16}$ **36.** $\frac{-5}{9} \times \frac{9}{-5} \times 1 = 1$

37. $\left(\frac{-4}{5} \times \frac{-3}{7}\right) + \left(\frac{-4}{5} \times \frac{-9}{13}\right) = \frac{-4}{5} \times \left(\frac{-3}{7} + \frac{-9}{13}\right)$

38. $\frac{4}{25} \times \left(\frac{-5}{11} \times \frac{-22}{25}\right) = \frac{-22}{25} \times \left(\frac{4}{25} \times \frac{-5}{11}\right)$

39. The product of a rational number and its reciprocal is always 1.

F. 40. Find the product of the reciprocals of $\frac{9}{-34}$ and $\frac{18}{-17}$

41. Supply the missing terms in $\frac{-25}{19} \times \frac{\ldots\ldots}{\ldots\ldots} = 1$

42. $\frac{8}{3}$ is the multiplicative inverse of $\frac{\ldots\ldots\ldots\ldots}{\ldots\ldots\ldots\ldots}$

43. $\frac{3}{-7} \times \frac{\ldots\ldots}{9} = \frac{4}{\ldots\ldots} \times \frac{\ldots\ldots}{-7}$

G. Name the *property of multiplication* **in each of the following :**

44. $\frac{-8}{15} \times \frac{5}{12} = \frac{5}{12} \times \frac{-8}{15}$ **45.** $\frac{2}{-3} \times \frac{-5}{7} = \frac{10}{21}$

46. $\frac{2}{3} \times \left(\frac{-5}{6} \times \frac{7}{15}\right) = \frac{7}{15} \times \left(\frac{2}{3} \times \frac{-5}{6}\right)$ **47.** $\frac{p}{q} \times 1 = 1 \times \frac{p}{q} = \frac{p}{q}$

48. $\frac{a}{b} \times \frac{b}{a} = 1$ **49.** $\frac{-4}{5} \times \left(\frac{2}{3} + \frac{-5}{9}\right) = \left(\frac{-4}{5} \times \frac{2}{3}\right) + \left(\frac{-4}{5} \times \frac{-5}{9}\right)$

50. *(a)* What will be the value of y, if it is its own reciprocal ?

(b) What will the value of y, if it is the reciprocal of x ?

(c) Is the product of a positive and a negative rational number always positive ?

H.51. Multiply $\frac{48}{53}$ by the reciprocals of 2, 3, 4 and 8.

52. Multiply the reciprocals of $\frac{1}{3}, \frac{-1}{6}, \frac{1}{9}$ and $\frac{-1}{18}$ by $\frac{1}{36}$.

53. Prove that $\frac{3}{11} \times 6\frac{1}{9}$ is equal to $1\frac{2}{3}$.

54. At first $\frac{7}{15}$ of a stick was cut off to shorten its length. Then $\frac{3}{16}$ of its remaining length was cut off. How long is the stick now left behind ?

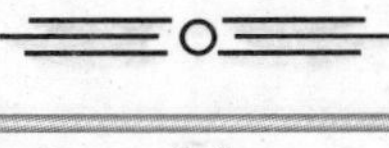

DIVISION OF RATIONAL NUMBERS

Division is a process just opposite to multiplication. So, we can say that **dividing 25 by 5** *is the same as* **multiplying 25 by the reciprocal of 5.**

If we extend this principle to rational numbers, we can say that—

(a) **dividing** $\frac{2}{3}$ **by** $\frac{11}{15}$ means **multiplying** $\frac{2}{3}$ **by** $\frac{15}{11}$ *(reciprocal of* $\frac{11}{15}$*)*

So, we can define the division of rational numbers as under :

If $\frac{a}{b}$ and $\frac{c}{d}$ are two rational numbers and $\frac{c}{d}$ is not zero, then

$$\frac{a}{b} \div \frac{c}{d} = \frac{a}{b} \times \frac{d}{c}.$$

Example : Suppose we are to divide $\frac{-28}{27}$ by $\frac{28}{15}$

Dividend $= \frac{-28}{27}$ and Divisor $= \frac{28}{15}$

$$\therefore \text{Quotient} = \frac{-28}{27} \div \frac{28}{15} = \frac{-28}{27} \times \frac{15}{28} = \mathbf{\frac{-5}{9}}$$

PROPERTIES OF DIVISION

PROPERTY 1

If a rational number is divided by a non-zero rational number, then the quotient is always a rational number.

Example : $\frac{-25}{32} \div \frac{-65}{48} = \frac{-25}{32} \times \frac{48}{-65} = \frac{-15}{-26} = \mathbf{\frac{15}{26}}$ ..... (a rational number)

We can generalise it as under :

If $\frac{a}{b}$ and $\frac{c}{d}$ are two rational numbers such that $\frac{c}{d} \neq 0$, then $\frac{a}{b} \div \frac{c}{d}$ is always a rational number.

PROPERTY 2

If a rational number is divided by 1, the quotient is the rational number itself.

Example : $\frac{-4}{5} \div 1 = \frac{-4}{5} \div \frac{1}{1} = \frac{-4}{5} \times \frac{1}{1} = \mathbf{\frac{-4}{5}}$

We can generalise it as under :

If $\frac{a}{b}$ is any rational number, then $\frac{a}{b} \div 1 = \frac{a}{b}$.

PROPERTY 3

If a rational number is divided by –1, the quotient is its opposite rational number *(additive inverse)*.

Example : $\frac{-4}{5} \div (-1) = \frac{-4}{5} \div \frac{-1}{1} = \frac{-4}{5} \times \frac{1}{-1} = \mathbf{\frac{4}{5}}$

We can generalise it as under :

If $\frac{a}{b}$ is any rational number, then $\frac{a}{b} \div (-1) = \frac{-a}{b}$.

PROPERTY 4

If any rational number is divided by itself, the quotient is 1.

Example : $\frac{4}{5} \div \frac{4}{5} = \frac{4}{5} \times \frac{5}{4} = \mathbf{1}$

We can generalise it as under :

If a non-zero rational number $\frac{a}{b}$ is divided by itself $(\frac{a}{b})$, the quotient is 1.

PROPERTY 5

If any non-zero rational number is divided by its opposite rational number, the quotient is –1.

Example : $\frac{7}{8} \div \frac{-7}{8} = \frac{7}{8} \times \frac{8}{-7} = \frac{7}{8} \times \frac{-8}{7} = \mathbf{-1}$

We can generalise it as under :

If a non-zero rational number $\frac{a}{b}$ is divided by its opposite rational number $(\frac{-a}{b})$, the quotient is –1.

Let us now solve some examples :

Example 1. Divide $3\frac{1}{17} \div \frac{39}{-34}$.

Solution : $3\frac{1}{17} \div \frac{39}{-34} = \frac{52}{17} \div \frac{39}{-34}$

$= \frac{52}{17} \times \frac{-34}{39} = \frac{-8}{3} = \mathbf{-2\frac{2}{3}}$ *Ans.*

Example 2. The product of two rational numbers is $\frac{-5}{7}$. If one of the numbers is $\frac{-15}{56}$, find the other.

Solution : The product of the numbers $= \frac{-5}{7}$

One of the numbers $= \frac{-15}{56}$

$\therefore$ Other number $= \frac{-5}{7} \div \frac{-15}{56} = \frac{-5}{7} \times \frac{56}{-15}$

$= \frac{8}{3} = \mathbf{2\frac{2}{3}}$ *Ans.*

Example 3. By what number must $\frac{-8}{39}$ be multiplied to obtain $\frac{5}{26}$?

Solution : The number to be obtained as product is $\frac{5}{26}$, *i.e.*

Reqd. product $= \frac{5}{26}$

given multiplicand $= \frac{-8}{39}$

$\therefore$ Reqd. multiplier $= \frac{5}{26} \div \frac{-8}{39} = \frac{5}{26} \times \frac{39}{-8}$

$= \frac{15}{-16} = \mathbf{\frac{-15}{16}}$ *Ans.*

Example 4. Compute $\left(\frac{4}{9} \div \frac{1}{-3}\right) \div \frac{1}{2}$ and $\frac{4}{9} \div \left(\frac{1}{-3} \div \frac{1}{2}\right)$ and find whether they are equal or not.

Solution : $\left(\frac{4}{9} \div \frac{1}{-3}\right) \div \frac{1}{2}$

$= \left(\frac{4}{9} \times \frac{-3}{1}\right) \div \frac{1}{2} = \frac{-4}{3} \div \frac{1}{2} = \frac{-4}{3} \times \frac{2}{1} = \mathbf{\frac{-8}{3}}$

and $\frac{4}{9} \div \left(\frac{1}{-3} \div \frac{1}{2}\right) = \frac{4}{9} \div \left(\frac{1}{-3} \times \frac{2}{1}\right)$

$= \frac{4}{9} \div \frac{2}{-3} = \frac{4}{9} \times \frac{-3}{2} = \frac{4 \times (-3)}{9 \times 2} = \frac{-12}{18} = \mathbf{\frac{-2}{3}}$

$\because \frac{-8}{3} \neq \frac{-2}{3}$

$\therefore$ **$\left(\frac{4}{9} \div \frac{1}{-3}\right) \div \frac{1}{2}$ is not equal to $\frac{4}{9} \div \left(\frac{1}{-3} \div \frac{1}{2}\right)$** *Ans.*

PRACTICE EXERCISES 6

A. Answer *yes* or *no* :

1. If a rational number is divided by 1, the quotient is the rational number itself.] ....

2. When a rational number is divided by a non-zero rational number, the quotient is not a rational number.] ....

3. Any rational number divided by –1 gives its opposite rational number as the quotient.] ....

4. If a rational number is divided by itself, the quotient is 1. [....................]

5. If a rational number is divided by its opposite rational number, the quotient is –1. [....................]

B. Perform the following divisions :

6. $\frac{-8}{35}$ by $\frac{2}{7}$ **7.** $\frac{16}{21}$ by $\frac{-4}{7}$ **8.** $\frac{-9}{20}$ by $\frac{3}{-5}$

9. $\frac{7}{15}$ by $\frac{2}{-3}$ **10.** $\frac{9}{85}$ by $\frac{3}{-34}$ **11.** $3\frac{1}{17}$ by $\frac{33}{-34}$

12. $\frac{7}{-6}$ by $\frac{-14}{15}$ **13.** $\frac{8}{-9}$ by $\frac{-5}{6}$ **14.** $\frac{-14}{27}$ by $\frac{7}{-9}$

15. $\frac{-8}{9}$ by $\frac{-7}{5}$ **16.** $\frac{-16}{7}$ by $\frac{-24}{35}$ **17.** $\frac{-9}{11}$ by $\frac{-5}{6}$

18. $\frac{-7}{18}$ by -6 **19.** $\frac{1}{22}$ by $\frac{-7}{11}$ **20.** $\frac{8}{9}$ by $\frac{-5}{6}$

C. 21. The product of two numbers is $\frac{-7}{12}$. One of them is $\frac{-2}{3}$, find the other.

22. By what number should –39 be multiplied to get $\frac{-8}{13}$ as product ?

23. By which rational number be $\frac{-5}{7}$ multiplied to get $\frac{-15}{28}$ as product ?

24. Compute $\left(\frac{2}{3} \div \frac{4}{15}\right) \div \frac{1}{-3}$ and $\frac{2}{3} \div \left(\frac{4}{15} \div \frac{1}{-3}\right)$ and find whether they are equal or unequal.

25. Prove that $\frac{5}{11} \div \frac{15}{22}$ and $\frac{15}{22} \div \frac{5}{11}$ are not equal.

26. Divide the product of $\frac{91}{12}$ and $\frac{19}{3}$ by their sum.

27. Divide the product of $2\frac{1}{3}$ and $3\frac{1}{2}$ by their difference.

28. Divide the difference of $\frac{8}{13}$ and $3\frac{1}{4}$ by their sum.

29. How many shirt-pieces each $2\frac{1}{4}$ m. long can be cut out of a roll of cloth 45 metres in length.

30. Complete each equation :

(a) $\frac{5}{11} \div \frac{\cdots\cdots}{\cdots\cdots} = \frac{2}{3}$ *(b)* $\frac{15}{22} \div \frac{\cdots\cdots}{\cdots\cdots} = \frac{5}{11}$

(c) $\frac{3}{5} + \ldots\ldots = \frac{4}{9}$ *(d)* $\frac{4}{9} - \ldots\ldots\ldots = \frac{-3}{5}$

5 RATIONAL NUMBERS
(ABSOLUTE VALUE AND DENSITY)

KNOW THESE TERMS :

1. **absolute value**—numerical value of a rational number irrespective of the sign before it
2. **density**—capacity of two rational numbers in terms of rational numbers that can lie between them.
3. **number line**—a line on which rational numbers are represented

ABSOLUTE VALUE

We have already learnt that the **absolute value** of an integer is its *numerical value* whatever sign may occur before it.

For example –5, 5 have each the same absolute value 5

This fact holds good for rational numbers as well.

For any rational number x, its absolute value is defined as under :

$$|x| = \begin{cases} x, \text{ if } x \text{ is greater than } 0. \\ 0, \text{ if } x \text{ is equal to } 0. \\ -x, \text{ if } x \text{ is less than } 0. \end{cases}$$

We already know that we use two vertical lines on both sides of a number to mark its absolute value

$$\left|-\frac{7}{12}\right|, \quad |-x|, \quad |5|, \quad \left|\frac{4}{-7}\right|$$

ABSOLUTE VALUE ON A NUMBER-LINE

Suppose we want to find the numbers with absolute value $\frac{2}{3}$ on a number line. For it, the following steps should be taken.

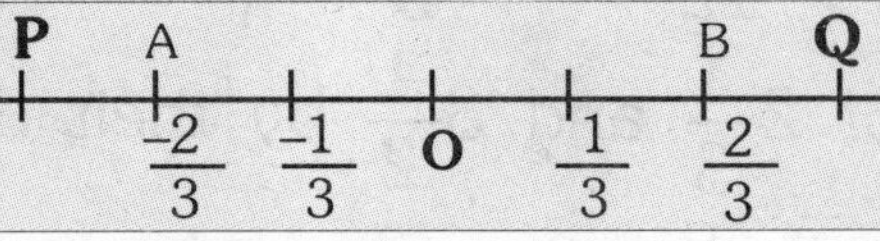

1. Draw a line and mark a point O on it.
2. Plot two other points P, Q on the line on both sides of O at an equal distance from O.
3. Divide OP and OQ each into three equal parts. Clearly OA, stands for $\frac{-2}{3}$ and OB for $\frac{2}{3}$.

So, the absolute value of both the numbers $\frac{-2}{3}$ and $\frac{2}{3}$ is $\mathbf{\frac{2}{3}}$.

If we take any other point on the line, its value cannot be $\frac{2}{3}$ because it will not be at a distance of $\frac{2}{3}$ from O.

Hence there are only two points on the number line that stand at a distance of $\frac{2}{3}$ from the point O.

There are only two numbers $\frac{2}{3}$ and $\frac{-2}{3}$ whose absolute value is $\frac{2}{3}$.

DENSITY OF RATIONAL NUMBERS

The word—**dense**—means *crowded*. So, the **density** *of two non-consecutive rational numbers* **means their capacity as to how many rational numbers** *can* **occur between them.**

IN THE CASE OF INTEGERS :

We know that there is no integer between two consecutive integers. For example, there is no integer between 4 and 5. Also, there is no integer between –4 and –5.

As for non-consecutive integers there can be a limited number of integers between them ; as—

(a) Between –3 and 2, there are four integers : –2, –1, 0, 1.

(b) Between –5 and 5, there are nine integers : –4, –3, –2, –1, 0, 1, 2, 3, 4

IN THE CASE OF RATIONAL NUMBERS

In the case of rational numbers, it is not so. Let us see what difference is there.

We know that the rational numbers between $\frac{-5}{9}$ and $\frac{2}{9}$ are :

$\frac{-4}{9}, \frac{-3}{9}, \frac{-2}{9}, \frac{-1}{9}, 0, \frac{1}{9}$ .... **six rational numbers**

Can there be more rational numbers, between $\frac{-5}{9}$ *and* $\frac{2}{9}$? Let us see.

We know that $\frac{-5}{9} = \mathbf{\frac{-50}{90}}$ and $\frac{2}{9} = \mathbf{\frac{20}{90}}$ *(Equivalent rational numbers)*

Clearly, there can be **69 rational numbers** between $\frac{-50}{90}$ and $\frac{20}{90}$; as—

$\frac{-49}{90}, \frac{-48}{90}, \frac{-47}{90}$ .... $\frac{18}{90}, \frac{19}{90}$ **(69 rational numbers)**

Can there be still more rational numbers between $\frac{-5}{9}$ *and* $\frac{2}{9}$? Let us see.

We know that $\frac{-5}{9} = \frac{-500}{900}$ and $\frac{2}{9} = \mathbf{\frac{200}{900}}$ *(Equivalent rational numbers)*

So, there can be still more (699) rational numbers between $\frac{-5}{9}$ and $\frac{2}{9}$; as—

$\frac{-499}{900}, \frac{-498}{900}, \frac{-497}{900}$................ $\frac{198}{900}, \frac{199}{900}$............... **(699 rational numbers)**

Similarly by taking $\frac{-5000}{9000}$ and $\frac{2000}{9000}$ as equivalent numbers of $\frac{-5}{9}$ and $\frac{2}{9}$, we can have **6999 rational numbers** between them.

Hence between any two rational numbers, we can find any number of rational numbers. This very property of rational numbers is called their **density**.

RATIONAL NUMBERS BETWEEN TWO RATIONAL NUMBERS

We have followed that between any two non-consucative rational numbers, we can find any number of rational numbers. We have also mastered the processes of addition and multiplication of rational numbers. So, we can easily find rational numbers between two given rational numbers. Let us have some examples.

Example 1. Find two rational numbers between $\frac{-2}{3}$ and $\frac{2}{3}$

Solution : Given rational numbers are $\frac{-2}{3}$ and $\frac{2}{3}$

Clearly $\frac{-2}{3} < \frac{2}{3}$ and their average $= \left(\frac{-2}{3} + \frac{2}{3}\right) \div 2$

$= \frac{0}{3} \times \frac{1}{2} = \mathbf{0}$

Again, $0 < \frac{2}{3}$

Now we shall find another rational number between 0 and $\frac{2}{3}$

Average of 0 and $\frac{2}{3} = \left(0 + \frac{2}{3}\right) \div 2 = \frac{2}{3} \times \frac{1}{2} = \frac{1}{3}$

$\therefore$ two rational number between $\frac{-2}{3}$ and $\frac{2}{3}$ are $\mathbf{0}, \mathbf{\frac{1}{3}}$ *Ans.*

Example 2. Find three rational numbers between $\frac{1}{5}$ and $\frac{1}{4}$.

Solution : Given rational numbers $= \frac{1}{5}$ and $\frac{1}{4}$

Clearly $\frac{1}{5} < \frac{1}{4}$

Average of $\frac{1}{5}$ and $\frac{1}{4} = \left(\frac{1}{5} + \frac{1}{4}\right) \div 2 = \left(\frac{4+5}{20}\right) \times \frac{1}{2}$

$= \frac{9}{20} \times \frac{1}{2} = \mathbf{\frac{9}{40}}$

Again $\frac{9}{40} < \frac{1}{4}$

Average of $\frac{9}{40}$ and $\frac{1}{4} = \left(\frac{9}{40} + \frac{1}{4}\right) \div 2 = \left(\frac{9+10}{40}\right) \times \frac{1}{2}$

$= \frac{19}{40} \times \frac{1}{2} = \mathbf{\frac{19}{80}}$

Clearly $\frac{19}{80} < \frac{1}{4}$

Again average of $\frac{19}{80}$ and $\frac{1}{4} = \left(\frac{19}{80} + \frac{1}{4}\right) \div 2 = \left(\frac{19 + 20}{80}\right) \times \frac{1}{2}$

$= \frac{39}{80} \times \frac{1}{2} = \mathbf{\frac{39}{160}}$

$\therefore$ Three rational numbers between $\frac{1}{5}$ and $\frac{1}{4}$ are $\mathbf{\frac{9}{40}, \frac{19}{80}, \frac{39}{160}}$ *Ans.*

Example 3. Verify that $|-x| = |x|$ if $x = \frac{5}{-8}$

Solution : $x = \frac{5}{-8}$ means $|x| = \left|\frac{5}{-8}\right| = \mathbf{\frac{5}{8}}$

$-x = \frac{-5}{-8} = \frac{5}{8}$ means $|x| = \left|\frac{5}{8}\right| = \mathbf{\frac{5}{8}}$

$\therefore$ Result in both the case is the same.

$\therefore$ **$|-x| = |x|$ is quite true, if $x = \frac{5}{-8}$**. *Ans.*

Example 4. Verify that $|x + y| \le |x| + |y|$ for $x = \frac{-9}{7}, y = \frac{3}{4}$

Solution : $x = \frac{-9}{7}$ and $y = \frac{3}{4}$

$|x + y| = \left|\left(\frac{-9}{7}\right) + \frac{3}{4}\right| = \left|\frac{-36 + 21}{28}\right| = \mathbf{\frac{-15}{28}}$

and $|x| + |y| = \left|\frac{-9}{7}\right| + \left|\frac{3}{4}\right| = \left|\frac{36}{7} + \frac{21}{4}\right| = \mathbf{\frac{57}{28}}$

Clearly $\frac{-15}{28} < \frac{57}{28}$

$\therefore$ **$|x + y| \le |x| + |y|$ is quite true, if $x = \frac{-9}{7}, y = \frac{3}{4}$** *Ans.*

Example 5. Verify that $|x \times y| = |x| \times |y|$ for $x = \frac{-7}{8}, y = \frac{1}{-4}$

Solution : $x = \frac{-7}{8}$ and $y = \frac{1}{-4}$

$|x \times y| = \left|\frac{-7}{8} \times \frac{1}{-4}\right| = \frac{-7}{-32} = \mathbf{\frac{7}{32}}$

and $|x| \times |y| = \left|\frac{-7}{8}\right| \times \left|\frac{1}{-4}\right| = \left|\frac{7}{8} \times \frac{1}{4}\right| = \mathbf{\frac{7}{32}}$

$\therefore$ **$|x \times y| = |x| \times |y|$ is quite true, if $x = \frac{-7}{8}, y = \frac{1}{-4}$.** *Ans.*

PRACTICE EXERCISES 7

A. Define—

1. *Absolute value* of a rational number.

2. *Density* of rational numbers.

B. Answer *yes* or *no* :

3. There is no integer between two consecutive integers. ....

4. There are a limited number of integers between two given integers. ....

5. The absolute value of a rational number is never negative. ....

6. There can be infinite rational numbers between two given rational numbers. ....

C. Write the absolute value of each of the following :

7. $\frac{5}{7}$ **8.** $\frac{-7}{9}$ **9.** $\frac{12}{-5}$ **10.** 0

11. $\frac{-9}{13}$ **12.** $\frac{-13}{-8}$ **13.** $\frac{11}{8}$ **14.** $\frac{-6}{13}$

D. Find the rational number whose absolute value is :

15. $\frac{1}{2}$ **16.** $\frac{3}{4}$ **17.** $\frac{5}{6}$

18. Verify that $|-x| = |x|$ by taking $x = \frac{-3}{4}$.

19. Verify that $|x + y| \leq |x| + |y|$ by taking $x = \frac{3}{4}$ and $y = \frac{-1}{2}$

20. Verify that $|x \times y| = |x| \times |y|$ by taking $x = \frac{3}{4}$ and $y = \frac{-4}{15}$

21. If $x = \frac{-4}{5}$ and $y = \frac{3}{7}$ then prove that $|x + y| < |x| + |y|$

22. Show that $\frac{1}{2} \times \frac{-1}{3} + \frac{1}{2}$ is a rational number that lies between $\frac{1}{3}$ and $\frac{1}{2}$

23. x and y are two rational numbers such that $x < y$. Show that the rational number $\frac{1}{2} \times (x + y)$ lies between x and y.

24. Find a rational number between $\frac{1}{3}$ and $\frac{1}{2}$.

25. Insert two rational numbers between –2 and 5.

26. Find three rational numbers between $\frac{1}{6}$ and $\frac{1}{3}$.

27. Find four rational numbers between $\frac{3}{4}$ and $\frac{2}{3}$.

6 RATIONAL NUMBERS (DECIMAL FORM)

KNOW THESE TERMS :

1. **terminating decimal**—rational number/fraction in decimal form that has a *finite decimal part* and that ends in an *exact division*
2. **non-terminating decimal**—rational number/fraction in decimal form that has a *never-ending decimal* part in which *one digit* or *digit-group recurs*

RATIONAL NUMBER TO DECIMAL

We already know how to convert a fraction into its decimal form. We know that—

$\frac{1}{2} = 0{\cdot}5$ and $\frac{1}{4} = 0{\cdot}25$ while $\frac{1}{8} = 0{\cdot}125$

Clearly $-\frac{1}{2} = -0{\cdot}5$ and $-\frac{1}{4} = -0{\cdot}25$ while $-\frac{1}{8} = -0{\cdot}125$

The common method of converting a fraction or rational number into decimal form is to **divide the numerator by its denominator.**

A rational number when converted into decimal form can have its *decimal part* in one of the following two forms.

1. **Terminating Decimals** 2. **Recurring Decimals**

TERMINATING DECIMALS

These decimals have a **finite decimal part** that ends in an exact division ; as : 0·5 ; 0·25 ; ·125 ; 0·375 etc.

RECURRING DECIMALS

These decimals have a **never-ending decimal-part** because the division never comes to an end. As a result, *one digit* or *a digit-group* repeats itself, *i.e.* **recurs** again and again ; as—

0·3333..... ; 0·6666..... ; 0·18888..... ; 0·142857142857.....

In order to express such decimals, the repeated digit or digit-group is put under *a bar* ; as : $0{\cdot}\overline{3}$, $0{\cdot}\overline{27}$, $0{\cdot}2\overline{34}$

Let us solve some examples of terminating decimals :

Example 1. Express each of the following rational numbers in decimal form :

(a) $\frac{3}{4}$ *(b)* $\frac{4}{5}$ *(c)* $\frac{13}{25}$ *(d)* $\frac{15}{8}$

Solution : (a) $\frac{4}{5}$ = **0·8** *Ans.*

(b) $\frac{3}{4}$ = **0·75** *Ans.*

(c) $\frac{13}{25}$ = **0·52** *Ans.*

(d) $\frac{15}{8}$ = **1·875** *Ans.*

5 | 4·00
  | 0·8
(a)

4 | 3·00
  | 0·75
(b)

25 | 13·00
  | 0·52
(c)

8 | 15·000
  | 1·875
(d)

Example 2. Express the rational number $\frac{3147}{256}$ in decimal form.

Solution : Given rational number = $\frac{3147}{256}$

The numerator and the denominator are large numbers

∴ We will perform long division.

So, $\frac{3147}{256}$ = **12·29296875** *Ans.*

```
        12·29296875
256 ) 3147·000000 (
      256                 2480
      587                 2304
      512                 1760
       750                1536
       512                2240
      2380                2048
      2304                1920
        760               1792
        512               1280
       2480               1280
                             0
```

NON-TERMINATING DECIMALS

These decimal rational numbers/fractions have **never-ending decimal parts**. In each decimal part, one digit or a group of digits **recurs** again and again.

Let us now solve some examples of non-terminating decimals

Example 3. Express the following rational numbers in decimal form.

(a) $\mathbf{\frac{1}{9}}$ (b) $\mathbf{\frac{5}{18}}$ (c) $\mathbf{\frac{5}{3}}$ (d) $\mathbf{\frac{3}{7}}$

Solution : (a) $\frac{1}{9}$ = 0·1111........

= **0·$\overline{1}$** *Ans.*

(b) $\frac{5}{18}$ = 0·2777..........

= **0·2$\overline{7}$** *Ans.*

(c) $\frac{5}{3}$ = 1·666............

= **1·$\overline{6}$** *Ans.*

(d) $\frac{3}{7}$ = **0·$\overline{428571}$** *Ans.*

```
(a)
9 | ·10
  | 1—1
  | 10—1
  | 10—1
  | 1......

(b)
18 | ·50
   | 2—14
18 | 140
   | 7—14
18 | 140
   | 7—14

(c)
3 | 5·0
  | 1—2
3 | 20
  | 6—2
3 | 20
  | 6—2

(d)
7 | ·30
  | 4—2
7 | 20
  | 2—6
7 | 60
  | 8—4
7 | 40
  | 5—5
7 | 50
  | 7—1
7 | 10
  | 1—3
```

Remember that—

(a) When a single digit recurs again and again, we may put a **dot** or bar on it.

(b) But when more-than-one digits recur, a **bar** is put on them.

(c) Every rational number can be expressed as either a **terminating decimal** or a **non-terminating decimal**.

HOW TO LOCATE THE TYPE OF A DECIMAL NUMBER

Observe all the examples given above. You will see that the rational numbers with denominators that have *prime factors* 2 and /or 5, end in **terminating decimal forms**.

But the rational numbers with denominators having *prime factors* **other than** 2 and 5 always have **non-terminating decimal forms**.

Example 4. Without actual division determine which of the following rational numbers have terminating and which have non-terminating decimal forms.

(a) $\mathbf{\frac{5}{8}}$ *(b)* $\mathbf{\frac{-2}{13}}$ *(c)* $\mathbf{\frac{-31}{20}}$ *(d)* $\mathbf{\frac{-121}{9}}$

Solution : *(a)* $\frac{5}{8} = \frac{5}{2 \times 2 \times 2}$

If we observe the prime factors of the denominator, we see that it contains 2 and no other prime factor.

$\therefore$ $\mathbf{\frac{5}{8}}$ **has a terminating decimal form.** *Ans.*

(b) $\frac{-2}{13} = \frac{-2}{1 \times 13}$

We observe that the denominator does not have 2 or 5 as its prime factors.

$\therefore$ $\mathbf{\frac{-2}{13}}$ **has a non-terminating decimal form.** *Ans.*

(c) $\frac{-31}{20} = \frac{-31}{2 \times 2 \times 5}$

As the denominator has only 2 and 5 as its prime factors.

$\therefore$ $\mathbf{\frac{-31}{20}}$ **has a terminating decimal form.** *Ans.*

(d) $\frac{-121}{9} = \frac{-121}{3 \times 3}$

The only prime factor of the denominator is 3

$\therefore$ $\mathbf{\frac{-121}{9}}$ **has a non-terminating decimal form.** *Ans.*

PRACTICE EXERCISES 8

A. Answer :

1. By which process do we convert a fraction/rational number into its decimal form ?

....

2. Which two forms can the decimal part of a rational number have ?

....

3. What is meant by a *terminating decimal* ?

....

....

4. What is meant by a *non-terminating decimal* ?

....

....

B. Express each rational number into its decimal form :

5. $\frac{3}{4}$ **6.** $\frac{15}{4}$ **7.** $\frac{23}{10}$ **8.** $\frac{13}{25}$

9. $\frac{1593}{625}$ **10.** $\frac{4}{5}$ **11.** $\frac{5}{4}$ **12.** $\frac{26}{25}$

13. $\frac{2157}{625}$ **14.** $\frac{12}{25}$ **15.** $\frac{11}{50}$ **16.** $\frac{3}{5}$

17. $\frac{5}{6}$ **18.** $\frac{7}{5}$ **19.** $\frac{5}{8}$ **20.** $\frac{9}{20}$

C. Express each rational number into its decimal form :

21. $\frac{5}{12}$ **22.** $\frac{1}{3}$ **23.** $\frac{4}{9}$ **24.** $\frac{2}{11}$

25. $\frac{1}{7}$ **26.** $\frac{16}{45}$ **27.** $\frac{24}{7}$ **28.** $\frac{8}{3}$

29. $\frac{22}{7}$ **30.** $\frac{-5}{18}$ **31.** $\frac{8}{3}$ **32.** $\frac{-19}{6}$

D. Without actual division, determine whether each of the following rational numbers will have terminating or non-terminating decimal part :

33. $\frac{11}{50}$ **34.** $\frac{5}{12}$ **35.** $\frac{5}{18}$ **36.** $\frac{17}{64}$

37. $\frac{9}{25}$ **38.** $\frac{43}{90}$ **39.** $\frac{25}{48}$ **40.** $\frac{53}{90}$

TERMINATING DECIMAL TO RATIONAL NUMBER

We learnt in the previous classes how to convert a decimal fraction into a common fraction. While doing so, we take the following steps :

1. We write the decimal fraction (say ·7)
2. We put a bar under the decimal fraction $\frac{\cdot 7}{}$
3. We put 1 under the decimal point. $\frac{\cdot 7}{1}$
4. We put as many zeroes to the right of 1 as there are digits to the right of the decimal point $\frac{\cdot 7}{10}$
5. Finally we remove the decimal point to get the desired common fraction as $\mathbf{\frac{7}{10}}$.

Similarly $\cdot 3 = \mathbf{\frac{3}{10}}$; $1\cdot 37 = \mathbf{\frac{137}{100}}$; $\cdot 485 = \mathbf{\frac{\cdot 485}{1000}}$

$$0\cdot 00093 = \frac{93}{100000}$$

This very process is used to change terminating decimals into rational numbers.

RECURRING DECIMAL TO RATIONAL NUMBER

Before proceeding to follow how to covert a recurring decimal into a rational number, grasp the following facts :

(a) A recurring decimal with all its decimal digits recurring, is called a **pure recurring decimal**.

Here are a few examples : $0\cdot\overline{3}$, $0\cdot\overline{6}$, $0\cdot\overline{27}$, $0\cdot\overline{16}$

(b) A recurring decimal that has at least one non-recurring digit in its decimal part is called a **mixed recurring decimal**.

Here are a few examples : $0\cdot 1\overline{6}$, $0\cdot 2\overline{7}$, $0\cdot 4\overline{92}$

Let us see how to convert both types of decimals into rational numbers.

A. CONVERTING PURE RECURRING DECIMALS

Example 5. Covert 0·3 into a rational number.

Solution : $1 \times 0\cdot\overline{3} = 0\cdot 333$..................(A)

$\therefore 10 \times 0\cdot\overline{3} = 3\cdot 333$..................(B) *(Decimal moves 1 place right)*

subtracting (A) from (B)

$(10 \times 0\cdot\overline{3}) - (1 \times 0\cdot\overline{3}) = (3\cdot 333 - 0\cdot 333)$

or $\mathbf{9} \times 0\cdot\overline{3} = \mathbf{3}$

$\therefore 0\cdot\overline{3} = \frac{3}{9} = \mathbf{\frac{1}{3}}$ *Ans.*

Example 6. Express $0\cdot\overline{27}$ as a rational number.

Solution : $1 \times 0\cdot\overline{27} = 0\cdot272727$.................(A)

$\therefore$ $100 \times 0\cdot\overline{27} = 27\cdot272727$...............(B) *(Decimal moves 2 places right)*

Subtracting (A) from (B)

$(100 \times 0\cdot\overline{27}) - (1 \times 0\cdot\overline{27}) = (27\cdot272727 - 0\cdot272727)$

or $99 \times 0\cdot\overline{27} = 27$

$\therefore$ $0\cdot\overline{27} = \frac{27}{99} = \frac{3}{11}$ *Ans.*

Example 7. Express $0\cdot\overline{321}$ as a rational number.

Solution : $1 \times 0\cdot\overline{321} = 0\cdot321321321$............(A)

$\therefore$ $1000 \times 0\cdot\overline{321} = 321\cdot321321321$......(B) *(Decimal moves 3 places right)*

Subtracting (A) from (B)

or $999 \times 0\cdot\overline{321} = 321$

$\therefore$ $0\cdot\overline{321} = \frac{321}{999} = \frac{107}{333}$ *Ans.*

A HANDY RULE :

If we observe the above examples, we can form the following rule for converting **pure recurring decimals** into *rational numbers* :

1. Write the recuring digit or digits only once as numerator.

2. Write as many nines as the denominator has the recurring digits.

Examples : $0\cdot\overline{1} = \frac{1}{9}$; $0\cdot\overline{17} = \frac{17}{99}$; $0\cdot\overline{492} = \frac{492}{999}$

B. CONVERTING MIXED RECURRING DECIMALS :

Example 8. Express $0\cdot2\overline{1}$ as a rational number.

Solution : $1 \times 0\cdot2\overline{1} = 0\cdot21111$.......................(A)

$\therefore$ $10 \times 0\cdot2\overline{1} = 2\cdot1111$.............(B) *(Decimal moves 1 place right)*

and $100 \times 0\cdot2\overline{1} = 21\cdot111$...........(C) *(Decimal moves 2 places right)*

Subtracting (B) from (C)

$90 \times 0\cdot2\overline{1} = (21\cdot111 - 2\cdot111) = 19$

$\therefore$ $0\cdot2\overline{1} = \frac{19}{90}$ *Ans.*

Example 9. **Express $0\cdot2\overline{31}$ as a rational number.**

Solution : $\mathbf{1} \times 0\cdot2\overline{31} = 0\cdot2313131$........................(A)

$\therefore$ $\mathbf{10} \times 0\cdot2\overline{31} = 2\cdot313131$................(B) *(Decimal moves 3 place right)*

and $\mathbf{1000} \times 0\cdot2\overline{31} = 231\cdot3131$............(C) *(Decimal moves 3 places right)*

Subtracting (B) from (C)

$\mathbf{990} \times 0\cdot2\overline{31} = (231\cdot3131 - 2\cdot3131) = \mathbf{229}$

$\therefore 0\cdot2\overline{31} = \dfrac{\mathbf{229}}{\mathbf{990}}$ *Ans.*

Example 10. **Express $0\cdot12\overline{63}$ as a rational number.**

Solution : $\mathbf{1} \times 0\cdot12\overline{63} = 0\cdot126363$.........................(A)

$\therefore$ $\mathbf{100} \times 0\cdot12\overline{63} = 12\cdot6363$..............(B) *(Decimal moves 2 places right)*

and $\mathbf{10000} \times 0\cdot12\overline{63} = 1263\cdot6363$.......(C) *(Decimal moves 4 places right)*

Subtracting (B) from (C)

$\mathbf{9900} \times 0\cdot12\overline{63} = (1263\cdot6363 - 12\cdot6363) = \mathbf{1251}$

$\therefore 0\cdot12\overline{63} = \dfrac{1251}{9900} = \dfrac{\mathbf{139}}{\mathbf{1100}}$ *Ans.*

A HANDY RULE :

If we observe the solutions of the above examples, we can form a rule to express **mixed recurring decimals** into *rational numbers.*

1. **Write the (mixed recurring decimal) – (non-recurring number) as numerator.**
2. **Put as many nines as in the recurring digits with as many zeroes to their right as non-recurring decimals as denominator.**

Examples : $\mathbf{0\cdot2\overline{1}} = \dfrac{21-2}{90} = \dfrac{\mathbf{19}}{\mathbf{90}}$; $\mathbf{2\cdot\overline{31}} = \dfrac{231-2}{990} = \dfrac{\mathbf{229}}{\mathbf{990}}$.

$\mathbf{0\cdot12\overline{63}} = \dfrac{1263-12}{9900} = \dfrac{1251}{9900} = \dfrac{\mathbf{139}}{\mathbf{1100}}$

Example 11. **Find the value of $1\cdot\overline{18} + 0\cdot24$**

Solution : $1\cdot\overline{18}$ is a mixed recurring decimal

$\therefore 1\cdot\overline{18} = 1 + \dfrac{18-0}{99} = \dfrac{\mathbf{117}}{\mathbf{99}}$ and $0\cdot\overline{24} = \dfrac{24-0}{99} = \dfrac{\mathbf{24}}{\mathbf{99}}$

$\therefore 1\cdot\overline{18} + 0\cdot\overline{24} = \dfrac{117}{99} + \dfrac{24}{99} = \dfrac{\mathbf{141}}{\mathbf{99}} = \mathbf{1\cdot\overline{41}}$ *Ans.*

PRACTICE EXERCISES 9

A. Answer :

1. What is the method to convert a terminating decimal into a rational number ?

....

....

2. What is a *pure recurring decimal* ?

....

....

3. What is a *mixed recurring decimal* ?

....

....

4. What is the rule to convert pure recurring decimals into rational numbers ?

(a) ....

(b) ....

5. What is the rule to convert mixed recurring decimals into rational numbers ?

(a) ....

(b) ....

B. Express the following pure recurring decimals into rational numbers :

6. $0\cdot\overline{8}$ **7.** $0\cdot\overline{16}$ **8.** $0\cdot\overline{234}$ **9.** $0\cdot\overline{3}$

10. $0\cdot\overline{13}$ **11.** $0\cdot\overline{4}$ **12.** $0\cdot\overline{32}$ **13.** $0\cdot\overline{133}$

D. Express the following mixed recurring decimals into rational numbers :

14. $0\cdot2\overline{8}$ **15.** $0\cdot1\overline{7}$ **16.** $0\cdot00\overline{387}$ **17.** $0\cdot2\overline{35}$

18. $0\cdot23\overline{1}$ **19.** $0\cdot4\overline{92}$ **20.** $0\cdot1\overline{254}$ **21.** $0\cdot1\overline{67}$

22. $0\cdot5\overline{36}$ **23.** $0\cdot4\overline{1}$ **24.** $0\cdot1\overline{263}$ **25.** $0\cdot0\overline{37}$

E. Find the value of

26. $4\cdot\overline{6} + 2\cdot\overline{1}$ **27.** $0\cdot\overline{62} - 0\cdot\overline{3}$ **28.** $0\cdot\overline{1} - 0\cdot\overline{4}$

29. $0\cdot\overline{1} + 0\cdot\overline{2} + 0\cdot\overline{16}$ **30.** $2\cdot\overline{6} + 2\cdot\overline{16}$

7 RATIONAL NUMBERS : EXPONENTS

KNOW THESE TERMS :

1. **exponent**—small numeral put on the top right of a rational number to show its power
2. **exponential notation**—writing a rational number/numbers in the exponential form
3. **base**—rational number or integer in exponential form *minus* the exponent
4. **index**—another word for the *exponent* of a rational number or integer

EXPONENT

We have already learnt a bit about powers. We know that $4 \times 4 \times 4 \times 4$ can be written as 4^4. It is read as **four raised to the power 4**.

We also know that in 4^5, **4** is called the **base.**

In 4^5, 5 is called the **index** or **exponent** of the 4's *power*. Similarly in the term -4^3, **−4** is the *base* while **3** is the *exponent*.

EXPONENTIAL NOTATION

The *form* **that indicates the product of an integer by itself several times through its exponent is called its** *exponential form.* **Writing of integers in their exponential forms is called** *exponential notation*.

This notation can be used for rational numbers as well. For example—

(a) $\left(\frac{1}{3}\right)^3 = \frac{1}{3} \times \frac{1}{3} \times \frac{1}{3}$ and it is read as $\frac{1}{3}$ **raised to the power 3**.

Here $\frac{1}{3}$ is the *base* and **3** is the *exponent* or *index*.

(b) $\left(\frac{-2}{3}\right)^4 = \left(\frac{-2}{3}\right) \times \left(\frac{-2}{3}\right) \times \left(\frac{-2}{3}\right) \times \left(\frac{-2}{3}\right) = \frac{16}{81}$

(c) $\left(\frac{-3}{5}\right)^3 = \left(\frac{-3}{5}\right) \times \left(\frac{-3}{5}\right) \times \left(\frac{-3}{5}\right) = -\frac{27}{125}$

Also recall that—

$(-1)^{\text{odd exponent}} = -1$ and $(-1)^{\text{even exponent}} = 1\ (+1)$

We can generalise it as under :

a × a × a..........*n* **times** $= a^n$ **where** *a* **is the** *base* **and** *n* **is the** *exponent.*

$\frac{p}{q} \times \frac{p}{q} \times \frac{p}{q}$............*n* **times** $= \left(\frac{p}{q}\right)^n$ **where** $\frac{p}{q}$ **is the** *base* **and** *n* **is the** *index* or *exponent.*

Let us now solve some examples :

Example 1. Find the value of :

(a) $\left(\frac{3}{4}\right)^4$ (b) $\left(\frac{3}{-4}\right)^3$ (c) $\left(\frac{-2}{7}\right)^5$

Solution : (a) $\left(\frac{3}{4}\right)^4 = \frac{3}{4} \times \frac{3}{4} \times \frac{3}{4} \times \frac{3}{4} = \frac{3 \times 3 \times 3 \times 3}{4 \times 4 \times 4 \times 4} = \frac{81}{256}$ *Ans.*

(b) $\left(\frac{3}{-4}\right)^3 = \left(\frac{3}{-4}\right) \times \left(\frac{3}{-4}\right) \times \left(\frac{3}{-4}\right) = \frac{3 \times 3 \times 3}{(-4) \times (-4) \times (-4)}$

$= \frac{27}{-64} = \frac{-27}{64}$ *Ans.*

(c) $\left(\frac{-2}{7}\right)^5 = \left(\frac{-2}{7}\right) \times \left(\frac{-2}{7}\right) \times \left(\frac{-2}{7}\right) \times \left(\frac{-2}{7}\right) \times \left(\frac{-2}{7}\right)$

$= \frac{(-2) \times (-2) \times (-2) \times (-2) \times (-2)}{7 \times 7 \times 7 \times 7 \times 7} = \frac{-32}{16807}$ *Ans.*

Example 2. Write the following in exponential notation :

(a) $\frac{2}{3} \times \frac{2}{3} \times \frac{2}{3} \times \frac{2}{3} \times \frac{2}{3}$ (b) $\frac{-7}{9} \times \frac{-7}{9} \times \frac{-7}{9} \times \frac{-7}{9}$

(c) $\frac{3}{-5} \times \frac{3}{-5} \times \frac{3}{-5}$

Solution : (a) $\frac{2}{3} \times \frac{2}{3} \times \frac{2}{3} \times \frac{2}{3} \times \frac{2}{3}$.............. ($\frac{2}{3}$ multiplied by itself **5 times**)

$= \left(\frac{2}{3}\right)^5$ *Ans.*

(b) $\frac{-7}{9} \times \frac{-7}{9} \times \frac{-7}{9} \times \frac{-7}{9}$.......... ($\frac{-7}{9}$ multiplied by itself **4 times**)

$= \left(\frac{-7}{9}\right)^5$ *Ans.*

(c) $\frac{3}{-5} \times \frac{3}{-5} \times \frac{3}{-5}$................. ($\frac{3}{-5}$ multiplied by itself **3 times**)

$= \left(\frac{3}{-5}\right)^3$ *Ans.*

Example 3. Simplify :

(a) $\left(\frac{1}{2}\right)^5 \times \left(\frac{-3}{4}\right)^3 \times \left(\frac{2}{-3}\right)^2$ **(b)** $\left(\frac{4}{7}\right)^3 \times \frac{245}{256} \times \left(\frac{-2}{5}\right)^2$

Solution : (a) $\left(\frac{1}{2}\right)^5 \times \left(\frac{-3}{4}\right)^3 \times \left(\frac{2}{-3}\right)^2 = \frac{(1)^5}{(2)^5} \times \frac{(-3)^3}{(4)^3} \times \frac{(2)^2}{(-3)^2}$

$= \frac{1}{32} \times \frac{-27}{64} \times \frac{4}{9} = \frac{-3}{512}$ *Ans.*

(b) $\left(\frac{4}{7}\right)^3 \times \frac{245}{256} \times \left(\frac{-2}{5}\right)^2 = \frac{(4)^3}{(7)^3} \times \frac{245}{256} \times \frac{(-2)^2}{(5)^2}$

$= \frac{64}{343} \times \frac{245}{256} \times \frac{4}{25} = \mathbf{\frac{1}{35}}$ *Ans.*

Example 4. Write the reciprocals of : (a) $\mathbf{(-5)^3}$ (b) $\mathbf{\left(\frac{2}{3}\right)^2}$ (c) $\mathbf{\left(\frac{-3}{4}\right)^8}$

Solution : (a) Reciprocal of $(-5)^3 = \frac{1}{(-5)^3} = \frac{(1)^3}{(-5)^3} = \mathbf{\left(\frac{1}{-5}\right)^3}$ *Ans.*

(b) Reciprocal of $\left(\frac{2}{3}\right)^2 = \frac{1}{\left(\frac{2}{3}\right)^2} = 1 \div \left(\frac{2}{3}\right)^2 = 1 \div \frac{(2)^2}{(3)^2}$

$= 1 \times \frac{(3)^2}{(2)^2} = \frac{(3)^2}{(2)^2} = \mathbf{\left(\frac{3}{2}\right)^2}$ *Ans.*

(c) Reciprocal of $\left(\frac{-3}{4}\right)^8 = \frac{1}{\left(\frac{-3}{4}\right)^8} = 1 \div \left(\frac{-3}{4}\right)^8$

$= 1 \div \frac{(-3)^8}{(4)^8} = 1 \times \frac{(4)^8}{(-3)^8}$

$= \frac{(4)^8}{(-3)^8} = \left(\frac{4}{-3}\right)^8 = \mathbf{\left(\frac{-4}{3}\right)^8}$ *Ans.*

Example 5. Find the product of the cube of $\mathbf{\frac{4}{-7}}$ and square of $\mathbf{\frac{-7}{8}}$.

Solution : Cube of $\frac{4}{-7} = \left(\frac{4}{-7}\right)^3 = \frac{(4)^3}{(-7)^3} = \frac{4 \times 4 \times 4}{(-7) \times (-7) \times (-7)} = \frac{64}{-343}$

Square of $\frac{-7}{8} = \left(\frac{-7}{8}\right)^2 = \frac{(-7)^2}{(8)^2} = \frac{(-7) \times (-7)}{8 \times 8} = \frac{49}{64}$

$\therefore$ Reqd Product $= \frac{64}{-343} \times \frac{49}{64} = \frac{1}{-7} = \mathbf{\frac{-1}{7}}$ *Ans.*

Example 6. Show that $\mathbf{\left(\frac{-4}{5}\right)^3 \times 5^2 \times \left(\frac{-1}{2}\right)^5 \times \left(\frac{1}{2}\right)^3 = \frac{1}{20}}$

Solution : $\left(\frac{-4}{5}\right)^3 \times 5^2 \times \left(\frac{-1}{2}\right)^5 \times \left(\frac{1}{2}\right)^3$

$= \frac{(-4)^3}{(5)^3} \times (5)^2 \times \frac{(-1)^5}{(2)^5} \times \frac{(1)^3}{(2)^3}$

$= \frac{-64}{125} \times 25 \times \frac{-1}{32} \times \frac{1}{8} = \frac{-64 \times 25 \times (-1) \times 1}{125 \times 32 \times 8}$

$= \frac{64 \times 25}{256 \times 125} = \mathbf{\frac{1}{20}}$

Hence the given statement is proved. *Ans.*

PRACTICE EXERCISES 10

A. Answer :

1. How is $3 \times 3 \times 3 \times 3$ written in brief ? ....
2. How do we read the term 5^6? ....
3. What is 3 in the term 3^7? ....
4. What is 7 in the term 3^7? ....
5. What is –1 raised to any *odd power* equal to ? ....
6. What is –1 raised to any *even power* equal to ? ....
7. How do we write 5 as a rational number ? ....
8. What is the reciprocal of 5 ? ....
9. What is $\frac{a}{b} \times \frac{a}{b} \times \frac{a}{b}$.............*m times* equal to ? ....

B. Find the value of :

10. $\left(\frac{3}{5}\right)^2$ 11. $\left(\frac{-4}{5}\right)^3$ 12. $\left(\frac{1}{-2}\right)^4$ 13. $\left(\frac{2}{3}\right)^5$

14. $\left(\frac{6}{11}\right)^3$ 15. $\left(\frac{-3}{8}\right)^4$ 16. $\left(\frac{2}{13}\right)^2$ 17. $\left(\frac{11}{-12}\right)^3$

18. $\left(\frac{3}{4}\right)^3$ 19. $\left(-\frac{2}{3}\right)^6$ 20. $\left(\frac{3}{7}\right)^4$ 21. $\left(\frac{-4}{5}\right)^5$

C. Show that—

22. $\left(\frac{p}{q}\right)^4 = \frac{p^4}{q^4}$

23. $\left(\frac{3}{4}\right)^2 \times \left(\frac{-2}{3}\right)^3 \times \left(\frac{-5}{6}\right)^2 = \frac{-25}{216}$

24. $\left(\frac{2}{3}\right)^3 \times \left(\frac{3}{4}\right)^2 = \frac{1}{6}$

25. $\left(\frac{-3}{5}\right)^2 \times \left(\frac{4}{9}\right)^4 \times \left(\frac{-15}{18}\right)^2 = \frac{64}{6561}$

26. $\left(\frac{-2}{3}\right)^3 \times \left(\frac{4}{-5}\right)^2 = \frac{-128}{675}$

27. $\left(\frac{1}{2}\right)^3 \times \left(\frac{-3}{5}\right)^2 \times \left(\frac{-4}{9}\right)^2 = \frac{2}{225}$

D. Express the following in exponential notation :

28. $\frac{2}{5} \times \frac{2}{5} \times \frac{2}{5} \times \frac{2}{5}$ 29. $\frac{-7}{8} \times \frac{-7}{8} \times \frac{-7}{8}$ 30. $\frac{-27}{64}$ 31. $\frac{1}{243}$

32. $\frac{-8}{125}$ 33. $\frac{-1}{27}$ 34. $\frac{49}{121}$ 35. $\frac{343}{512}$ 36. $\frac{125}{512}$

37. $\frac{-1000}{729}$ 38. $\frac{625}{2401}$ 39. $\frac{1024}{3125}$ 40. $\frac{p}{q} \times \frac{p}{q} \times \frac{p}{q}$

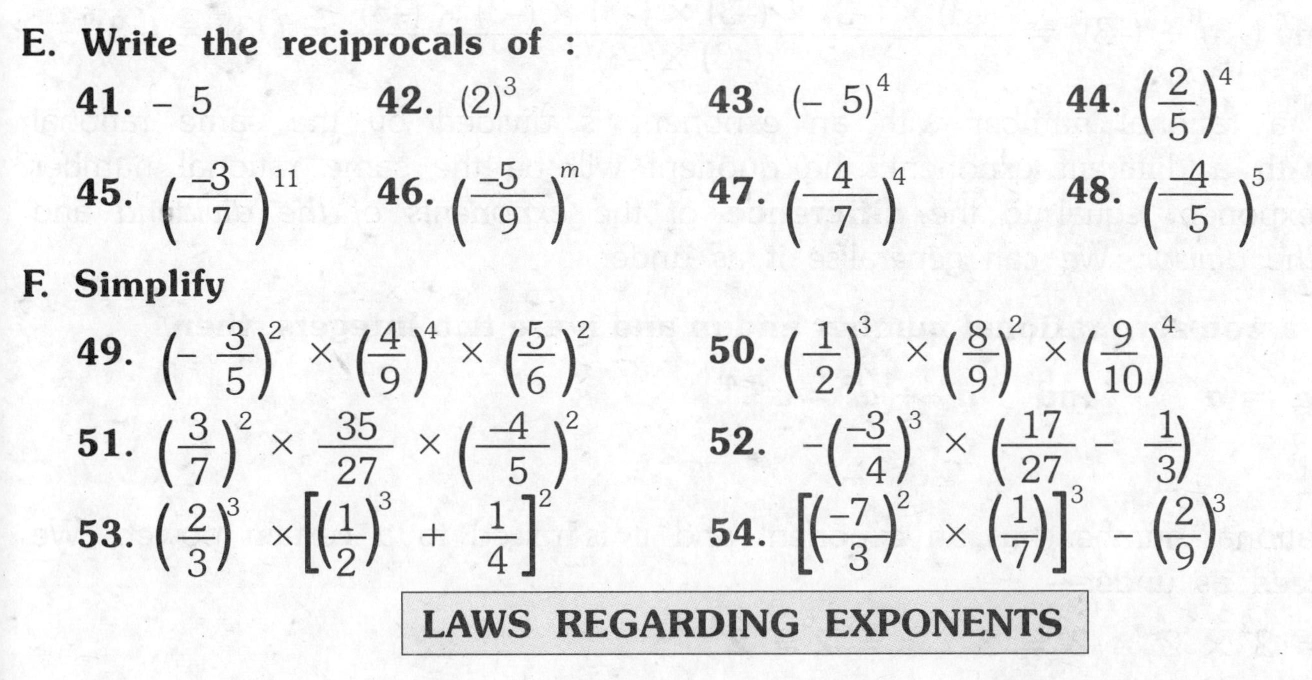

E. Write the reciprocals of :

41. -5 **42.** $(2)^3$ **43.** $(-5)^4$ **44.** $\left(\frac{2}{5}\right)^4$

45. $\left(\frac{-3}{7}\right)^{11}$ **46.** $\left(\frac{-5}{9}\right)^m$ **47.** $\left(\frac{4}{7}\right)^4$ **48.** $\left(\frac{-4}{5}\right)^5$

F. Simplify

49. $\left(-\frac{3}{5}\right)^2 \times \left(\frac{4}{9}\right)^4 \times \left(\frac{5}{6}\right)^2$ **50.** $\left(\frac{1}{2}\right)^3 \times \left(\frac{8}{9}\right)^2 \times \left(\frac{9}{10}\right)^4$

51. $\left(\frac{3}{7}\right)^2 \times \frac{35}{27} \times \left(\frac{-4}{5}\right)^2$ **52.** $-\left(\frac{-3}{4}\right)^3 \times \left(\frac{17}{27} - \frac{1}{3}\right)$

53. $\left(\frac{2}{3}\right)^3 \times \left[\left(\frac{1}{2}\right)^3 + \frac{1}{4}\right]^2$ **54.** $\left[\left(\frac{-7}{3}\right)^2 \times \left(\frac{1}{7}\right)\right]^3 - \left(\frac{2}{9}\right)^3$

LAWS REGARDING EXPONENTS

Exponents are solved according to some **rules** or **laws**. These laws are very helpful in the simplification of rational numbers with exponents.

LAW 1

We know that $2 = 2^1$,

$\therefore\ 2 \times 2 \times 2 = \mathbf{2^1 \times 2^1 \times 2^1}$

Also, we know that $2^1 \times 2^1 \times 2^1 = 8 = \mathbf{(2)^3}$

$\therefore\ 2^1 \times 2^1 \times 2^1 = (2)^3$ or $2^1 \times 2^1 \times 2^1 = \mathbf{2^3} = \mathbf{2^{1+1+1}}$

Similarly $(-4)^4 \times (-4)^3 = (-4)^{4+3} = \mathbf{(-4)^7}$

And $\left(\frac{3}{4}\right)^2 \times \left(\frac{3}{4}\right)^3 = \left(\frac{3}{4}\right)^{2+3} = \left(\mathbf{\frac{3}{4}}\right)^{\mathbf{5}}$

We see that if a rational number with two different exponents undergoes multiplication, the product will have the same number raised to the exponent **equal to the sum of the two exponents**. We can generalise it as under :

If *a* is a non-zero rational number and *m* and *n* are two integers, then $a^m \times a^n = a^{m+n}$.

LAW 2

If we are to divide a rational number with an exponent by the same rational number with a different exponent, we will proceed as under :

$$7^4 \div 7^3 = \frac{7^4}{7^3}\ \frac{7 \times 7 \times 7 \times 7}{7 \times 7 \times 7} = 7 = 7^1 = \mathbf{7^{4-3}}$$

Similarly $(-3)^6 \div (-3)^2 = \dfrac{(-3) \times (-3) \times (-3) \times (-3) \times (-3) \times (-3)}{(-3) \times (-3)} = (-3)^4 = \mathbf{(-3)^{6-2}}$

So, if a rational number with an exponent is divided by the same rational number with a different exponent, the quotient will be the same rational number with an exponent equal to the **difference** of the *exponents of the dividend* and *those of the divisor*. We can generalise it as under :

If *a* is a non-zero rational number and *m* and *n* are two integers, then

$\boldsymbol{a^m \div a^n = a^{m-n}}$ **and** $\boldsymbol{a^n \div a^m = a^{n-m}}$

LAW 3

If a rational number has an exponent and it is raised to a certain power. We shall proceed as under—

$(2^2)^3 = 2^2 \times 2^2 \times 2^2 = 2^{2+2+2} = 2^6 = \mathbf{2^{2\times3}}$

$\left[\left(\frac{3}{4}\right)^3\right]^3 = \left(\frac{3}{4}\right)^3 \times \left(\frac{3}{4}\right)^3 \times \left(\frac{3}{4}\right)^3$

$= \left(\frac{3}{4}\right)^{3+3+3} = \left(\frac{3}{4}\right)^9 = \boldsymbol{\left(\frac{3}{4}\right)^{3\times3}}$

We can generalise it as under :

If *a* is a non-zero rational number and *m*, *n* are integers, then $\boldsymbol{(a^m)^n = a^{m\times n}}$

LAW 4 *Negative Exponent*

If a rational number has a negative integer as its exponent, we proceed as under :

$7^{-3} = 7^{2-5} = 7^2 \div 7^5 = 7^2 \times \frac{1}{7^5} = \dfrac{7 \times 7}{7 \times 7 \times 7 \times 7 \times 7}$

$= \dfrac{1}{7 \times 7 \times 7} = \boldsymbol{\dfrac{1}{7^3}}$

Similarly $\left(\frac{3}{4}\right)^{-2} = \dfrac{(3)^{-2}}{(4)^{-2}} = \dfrac{3^{2-4}}{4^{2-4}} = \dfrac{3^2 \div 3^4}{4^2 \div 4^4}$ (*exponents are subtracted in division*)

$= \left(3^2 \times \frac{1}{3^4}\right) \div \left(4^2 \times \frac{1}{4^4}\right)$

$= \dfrac{3 \times 3}{3 \times 3 \times 3 \times 3} \div \dfrac{4 \times 4}{4 \times 4 \times 4 \times 4}$

$= \dfrac{3 \times 3}{3 \times 3 \times 3 \times 3} \times \dfrac{4 \times 4 \times 4 \times 4}{4 \times 4}$

$= \dfrac{1}{3 \times 3} \times \dfrac{4 \times 4}{1} = \dfrac{4^2}{3^2} = \boldsymbol{\left(\frac{4}{3}\right)^2}$

So, we can generalise it as under :

If a rational number has a negative integer as its exponent, it will be equal to its reciprocal with the same positive exponent, *i.e.*

If rational number a has $-m$ as its exponent, then $a^{-m} = \frac{1}{a^m}$

LAW 5 Zero Exponent

If a rational number has 0 as its exponent, we shall proceed as under :

$7^0 = 7^{1-1} = 7^1 \div 7^1 = 7 \times \frac{1}{7} = \mathbf{1}$

Similarly $5^0 = 5^{2-2} = 5^2 \div 5^2 = 5^2 \times \frac{1}{5^2} = 25 \times \frac{1}{25} = \mathbf{1}$

So, we can generalise it as under :

If a rational number has zero as its exponent, it is equal to 1, *i.e.*

If any rational number a has 0 as its exponent, then $a^0 = 1$

LAW 6

If two different rational numbes with the same exponent are multiplied, we shall proceed as under :

$2^4 \times 3^4 = (2 \times 2 \times 2 \times 2) \times (3 \times 3 \times 3 \times 3)$
$= 2 \times 2 \times 2 \times 2 \times 3 \times 3 \times 3 \times 3$
$= (2 \times 3) \times (2 \times 3) \times (2 \times 3) \times (2 \times 3)$
$= (2 \times 3)^4 = \mathbf{6^4}$

We can generalise it as under :

If a, b are two rational numbers and m is an integer, then $a^m \times b^m = (ab)^m$

Let us solve some examples :

Example 7. Solve the following :

(a) $(-3)^4 \times (-3)^2$ (b) $(-4)^5 \div (-4)^3$

(c) $\left(\frac{3}{2}\right)^3 \div \left(\frac{3}{2}\right)^4$ (d) $\left[\left(\frac{-2}{3}\right)^3\right]^2$

(e) $\left(\frac{9}{11}\right)^{-2}$ (f) $\left(\frac{1}{5}\right)^0$

Solution : (a) $(-3)^4 \times (-3)^2 = (-3)^{4+2} = 3^6 = \mathbf{729}$ *Ans.* *(Law 1)*

(b) $(-4)^5 \div (-4)^3 = (-4)^{5-3} = (-4)^2 = \mathbf{16}$ *Ans.* *(Law 2)*

(c) $\left(\frac{3}{2}\right)^3 \div \left(\frac{3}{2}\right)^4 = \left(\frac{3}{2}\right)^{3-4} = \left(\frac{3}{2}\right)^{-1} = \frac{3^{-1}}{2^{-1}} = \frac{2^1}{3^1} = \mathbf{\frac{2}{3}}$ *Ans.*

(Law 4)

(d) $\left[\left(\frac{-2}{3}\right)^3\right]^2 = \left(\frac{-2}{3}\right)^{3\times 2} = \left(\frac{-2}{3}\right)^6 = \frac{(-2)^6}{(3)^6} = \mathbf{\frac{64}{729}}$ *Ans.* (Law 3)

(e) $\left(\frac{9}{11}\right)^{-2} = \frac{(9)^{-2}}{(11)^{-2}} = \frac{(11)^2}{(9)^2} = \mathbf{\frac{121}{81}}$ *Ans.* (Law 5)

(f) $\left(\frac{1}{5}\right)^0 = \frac{(1)^0}{(5)^0} = \frac{1}{1} = \mathbf{1}$ *Ans.* (Law 6)

Example 8. By what should (–5) be multiplied so that the product may be 8.

Solution : Let the required number be x

$\therefore (-5) \times x = 8$ or $-5x = 8$ or $x = \frac{8}{-5}$

$\therefore$ Reqd. No. $= \mathbf{\frac{8}{-5}}$ *Ans.*

Example 9. Simplify (a) $\frac{\left(\frac{-3}{4}\right)^4 \times \left(\frac{5}{3}\right)^3}{\left(\frac{5}{3}\right)^2 \times \left(\frac{3}{4}\right)^2}$ (b) $\left[\left(\frac{2}{5}\right)^6 \div \left(\frac{2}{5}\right)\right] \div \frac{2}{5}$

Solution : (a) $\frac{\left(-\frac{3}{4}\right)^4 \times \left(\frac{5}{3}\right)^3}{\left(\frac{5}{3}\right)^2 \times \left(\frac{3}{4}\right)^2} = \frac{\left(-\frac{3}{4}\right)^4 \times \left(\frac{3}{4}\right)^{-2}}{\left(\frac{5}{3}\right)^2 \times \left(\frac{5}{3}\right)^{-3}}$ (Law 5)

$= \frac{\left(-\frac{3}{4}\right)^{4+(-2)}}{\left(\frac{5}{3}\right)^{2+(-3)}} = \frac{\left(-\frac{3}{4}\right)^{4-2}}{\left(\frac{5}{3}\right)^{2-3}} = \frac{\left(-\frac{3}{4}\right)^2}{\left(\frac{5}{3}\right)^{-1}} = \left(\frac{-3}{4}\right)^2 \times \left(\frac{5}{3}\right)^1$

$= \left(-\frac{3}{4}\right) \times \left(-\frac{3}{4}\right) \times \frac{5}{3} = \frac{9}{16} \times \frac{5}{3} = \mathbf{\frac{15}{16}}$ *Ans.*

(b) $\left[\left(\frac{2}{5}\right)^6 \div \left(\frac{2}{5}\right)\right] \div \frac{2}{5} = \left(\frac{2}{5}\right)^{6-1} \div \frac{2}{5}$

$= \left(\frac{2}{5}\right)^5 \div \left(\frac{2}{5}\right)^1 = \left(\frac{2}{5}\right)^{5-1} = \left(\frac{2}{5}\right)^4 = \frac{2^4}{5^4} = \mathbf{\frac{16}{625}}$ *Ans.*

Example 10. Find the value of x so that $\left(\frac{2}{3}\right)^{-2} \times \left(\frac{2}{3}\right)^{-9} = \left(\frac{2}{3}\right)^{2x+1}$

Solution : $\left(\frac{2}{3}\right)^{-2} \times \left(\frac{2}{3}\right)^{-9} = \left(\frac{2}{3}\right)^{2x+1}$

or $\left(\frac{2}{3}\right)^{(-2)+(-9)} = \left(\frac{2}{3}\right)^{2x+1}$ or $\left(\frac{2}{3}\right)^{-11} = \left(\frac{2}{3}\right)^{2x+1}$

$\because$ base is the same on both sides, so exponents must be equal.

$\therefore -11 = 2x + 1$ or $-11 - 1 = 2x$ or $-12 = 2x$, Hence $\mathbf{x = -6}$ *Ans.*

Example 11. Find the value of $\left(\frac{2}{5}\right)^{-3} \times \left(\frac{3}{5}\right)^{-3}$

Solution : $\left(\frac{2}{5}\right)^{-3} \times \left(\frac{3}{5}\right)^{-3} = \left(\frac{2}{5} \times \frac{3}{5}\right)^{-3}$ (*Law 6*)

$= \left(\frac{6}{25}\right)^{-3} = \left(\frac{25}{6}\right)^{3}$ (*Law 4*)

$= \mathbf{\frac{15625}{216}}$ *Ans.*

PRACTICE EXERCISES 11

A. Complete each statement :

1. $a^m \times a^n = a^{\cdots\cdots}$

2. $a^m a^n = a^{\cdots\cdots}$

3. $(a^m)^n = a^{\cdots\cdots}$

4. $a^{-m} = \frac{\cdots\cdots}{\cdots\cdots}$

5. $a^0 = \ldots\ldots\ldots\ldots$

6. $a^{m-n} = \frac{1}{a^{\cdots\cdots}}$

B. Find the value of :

7. $(-3)^3 \times (-3)^2$

8. $(-3)^5 \div (-3)^2$

9. $(-1)^4 \times (-1)^5$

10. $\left(-\frac{4}{5}\right)^2 \times \left(-\frac{4}{5}\right)^4$

11. $\left(\frac{6}{7}\right)^{-2}$

12. $\left(\frac{9}{11}\right)^{-2}$

13. $\left(\frac{1}{3}\right)^{-m}$

14. $\left[\left(\frac{2}{3}\right)^3\right]^2$

15. $\left(\frac{-3}{5}\right)^0$

C. Solve :

16. $\left(\frac{6}{7}\right)^3 \times \left(\frac{6}{7}\right)^{-3} \times \left(\frac{6}{7}\right)^0$

17. $\left(\frac{5}{4}\right)^9 \div \left(\frac{5}{4}\right)^6 \times \left(\frac{5}{4}\right)^0$

18. $\left[\left(\frac{1}{3}\right)^3\right]^2 \div \left(\frac{1}{3}\right)^6$

19. $\left(\frac{-2}{7}\right)^2 \div \left(\frac{-2}{7}\right)^2 \times \frac{7}{8}$

20. $\left(\frac{-3}{5}\right)^3 \div \left(\frac{-3}{5}\right)^5 \times \left(\frac{8}{9}\right)^0$

21. $\left(\frac{17}{20}\right)^0 \times \left(\frac{17}{20}\right)^{-1} \times \left(\frac{17}{20}\right)^2$

22. $\left(\frac{5}{7}\right)^{-3} \div \left(\frac{3}{4}\right)^{-3}$

23. $\left(\frac{-2}{3}\right)^{-4} \times \left(\frac{2}{9}\right)^{-4}$

24. $\left(\frac{4}{3}\right)^{-2} \div \left(\frac{5}{6}\right)^0$

25. $\left[\left(\frac{3}{4}\right)^3\right]^3 \div \left(\frac{3}{4}\right)^3 \times \left(\frac{1}{3}\right)^{-1} \times \left(\frac{1}{6}\right)^{-1}$

D. Simplify :

26. $\dfrac{\left(-\dfrac{3}{4}\right)^4 \times \left(\dfrac{5}{3}\right)^3}{\dfrac{25}{9} \times \left(\dfrac{3}{4}\right)^2}$ **27.** $\dfrac{\left(\dfrac{4}{7}\right)^5 \times \left(\dfrac{2}{3}\right)^3}{\left(\dfrac{2}{3}\right)^5 \times \left(\dfrac{4}{7}\right)^3}$ **28.** $\left(\dfrac{1}{2}\right)^{-2} \div \left(\dfrac{3}{4}\right)^{-2} \times \left(\dfrac{2}{3}\right)^{-2}$

29. $[(-4)^2 \times -4)^3] \div (-4)^{-12}$ **30.** $\left[\left(\dfrac{2}{5}\right)^6 \div \left(\dfrac{2}{5}\right)^5\right] \div \left(\dfrac{5}{2}\right)^{-1}$

E. Which of the following statements are true ?

31. $\left(\dfrac{-2}{9}\right)^8 \div \left(\dfrac{-2}{9}\right)^6 = \dfrac{(2)^2}{(3)^4}$ **32.** $\left[\left(\dfrac{4^2}{7}\right)\right]^5 = \left[\left(\dfrac{4}{7}\right)^2\right]^{10}$

33. $\left(\dfrac{5}{3}\right)^3 \div \left(\dfrac{5}{3}\right)^2 \times \dfrac{3}{5} = 1$ **34.** $\left(\dfrac{9}{5}\right)^{-3} \times \left(\dfrac{9}{5}\right)^0 \times (5)^{-2} \times \left(\dfrac{1}{9}\right)^{-1} = \dfrac{5}{81}$

F. Solve :

35. Find the value of $\left[\left\{\left(\dfrac{3}{4}\right)^2\right\}^3 \div \left(\dfrac{3}{4}\right)^2\right] \times \left(\dfrac{1}{3}\right)^{-2} \times (3)^{-1} \times \left(\dfrac{1}{6}\right)^{-1}$

36. Find the value of $\left(\dfrac{a}{b}\right)^{-2}$ if $\dfrac{a}{b} = \left(\dfrac{4}{3}\right)^{-2} \div \left(\dfrac{7}{8}\right)^0$

37. Find the value of x if $\left(\dfrac{3}{5}\right)^2 \times \left(\dfrac{3}{5}\right)^{-5} = \left(\dfrac{3}{5}\right)^{2x+1}$

38. By what number should $\left(\dfrac{-2}{3}\right)^{-2}$ be multiplied to get $\dfrac{3}{2}$?

39. By what number should $(8)^{-2}$ be multiplied to get (10) ?

40. Find the value of $\left(\dfrac{1}{2}\right)^{-2} \div \left(\dfrac{2}{3}\right)^{-3}$ and find the reciprocal of the resultant rational number.

41. Find the value of $\left[\left(\dfrac{2}{3}\right)^2\right]^3 \times \left(\dfrac{1}{3}\right)^{-4} \times (3)^{-1} \times \dfrac{1}{6}$ and then find the reciprocal of the resultant rational number.

42. Is it true that $\left[\left(\dfrac{3}{4}\right)^3\right]^{-2} = \dfrac{4096}{729}$ or not ?

43. Find the value of x if $2^{-3x} = \dfrac{1}{8}$

44. Find the value of m if $\left(\dfrac{2}{9}\right)^3 \times \left(\dfrac{2}{9}\right)^{-6} = \left(\dfrac{2}{9}\right)^{2m-1}$

SCIENTIFIC NOTATION

The distance of the sun from the earth is 150000000 kilometres. If we write this numeral in the place-value chart, we shall see that we have 1 in the *ten-crore's place* and **5** in the *crore's place*. All other places have zeroes (0). So, we read it as **fifteen crore**. Writing such a large number in full is not so easy. So, we use *exponential notation* to express such numbers for convenience and for saving *time* and *space* as well.

Let us have some examples :

Example 1. By what power of 10 should 2·5 be multiplied to get :

(a) **25** *(b)* **250** *(c)* **2500** *(d)* **25000**

Solution : It is quite clear

$25 = 2{\cdot}5 \times 10\ (10^1)$ *(dividing and then multiplying by 10)*

$250 = 2{\cdot}5 \times 100\ (10^2)$ (" " " " " *100*)

$2500 = 2{\cdot}5 \times 1000\ (10^3)$ (" " " " " *1000*)

$25000 = 2{\cdot}5 \times 10000\ (10^4)$ (" " " " " *10000*)

$250000 = 2{\cdot}5 \times 100000\ (10^5)$ (" " " " " *100000*)

We saw that the number 2·5 lies between **1** and **10**. So, we can express it as **$1 < 2{\cdot}5 < 10$.**

When this number is multiplied by 10 it becomes greater than 10 and when multiplied by 100, it becomes greater than 100... and so on. So, it is clear that large numbers can be written in this form to save, **time, space** and **effort**. This form is called the **standard/scientific form** of a number and writing numbers in this form is called **scientific notation**.

Let us now solve some more examples :

Example 2. Write the following numbers in their standard form :

(a) **5 million** *(b)* **15 lakh** *(c)* **150000000**

Solution : *(a)* 5 million = 5000000

5 is already between 1 and 10

Six zeroes are already there to its right

So, $5000000 = 5 \times 10^6 = \mathbf{5{\cdot}0 \times 10^6}$ *Ans.*

(b) 15 lakh = 1500000

= 15 × 100000

But in scientific notation 15 = 1·5 × 10

(dividing and then multiplying by 10)

So, 1500000 will become 1·5 × 1000000 (*6 zeroes instead of 5*)

Hence 1500000 = $\mathbf{1{\cdot}5 \times 10^{6}}$ *Ans.*

(c) 150000000 = 1·5 × 100000000 (*8 zeroes instead of 7 zeroes*)

= $1{\cdot}5 \times 10^{8}$

NUMBERS LESS THAN 1

Example 12. Express 0·00029 in scientific notation :

Solution : We know that $0{\cdot}29 = \frac{2{\cdot}9}{10}$ (*multiplying and then dividing by 10*)

$$= 2{\cdot}9 \times \frac{1}{10} = 2{\cdot}9 \times 10^{-1}$$

$$\therefore \quad 0{\cdot}029 = \frac{2{\cdot}9}{100} = 2{\cdot}9 \times \frac{1}{10^2} = \mathbf{2{\cdot}9 \times 10^{-2}}$$

Similarly $$0{\cdot}0029 = \frac{2{\cdot}9}{1000} = 2{\cdot}9 \times \frac{1}{10^3} = \mathbf{2{\cdot}9 \times 10^{-3}}$$

And $$0{\cdot}00029 = \frac{2{\cdot}9}{10000} = 2{\cdot}9 \times \frac{1}{10^4} = \mathbf{2{\cdot}9 \times 10^{-4}} \text{ Ans.}$$

Remember that

1. For numbers > 1, exponents of 10 are always *positive.*

2. For numbers < 1, exponents of 10 are always *negative.*

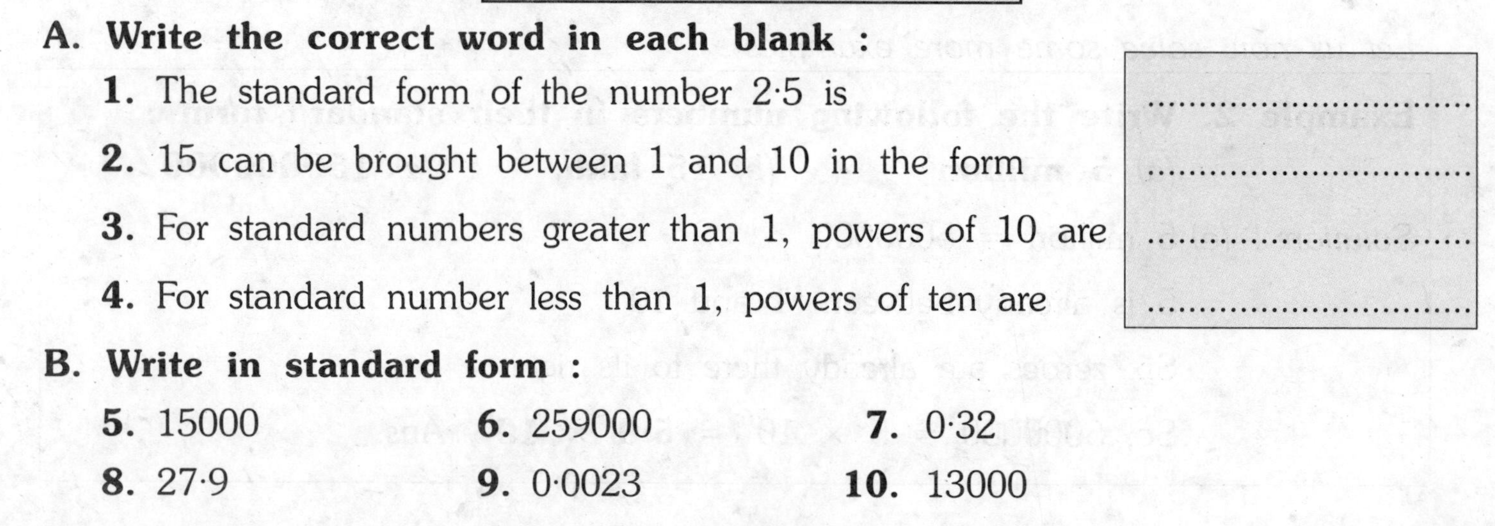

PRACTICE EXERCISES 12

A. Write the correct word in each blank :

1. The standard form of the number 2·5 is ....

2. 15 can be brought between 1 and 10 in the form ....

3. For standard numbers greater than 1, powers of 10 are ....

4. For standard number less than 1, powers of ten are ....

B. Write in standard form :

5. 15000	**6.** 259000	**7.** 0·32
8. 27·9	**9.** 0·0023	**10.** 13000

C. Write in scientific notation :

11. 0·0029 **12.** 0·0000073 **13.** 0·00092

14. 0·000037 **15.** 0·0000074 **16.** 0·000029

D. 17. The speed of light is 300000000 metres per second. Write it in standard form.

18. The speed of sound is 33000 cm. per second. Write it in scientific notation.

19. The distance travelled by a light-ray in a year is 9460500000000000 kilometres. Write it in scientific notation.

20. The distance of the moon from the earth is 384400000 kilometres. Write it in the standard form.

21. The diameter of an atom is $1{\cdot}5 \times \frac{1}{100000000}$ cm. Write it scientifically.

E. Write the following scientific numbers in common form :

22. $5{\cdot}98 \times 10^{8}$ **23.** $4{\cdot}10^{-6}$ **24.** $9{\cdot}8 \times 10^{-7}$

25. $1{\cdot}06 \times 10^{9}$ **26.** $7{\cdot}03 \times 10^{-6}$ **27.** $7{\cdot}3 \times 10^{-6}$

28. 18 thousand **29.** $2{\cdot}89 \times 10^{5}$ **30.** $9{\cdot}3 \times 10^{5}$

F. 31. A star is about $8{\cdot}1 \times 10^{13}$ kilometres from the earth. If light be travelling at $3{\cdot}0 \times 10^{5}$ km. per second, how long will it take the light of the star to reach the earth ?

32. The needle of a record-player makes 900 revolutions to play a song. It has to move over a distance of 7·2 cm. in all. Find the width of the groove of the record-player.

33. An aeroplane is to fly over a distance of $3{\cdot}5 \times 10^{5}$ kilometres at the speed of $7{\cdot}0 \times 10^{5}$ metres per hour. How long will it take the aeroplane to cover the distance ?

34. A jet aeroplane has a speed of $8{\cdot}0 \times 10^{5}$ kilometres in an hour. How long will it take the jet to cover a journey $4{\cdot}0 \times 10$ kilometres long.

35. The diameter of an atom is $\frac{1{\cdot}5}{100000000}$ cm. Write it in standard form.

MISCELLANEOUS EXERCISES I

A. Answer *yes* **or** *no* :

1. Every natural number is a rational number too. ....

2. 0 was invented to form the integers. ....

3. Between every two consecutive integers, there is an integer. ....

4. Between two rational numbers, there is a rational number. ....

5. The product of two positive rational numbers is always positive. ....

6. The reciprocal of $-3 = \frac{1}{-3}$ ....

7. The additive inverse of $-\frac{3}{4}$ is $\frac{4}{3}$ ....

8. Every rational number has a decimal form. ....

9. Every rational number is necessarily in natural number. ....

10. Any rational number + zero equals the rational number itself. ....

11. Every negative rational number is smaller than zero. ....

12. $\frac{p+r}{q} = \frac{p}{q} + \frac{r}{q}$ ....

13. The reciprocal of a number is called its *multiplicative inverse* also. ....

14. The multiplicative inverse of 0 is 0 itself. ....

B.15. Show the following rational numbers on a number line :

(a) $\frac{3}{4}$ (b) $\frac{2}{3}$ (c) $1\frac{1}{3}$

C. Solve :

16. $\left(\frac{-4}{25} + \frac{11}{15}\right) \div \left(\frac{17}{75} + \frac{3}{25}\right)$

17. $\left(\frac{-27}{32} + \frac{7}{8}\right) - \left(\frac{13}{16} + \frac{1}{4}\right)$

18. $\left(\frac{41}{2} + \frac{35}{2}\right) \div \left(\frac{23}{7} - \frac{11}{14}\right)$

19. $\frac{2}{5} \times \left(\frac{7}{9} - \frac{11}{117}\right) \times \frac{13}{16}$

20. Express $\frac{3147}{256}$ in decimal form :

21. What must be subtracted from $\frac{41}{16}$ to get $-\frac{23}{48}$

22. Subtract the sum of $3\frac{4}{11}$ and $\frac{3}{22}$ from the difference of $\frac{11}{4}$ and $\frac{-7}{4}$.

23. Arrange the following in descending order :

$\frac{7}{2}, \frac{-3}{4}, \frac{7}{20}, 0, \frac{-3}{7}, \frac{9}{40}, \frac{5}{8}$

24. Which of the following are terminating decimals ?

$\frac{41}{8}, \frac{-5}{11}, \frac{21}{20}, \frac{47}{64}$

25. Solve : (a) $2{\cdot}0 \times 10^5 \times 1{\cdot}9 \times 10^{-3}$ (b) $1{\cdot}8 \times 10^8 \times 7{\cdot}3 \times 10^{-7}$

D. Simplify :

26. (a) $\left(\frac{4}{5}\right)^7 \times \left(\frac{4}{5}\right)^9 \times \left(\frac{4}{5}\right)^{-16}$ (b) $(a^3 b^2) \div (a^2 b^3)^3$

27. $(x)^{3b-c} \times (x)^{c-a} \times (x)^{a-b}$

28. $(5^3)^2 \div (5^2)^3$

29. $(p)^{x-y+z} \times (p)^{x-y+z} \times (p)^{x-y+z}$

30. $3^{x+2} = 3^{2x+4}$

E. Solve the equations : 31. $2 \times 2 \div 2 = 16$ **32.** $3 \times 3 \times 3 = 9$

F. If $x = 2$, $y = 3$ find the value of :

33. $\left(\frac{1}{x} + \frac{1}{y}\right)^y$ **34.** $\left(\frac{x}{y} + \frac{y}{x}\right)^3$ **35.** $\frac{x^y + y^x}{x^y - y^x} \times \frac{x}{y}$

36. $\frac{x^4 + y^4}{x^4 - y^4} \times \left(\frac{1}{x} + \frac{1}{y}\right)$ **37.** $3^{3x} - 3^{2y}$

38. Compare the rational numbers $\frac{5}{-8}$ and $\frac{-7}{12}$

39. Write two rational numbers between $\frac{-6}{11}$ and $\frac{5}{6}$.

G. Complete each statement :

40. Two rational numbers can be added in any ....

41. Additive inverse of a rational number is its own ....

42. Multiplicative inverse of a number is its ....

43. The number to be added to $\frac{4}{9}$ to get $\frac{-7}{8}$ is ....

44. Prove that $\frac{-3}{11} \times \frac{5}{21} = \frac{5}{21} \times \frac{-3}{11}$ ....

H. Fill up the blanks :

45. $a(b + c) = (a \times \ldots) + (\ldots \times c)$ **46.** $p \times (q \times r) = r \times (\ldots \times \ldots)$

47. $\frac{-25}{19} \times \frac{\ldots}{\ldots} = -1$ **48.** $\frac{3}{-7} \times \frac{\ldots}{9} = \frac{4}{\ldots} \times \frac{\ldots}{\ldots}$

49. The product of two rational numbers is $\frac{-5}{7}$. One of the numbers is $\frac{-15}{56}$. Find the other.

50. Write the following in scientific form.

(a) 846×10 (b) $1 \div 100000$ (c) 372×10

MEMORABLE FACTS

1. 0 is a rational number in the form $\frac{0}{1}$, $\frac{0}{2}$, or $\frac{0}{3}$ etc.
2. A rational number is positive if its numerator and denominator have *similar signs* before them.
3. A rational number is negative if its numerator and denominator have *different signs* before them.
4. An integer can be expressed as a rational number by writing it as the *numerator* and writing 1 as its *denominator*.
5. In order to *compare* two rational numbers, we have to *reduce them to the same denominator*.
6. The *sum* of two rational numbers is *also a rational number.*
7. Rational numbers can be added up *in any order* and *in any grouping*.
8. The *negative* and *positive* forms of a rational number form *additive inverse forms* of each other.
9. The *difference* of any two rational numbers is *also a rational number.*
10. The *product* of two rational numbers is *also a rational number.*
11. The *product* of two rational numbers is equal to the *product of their numerators* divided by the *product of their denominators.*
12. A rational number *multiplied by zero* is equal to *zero*.
13. The *reciprocal* of a rational number is obtained by *changing the places of* its *numerator* and *denominator.*
14. The *reciprocal* of a rational number is called its *multiplicative inverse* also.
15. If a rational number, *is divided* by a non-zero rational number the quotient is *also a rational number.*
16. A rational number *divided by its additive inverse gives* –1 as quotient.
17. A rational number *added to its additive inverse* is equal to zero.
18. A rational number *divided by its reciprocal* gives 1 as quotient.
19. Rational numbers have *two types of decimal forms* : *terminating form* and *recurring form.*
20. Some laws *regarding exponents of rational numbers* are :

    (a) $a \times a \times a \times a......n$ times $= a^n$ (b) $a^m \times a^n = a^{m+n}$

    (c) $a^m \div a^n = a^{m-n}$ (d) $a^{-m} = \frac{1}{a^m}$ (e) $a^0 = 1$ (f) $a^m \times b^m = (ab)^m$

UNIT II

COMMERCIAL ARITHMETIC

Unitary Method, Laws of Variation *(Ratios, Proportions)* and **Percentage** are the chief tools employed in Commercial Arithmetic.

IN THIS UNIT—

8 VARIATION : DIRECT, INVERSE

KNOW THESE TERMS :

1. **direct variation**—variation in which two quantities vary constantly i.e. one of them increases or decreases just as the other does
2. **inverse variation**—variation in which two quantities very inversely i.e. one of them decreases constantly as the other increases or *vice versa*.

What is *variation* ?

Variation means **change in the value** of an item **due to change** in its **number** or **quantity** and *vice versa.*

Variation can take place in two different ways as under :

(a) Direct Variation *(b)* Indirect or Inverse Variation

DIRECT VARIATION

(a) I buy **1** *packet of bread* for **Rs. 5** every day.

(b) If some friends visit me, I shall buy **2** or **3** *packets of bread.* Clearly, I shall buy 2 packets for **Rs. 10**.

(c) Similarly, **3** *packets* will cost **Rs. 15** and **4** *packets* will cost **Rs. 20**.

We see that as the **number of packets** *increases*, **the cost** *also increases*. Conversely, if the **number of packets** *decreases*, **the cost** also decreases.

Such a variation is called DIRECT VARIATION.

In this type of variation—

$\dfrac{\textit{No. of Bread-Packets}}{\textit{No. of Rupees}}$ is the **ratio of variation.**

This ratio always remains the same (*constant*) ; as—

Packets	*Price in Rs.*	=	*Ratio*
1	5	=	**1 : 5**
2	10	=	2 : 10 = **1 : 5**
3	15	=	3 : 15 = **1 : 5**

We can generalise it as under :

Two quantities *a* **and** *b* are **in direct variation, if their ratio** *(a : b)* **remains constant,** ***i.e.*** **if one of them increases or decreases just as the other does.**

Let us now solve some examples :

Examples 1. The cost of 15 oranges is Rs. 35. Find the cost of 39 oranges.

Solution : Let the cost of 39 oranges be x

Oranges	15	39
Rupees	35	x

$\because$ No of oranges have increased

$\therefore$ Cost will also increase

So, It is a case of *direct variation*.

$\therefore \frac{15}{39}$ must be equal to $\frac{35}{x}$ or $15x = 35 \times 39$

or $x = \frac{35 \times 39}{15} = 91$; Hence cost of 39 oranges = **Rs. 91** *Ans.*

Examples 2. If a car needs 36 litres oil to cover 522 kilometres. How much oil will it need to cover 203 kilometres.

Solution : Let the reqd. quantity of oil be x

kilometres	522	203
litres	36	x

$\because$ No. of kilometres has decreased

$\therefore$ litres of oil must also decrease

So, it is a case of *direct variation*

$\therefore \frac{522}{203} = \frac{36}{x}$ or $522x = 203 \times 36$

or $x = \frac{203 \times 36}{522} = 14$

Hence Reqd. quantity of oil = **14 litres** *Ans.*

Examples 3. The cost of 37 metres of silk is Rs. 2090·50. How many metres of silk can be bought for Rs. 2373 ?

Solution : Let the reqd. no of metres be x

Rupees	2090·50	2373
Metres	37	x

$\because$ Cost has increased

$\therefore$ metres must also increase

So, it is a case of *direct variation*

$\therefore \frac{2090{\cdot}50}{2373} = \frac{37}{x}$ or $x\,(2090{\cdot}50) = 2373 \times 37$

or $x = \frac{2373 \times 37}{2090{\cdot}50} = \frac{2373 \times 37 \times 2}{4181} = 42$

Hence Reqd. length of silk = **42 metes** *Ans.*

Examples 4. A worker is paid Rs. 213 after working for 6 days. His total wages for the month were Rs. 923. How many days did he work during the month ?

Solution : Let the reqd. no of days be x

Rupees	213	923
Days	6	x

$\because$ Wages have increased

$\therefore$ days must also increase

So, it is a case of *direct variation*

$$\therefore \frac{213}{923} = \frac{6}{x} \quad \text{or} \quad 213x = 6 \times 923$$

$$\text{or } x = \frac{6 \times 923}{213} = 26$$

So, the worker worked for **26 days** *Ans.*

PRACTICE EXERCISES 13

A. Answer :

1. What is meant by *variation* ?

2. What is meant by *direct variation* ?

3. If $\frac{a}{b} = k$ and k is constant, is it a case of direct variation ?

B. Which of the following tables show direct variation ?

4.

x	1	2	3	4	5
y	2	1	3	3	4

5.

x	10	20	30	40	50
y	19	38	57	76	95

6.

x	4·5	9	12	16·5	19·5
y	3	6	8	11	13

7.

x	10	12·50	30	40	50
y	22	27·50	66	76	95

C. 8. The cost of 6 metres of cloth is Rs. 24·00. Find the cost of 2, 3, 9, 12, 15 metres of cloth writing them in a table to show direct variation.

9. 6 sheets of paper weigh 45 grams. What will be the weight of 200 such sheets.

10. 5 litres of petrol cost Rs. 130. What will be the cost of 8 litres of petrol ?

11. 50 kilograms of flour is needed every day for 200 men living in a hostel. How many men can be fed every day with 112·5 kilograms of floor ?

12. A bus covers 150 km. in 3 hours. In how many hours will it cover 400 km. ?

13. 72 books can be packed in 4 cartons of the same size. How many cartons will be needed for 288 such books to be packed ?

14. 12 exercise-books with 250 pages each cost Rs. 60. What will be the cost of 20 exercise-books with 250 pages each ?

15. A rich man distributed 35 blankets to beggars which cost him Rs. 1680. How much money will he have to spend to distribute 40 such blankets ?

16. 8 small calculators can be bought for Rs. 300. How much will 18 such calculators cost ?

17. 30 metres of woollen cloth cost Rs. 1455. How many metres of this cloth can be bought for Rs. 970 ?

18. 13 metres of iron wire weigh 23·4 kilograms. What length of the wire shall weigh 10·8 kilograms ?

19. The shadow cast by a pole 3 metres high is 3·6 metres in length. How high a pole will cast a shadow 54 metres in length ?

20. 8 cartons of the same size can contain 1152 cakes of Rexona Soap. How many cartons will be needed for 3888 such cakes ?

21. The monthly consumption of refined oil in a commune of 60 persons is 1350 litres. What will the consumption be if 16 more persons join the commune ?

22. 7·5 kilogram of tea cost Rs. 56·25. How much should be paid for 2·4 kilograms of the same tea ?

23. A car covers a certain distance in $3\frac{1}{2}$ hours running at a speed of 25 kilometres an hour. How long will it take to cover the same distance at a speed of 42 kilometres an hour ?

24. A 54 horse-power pumping–set raises 1530 litres of water per minute from a certain depth. What horse-power is needed to raise 2805 litres per minute from the same depth ?

D. Write True or False against each statement :

25. $x = k$ shows direct variation if k is constant. ....

26. $\frac{x}{y} = k$ is a case of direct variation if y is constant. ....

27. $\frac{x}{y} = k$ shows direct variation if x is constant. ....

28. The variation is direct if a car covers 300 km. in 5 hours and 540 km. in 9 hours. ....

INVERSE VARIATION

We read in the case of direct variation that two quantities undergo increase or decrease together. But sometimes the case is just inverse. It is mostly in the case of **time** *taken for* **a job**. For example :

(*a*) 6 men do a job in 4 days. But 5 of the men fall ill and only 1 man is left to do the job. He will take many more days to do the job.

Clearly, **1 man will do the in 4 × 6 = 24 days.**

(*b*) Again, if 8 men are put to do the job, they will do it in fewer days than 6 men even.

Clearly, **8 men will do the job in 24 ÷ 8 = 3 days.**

We can tabulate these facts as under :

Men	1	2	3	4	6	8	12
Days	24	12	8	6	4	3	2

It is quite clear that—

1. **If the number of men** *decreases,* **the number of days** *increases.*
2. **If the number of men** *increases,* **the number of days** *decreases.*

Such a variation is called **inverse variation.**

Let us consider what happens to the ratio in the case of an inverse variation. Observing the table given above closely, we see that the **product of the men and the corresponding days** remains the same, *i.e. constant.*

We can generalise it as under :

Two quantities *a* **and** *b* **are in inverse variation if their product remains constant,** ***i.e.*** **one of them** *decreases* **constantly as the other** *increases* **; as—**

Men	×	Time (days)	=	Product
1	×	24	=	24
2	×	12	=	24
3	×	8	=	24
4	×	6	=	24

Men	:	Time (days)	=	Product
6	:	4	=	24
8	:	3	=	24
12	:	2	=	24
24	:	1	=	24

Let us now solve some examples :

Examples 5. A school boarding-house has provisions to last 15 days for 400 students. How many days will the provisions last if 100 more students join in ?

Solution : Suppose Reqd. No. of days = x

∵ No of students has *increased*

∴ No of days will **decrease**

students	400	400 + 100 = 500
days	15	x

So, it is a case of *inverse variation*

∴ Product 400 × 15 must be equal to the product of $x \times 500$

or $500x = 400 \times 15$ or $x = \frac{400 \times 15}{500} = 12$

Hence the provisions will last **12 days** *Ans.*

Examples 6. 16 horses graze a green field in 25 days. In how days would 40 horses have grazed it ?

Solution : Suppose Reqd. No. of days = x

∵ No of horses has *increased*

∴ No of days will **decrease.**

horses	16	40
days	25	x

So, it is a case of *inverse variation*

∴ Product of 16 × 25 must be equal to the product of $40 \times x$

or $40x = 16 \times 25$ or $x = \frac{16 \times 25}{40} = 10$

Hence 40 horses would have grazed the field in **10 days** *Ans.*

Examples 7. A contractor promises to construct a building in 9 months with a work-force of 560 men. How many extra men will he have to employ if the building is to be built in 7 months.

Solution : Suppose new number of men = x

∵ Months have *decreased*

∴ men will **increase** in number

Months	9	7
Men	560	x

So, it is a case of *inverse variation*

∴ Product of 9 × 560 must be equal to Product of $7 \times x$

or $7x = 9 \times 560$ or $x = \frac{9 \times 560}{7} = 720$

∴ No. of extra men employed = 720 − 560 = **160** *Ans.*

PRACTICE EXERCISES 14

A. Which of the following show inverse variation ?

1.

days	8	16	32
men	4	2	1

2.

km.	80	40	20	160
hrs.	8	16	32	1

B. Complete each table so that it shows inverse variation :

3.

Flour in kg.	......	125	......	500	......
Men	25	20	10	.....	1

4.

a	36	8	6	.....	3
b	.....	9	.....	18	.....

C. 5. An insurance company undertakes to pay Rs. 2000 to the wife of a man at his death against different premiums to be paid at different ages. Taking the premium Rs. 56 at the age of 35 as a standard, determine the other premiums so that the age and the premium remain in inverse proportion

Age	25	30	35	40	45
Premium in Rs.	.....	.....	56	.....	.....

6. 36 men do a job in 25 days. In how many days will 15 men do it ?

7. A gang of 540 men can construct a building in 7 months. How many men should be removed from work to finish the building in 9 months ?

8. A garrison of 800 soldiers had provisions for 15 days in a fort. But 300 men escape through a secret tunnel. How long will the provisions last now.

9. 12 pumps were put to work to empty a tank in 20 minutes. Suddenly 2 pumps went out of order. How long will the remaining pumps take to empty the tank ?

10. A working ladies' hostel has food-stuffs enough to last 40 days for 25 ladies. How many ladies must leave so that the food-stuffs may last 50 days ?

11. Mohan has enough money to buy 4 kilogram of potatoes at Rs. 5·00 per kg. If the price goes up to be Rs. 8·00 per kg., how much potatoes shall Mohan buy ?

12. A hostel has flour for 300 children to last 42 days. If 50 more children reach suddenly, how long will the flour last ?

13. A regiment of 500 soldiers garrisoned in a fort have provisions for 24 days. Suddenly 700 more soldiers arrive. How long will the provisions last now ?

14. A contractor puts 420 men to construct a bridge in 9 months. How many extra men must he employ to build the bridge in 7 months ?

15. A car covers a certain distance in 3 hours at a speed of 45 km. per hour. How long will it take the car to cover the same distance at 36 km. per hour ?

COMPOUND RATIOS (THE CHAIN RULE)

The chain rule means the use of rules of variation more than once in one and the same problem. In this case, we form a **ratio** or **product** for each rule and solve the problem using the compounded facts. Let us solve some examples.

Examples 8. 70 patients in a hospital consume 1350 litres of milk in 30 days. How many patients will use up 1710 litres of milk in 28 days ?

Solution : Suppose the Reqd. No. of patients = x

litres	1350	1710
days	30	28
patients	70	x

$\because$ litres have *increased*, patients must also **increase**. (*direct variation*)

$\therefore$ the ratio will be $\mathbf{\frac{1710}{1350}}$

$\because$ days have *decreased*, patients, will **increase**. (*inverse variation*)

$\therefore$ the ratio will be $\mathbf{\frac{30}{28}}$

Given No. of patients = **70**

$\therefore$ Reqd. No. of patients = $\frac{1710}{1350} \times \frac{30}{28} \times 70 = \mathbf{95}$ *Ans.*

☞ **Master the rule given in the box below to solve problems involving compound ratios.**

RULE :
1. Make the table of ratios/prodcuts.
2. Observe each ratio one by one and decide whether the answer is to be *more* or *less* than the given quantity.
3. If **more**, make the larger quantity the numerator of the ratio and the other its denominator.
4. If the answer is to be **less** than the given quantity, make the smaller quantity the numerator of the ratio and the other its denominator.
5. Multiply all the ratios and the given quantity of the item that is to be found.

Examples 9. 36 men can build a wall 140 metres long and 3 metres high in 21 days. How many men will take 14 days to build a wall 60 metres long and 3·5 metres high ?

Solution : Suppose the Reqd. No. of men = x

Length in metres	140	60
Height in metres	3	3·5
Days	21	14
Men	36	x

∵ **Length** has *decreased,* men will also **decrease.**

∴ Its ratio = $\mathbf{\frac{60}{140}}$

∵ **Height** has *increased,* men will ***increase***

∴ Its ratio = $\frac{3 \cdot 5}{3} = \frac{7}{2 \times 3} = \mathbf{\frac{7}{6}}$

∵ **Days** have *decreased,* men will **increase**

∴ Their ratio = $\mathbf{\frac{21}{14}}$

Given number of men = **36**

∴ Reqd. No. of men = $\frac{60}{140} \times \frac{7}{6} \times \frac{21}{14} \times 36$ = **27 men** *Ans.*

Examples 10. A regiment of 600 soldiers in a fort has food-stuffs to last 35 days at a certain rate of ration per head. How long will the food-stuffs last if the soldiers increase to be 900 and the rate of ration is reduced in the ratio 5:6.

Solution : Suppose the Reqd. No. of days = x

Soldiers	600	900
Ration	6	5
Days	35	x

Soldiers have *increased,* days will **decrease**

Their Ratio = $\mathbf{\frac{600}{900}}$

Ration has *reduced,* it will last for **more days**

Their Ratio = $\mathbf{\frac{6}{5}}$

Given number of days = **35**

Reqd. No, of days = $\frac{600}{900} \times \frac{6}{5} \times 35$ = **28 days** *Ans.*

PRACTICE EXERCISES 15

1. The cost of 16 packets of salt each weighing 900 grams is Rs. 28. Find the cost of 27 packets of salt each of which weighs 1 kilogram.

2. 30 labourers working 7 hours a day can finish a job in 18 days. How many labourers working 6 hours a day can finish the job in 30 days ?

3. 40 persons use up 60 kg. rice in 15 days. In how many days will 30 persons consume 12 kg. rice ?

4. In a school-hostel, flour is enough for 300 students to last 42 days at 250 grams per head. How long will the flour last if 50 more students join the hostel and the daily ration is reduced to 200 grams per head.

5. A rectangle has an area of 150 square metres. What will its area be if its length increases in the ratio 4 : 3 and its breadth increases in the ratio 3 : 2 ?

6. A car covers 96 kilometres at a certain speed in a certain period of time. How much distance will its cover if its speed decreases in the ratio 3 : 4 and time decreases in the ratio 5 : 8 ?

7. A work is completed in 20 days by 32 men working $7\frac{1}{2}$ hours a day. How many men will do the same work in 8 days working 10 hours a day ?

8. A hand-written script has 120 pages of 28 lines each and each line has 7 words. In how many pages will it get printed if each printed page has 42 lines of 10 words each ?

9. A garrison of 1500 soldiers in a fort has food-stuffs for 12 weeks. How many soldiers can be fed with the same amount of food-stuffs for 20 weeks if the daily ration per head is reduced in the ratio 9 : 10 ?

10. The freight for carrying 42 quintals over 98 kilometres is Rs. 49. What will be the freight for carrying 27 quintals over 28 kilometres at the same rate per quintal ?

11. A car running at 88 kilometres per hour covers a certain journey in $3\frac{1}{2}$ hours. How long will it take a bus to cover two-thirds of the journey if its speed bears the ratio 4 : 9 to that of the car.

12. 5 harvesters reap a crop in 16 days working 9 hours a day. In how many days will 8 harvesters reap the same crop working 10 hours a day ?

9 TIME AND WORK

KNOW THESE TERMS :

1. **work**—any job undertaken to be done. Complete work is always referred to as 1
2. **time**—period (days, hours, etc.) taken by a *doer/doers* to complete a work
3. **distance**—journey travelled by a person or vehicle etc.
4. **speed**—distance covered by a person/vichicle in a unit time (*hour* etc.)

We have already learnt from the sums on variation that—

(*a*) More **working hands** take **less time** to complete a work.

(*b*) **Less time** given for a job needs **more working hands**.

(*c*) **More daily hours for work** mean **fewer days** to complete a job.

(*d*) **Fewer daily hours** for work mean **more days** to complete a job.

(*e*) **1. If A completes a job in 6 days, he does $\frac{1}{6}$ of the job in 1 day.**

2. If A does $\frac{1}{6}$ of the job in 1 day, he will do the job in 6 days.

Let us solve some examples :

Example 1. Monu can do a work in 30 days while Sonu can do it in 20 days. How long will they take to do it if they work together.

Solution : $\because$ Monu can do the work in 30 days.

$\therefore$ He does $\frac{1}{30}$ of the wprk in 1 day

$\because$ Sonu can do the work in 20 days.

$\therefore$ He does $\frac{1}{20}$ of the work in 1 day.

$\therefore$ Both will do $\left(\frac{1}{30} + \frac{1}{20}\right)$ or $\frac{2 + 3}{60} = \frac{5}{60}$ of the work in 1 day.

Hence they will do the job in $\frac{60}{5}$ or **12 days** *Ans.*

A HANDY RULE :

If A does a work in *m* days and B in *n* days

A's 1 day's work $= \frac{1}{m}$ and B's 1 day's work $= \frac{1}{n}$

$\therefore$ (A + B)'s 1 day's work $= \frac{1}{m} + \frac{1}{n} = \frac{n+m}{mn}$

So, they will do the job together in $\frac{mn}{m+n}$ days.

Applying this rule to this example :

A does the work in 30 days.

B does the work in 20 days.

$\therefore$ Both will do it in $\frac{30 \times 20}{30 + 20}$ days

i.e. in $\frac{600}{50}$ or **12 days**

Example 2. **Akbar and Anthony can together harvest a field in 4 days. If Akbar can harvest the field alone in 12 days, how long will it take Anthony to harvest it alone ?**

Solution : Both can harvest the field in 4 days

$\therefore$ Their 1 day's work $= \mathbf{\frac{1}{4}}$

Akbar can harvest the field alone in 12 days

$\therefore$ Akbar's 1 day's work $= \mathbf{\frac{1}{12}}$

Clearly, Anthony's 1 day's work $= \frac{1}{4} - \frac{1}{12} = \frac{3-1}{12} = \frac{2}{12} = \mathbf{\frac{1}{6}}$

Hence Anthony can do the job alone in **6 days** *Ans.*

Example 3. **Working 8 hours a day, Sohan can copy a book in 18 days. How many hours a day must he work to copy it in 12 days ?**

Days	18	12
Hours	8	x

Solution : Suppose the reqd. No. of hours $= x$

$\because$ **Days** have *decreased*, hours must **increase**

$\therefore$ Their Ratio $= \mathbf{\frac{18}{12}}$

Given No. of hours $=$ **8**

$\therefore$ Reqd. No. of hours $= \frac{18}{12} \times 8 =$ **12 hrs.** *Ans.*

Example 4. **A and B can do a job in 18 days ; B and C in 24 days while A and C in 36 days, how long will all the three take to finish it together as well as separately ?**

Solution : (A + B)'s one day's work $= \frac{1}{18}$

(B + C)'s one day's work $= \frac{1}{24}$

(A + C)'s one day's work $= \frac{1}{36}$

$\therefore$ (A + B)'s + (B + C)'s + (A + C)'s 1 day's work

or 2(A + B + C)'s 1 day's work $= \frac{1}{18} + \frac{1}{24} + \frac{1}{36}$

$= \frac{4+3+2}{72} = \frac{9}{72} = \frac{1}{8}$

$\therefore$ (A + B + C)'s 1 day's work $= \frac{1}{8} \times \frac{1}{2} = \frac{1}{16}$

So, A, B, C can finish the job together in **16 days** *Ans.*

Now, A's 1 day's work = (A+B+C)'s 1 day's work – (B+C)'s 1 day's work

$= \frac{1}{16} - \frac{1}{24} = \mathbf{\frac{1}{48}}$; so **A** can do the job in **48 days**. *Ans.*

Similarly B's 1 day's work $= \frac{1}{16} - \frac{1}{36} = \frac{9-4}{144} = \mathbf{\frac{5}{144}}$,

So, **B** can do it in $\frac{144}{5}$ or $\mathbf{28\frac{4}{5}}$ **days** *Ans.*

And C's 1 day's work $= \frac{1}{16} - \frac{1}{18} = \frac{9-8}{144} = \mathbf{\frac{1}{144}}$

So, **C** can do the work in **144 days** *Ans.*

Example 5. A and B can do a piece of work in 6 days and 4 days respectively. A starts the work and works at it for 2 days. Then B joins him. How long will it take them to finish the remaining work ?

Solution : A can do the work in 6 days, so his 1 day's work $= \frac{1}{6}$

B can do the work in 4 days, so his 1 day's work $= \frac{1}{4}$

$\therefore$ (A+B)'s 1 day's work $= \frac{m+n}{mn} = \frac{6+4}{6 \times 4} = \frac{10}{24} = \mathbf{\frac{5}{12}}$

Now, A worked alone for 2 days

So, work done by him $= \frac{1}{6} \times 2 = \mathbf{\frac{1}{3}}$

Remaining work $= 1 - \frac{1}{3} = \mathbf{\frac{2}{3}}$ *(complete work is taken to be 1)*

This work will be done by A and B together

(A+B)'s 1 day's work $= \frac{5}{12}$

$\therefore$ They do $\frac{2}{3}$ of the work in $= \frac{2}{3} \div \frac{5}{12}$ days

$= \frac{2}{3} \times \frac{12}{5} = \frac{8}{5}$ days

$= \mathbf{1\frac{3}{5}}$ **days** *Ans.*

Example 6. Pipe A can fill an empty tank in 10 hours while pipe B can empty the full tank in 15 hours. If both the pipes are opened when the tank is empty, how much time will it take the tank to get filled ?

Solution : Pipe A can fill the tank in 10 hours

So, work done by pipe A in 1 hour $= \frac{1}{10}$

Pipe B can empty the tank in 15 hours

So, work done by pipe B in 1 hour $= \frac{1}{15}$

If both the pipes are opened together, they will work against each other.

Work done in 1 hour by both the pipes $= \frac{1}{10} - \frac{1}{15} = \mathbf{\frac{1}{30}}$

Hence the tank will get filled in **30 hours** *Ans.*

Example 7. 4 men or 7 boys can dig a tank in 15 days. How long will 2 men and 4 boys take to dig the same tank working together ?

Solution : 4 men = 7 boys

1 man $= \frac{7}{4}$ boys and 2 men $= \frac{7}{4} \times 2 = \frac{7}{2}$ boys

In the second case, 2 men + 4 boys will work together

In other words, $\left(\frac{7}{2}\text{ boys} + 4\text{ boys}\right)$ or $\frac{15}{2}$ boys will work together

Now using *unitary method*—

7 boys dig the tank in 15 days

1 boy will dig it in 15 × 7 = 105 days

and $\frac{15}{2}$ boys will dig it in $105 \times \frac{2}{15} =$ **14 days** *Ans.*

Example 8. A, B, C can do a job in 6, 8 and 12 days separately each working alone. B and C work together for 2 days and then A replaces C. In how much time will the total work finish ?

Solution : A's 1 day's work $= \frac{1}{6}$, B's 1 day's work $= \frac{1}{8}$ and C's 1 day's work $= \frac{1}{12}$

Now B and C work together for 2 days

$\therefore$ They do $\left(\frac{1}{8} + \frac{1}{12}\right) \times 2 = \frac{5}{24} \times 2 = \mathbf{\frac{5}{12}}$ of the work

Remaining work $= 1 - \frac{5}{12} = \frac{7}{12}$

Now B and A work together as C leaves

(B+A)'s 1 day's work $= \frac{1}{6} + \frac{1}{8} = \frac{7}{24}$

In other words, they do $\frac{7}{24}$ of the work in 1 day.

$\therefore$ They will do the remaining $\frac{7}{12}$ of the work in $\frac{7}{12} \div \frac{7}{24}$ days

$$= \frac{7}{12} \times \frac{24}{7} = \mathbf{2} \text{ days}$$

So, total time taken to do the work = 2 + 2 = **4 days** *Ans.*

PRACTICE EXERCISES 16

A. Complete each statement :

1. More men employed at a job take .... time to do it.

2. Less time allowed for a job needs .... men to be employed to do it.

3. More working hours daily complete the job in .... time.

4. Fewer working hours daily complete the job in .... time.

B. 5. Ritu knits a sweater in 14 days completely. What amount of knitting does she do in 5 days ?

6. Dinu ploughs a field in 6 days while Ramu can plough it in 12 days. How long will it take for the field to be tilled if Dinu and Ramu work together ?

7. Rajesh and Manish can complete a job in 8 days. But Rajesh alone can do it in 12 days. How long will it take Manish to complete it alone ?

8. Two pipes A and B can fill a tank in 6 and 8 hours respectively A third pipe can empty off the full tank in 15 hours. In how much time will the tank get filled if all the three pipes are opened together ?

9. 12 men working 8 hours a day complete $\frac{1}{4}$ of a job in 10 days. How long will 16 men working $7\frac{1}{2}$ hours a day take to finish the remaining $\frac{3}{4}$ of the same job ?

10. 2 men or 3 boys can harvest a field in 10 days. How long will 2 men and 2 boys take to finish this job ?

11. A alone can dig a pit in 12 days while B can fill it up with earth in 15 days. If they work at the pit daily in turn each for half the day, in how many days will the pit get filled up ?

12. Mohan and Sohan can do a certain job together in 12 days. But Mohan alone can do it in 20 days. In how many days can Sohan do it alone ?

13. A and B can do a piece of work in 12 days ; B and C in 15 days while C and A in 20 days. In how many days will they finish it together as well as separately ?

14. A can do a work in 25 days and B can complete it in 20 days. They work together for 4 days when A leaves the work. In how many days will the remaining job be completed by B alone ?

15. A cistern can be filled up by one pipe in 8 hours and by another in 4 hours. In how much time will both the taps fill the cistern together ?

16. Pipe A can fill an empty cistern in 4 hours while pipe B can empty it up in 6 hours. If both the pipes are opened together, in how much time will they fill the tank ?

17. Pipes A and B can fill an empty tank in 12 and 16 hours respectively pipe C can empty off the full tank in 8 hours. If all the three pipes are opened together, how long will the tank take to get filled up ?

18. After doing $\frac{4}{15}$ of a work in 20 days, A calls B for help and finishes the job in 22 days more. In how much time can either of them do the work alone ?

19. Pipe A can fill an empty tank in 3 hours. Pipes B and C can empty off the full tank in 4 and 6 hours respectively. If the tank is empty, find—

(a) in what time will the pipes A, B fill it together ?

(b) in what time will the full tank become empty if all the pipes are opened ?

20. A and B can do a work in 12 days. After they have worked for 2 days, they call C who works at the same rate as A. Thus the work takes only $6\frac{1}{4}$ days more to be complete. In what time can B do it alone ?

21. A and B can do a job in $1\frac{1}{2}$ days together ; A and C in 2 days together and B and C in 3 days together. They work together and finish the job. They are paid Rs. 9 for the entire job. How will they divide the money ?

22. A and B together can build a wall in 25 days. they work together for 15 days and then A alone finishes it in 20 days. In how many day's can either of them build the wall alone ?

23. Mohan and Sohan reap a field in 9 hours and 6 hours respectively. They begin reaping it at 6:00 a.m. When will they finish the job ?

10 TIME AND DISTANCE

KNOW THESE TERMS :

1. **resultant**—quantity obtained as a result of a basic operation
2. **distance**—length covered by a journey or moving body
3. **speed**—rate at which a body moves to cover a distance
4. **time**—period taken to cover a distance by a moving body

Problems on **time** and **distance** are directly related to speeds of various moving things—vehicles or living-beings. Different objects have different speeds. Not only this, the speed of one and the same object is not always the same. A train starts with a slow speed, then moves fast and again slows down to stop at the next station. A moving body covers a certain **distance**, in a certain **time** moving at a certain **speed**. So, these three items are involved in the problems on *Time and Distance*. If we know any two of them, we can find the third using the following formulae :

1. Distance = *speed* × *Time* **2. Time** = $\frac{Distance}{Speed}$ **3. Speed** = $\frac{Distance}{Time}$

Let us solve some examples :

Example 1. Express the speed of 54 kilometrs per hour into metres per second.

Solution : Given speed = 54 km. per hour

= 54000 metres every 60 minutes

= 54000 metres every 60 × 60 or 3600 seconds

∴ Speed per second = $\frac{54000}{3600} = \frac{30}{2}$ = **15 metres** *Ans.*

Example 2. Express the speed of 10 metres per second into kilometres per hour.

Solution : Given speed = 10 metres per second

= 10 × 60 metres per minute

= 10 × 60 × 60 metres per hour

= $\frac{10 \times 60 \times 60}{1000}$ km. per hour

= **36 kilometres per hour** *Ans.*

Example 3. Ahmad drives his motor-bike at 42 kilometres per hour. How much distance will he cover in 2 hours 20 minutes ?

Solution : *Speed* of the motor-bike = 42 km. per hour

Time = 2 hours 20 minutes = $2\frac{20}{60}$ hrs. = $2\frac{1}{3}$ hrs. = $\frac{7}{3}$ hrs

∴ Reqd. distance = Speed × Time

= $42 \times \frac{7}{3}$ km. = **98 km.** *Ans.*

Example 4. Jyoti is cycling at 18 km. per hour. How long will it take her to cover 400 metres ?

Solution : Jyoti's speed = 18 km./hour = 18000 m./hr.

Distance = 400 metres

∴ Time = $\frac{\text{Distance}}{\text{Speed}} = \frac{400}{18000}$ hrs. = $\frac{1}{45}$ hrs.

= $\frac{1}{45} \times 60$ minutes = $\frac{4}{3}$ minute

= **1 min. 20 seconds** *Ans.*

Example 5. Raju goes to Hardwar in his car that runs at a certain speed. He covers 144 kilometres in $2\frac{1}{4}$ hours. At what speed does his car run ?

Solution : Distance covered = 144 km.

Time taken = $2\frac{1}{4}$ hours = $\frac{9}{4}$ hours

∴ Speed = $\frac{\text{Distance}}{\text{Time}}$ = 144 km. ÷ $\frac{9}{4}$

= $144 \times \frac{4}{9}$ km./per hour = **64 km. per hour**. *Ans.*

Example 6. A boy goes to school on his bicycle at 12·5 km. per hour but reaches late by 3 minutes. Had he travelled at 15 km. an hour, he would have reached 5 minutes too early. Find the distance of his school from his home.

Solution : Suppose the Reqd. distance = 1 km.

Time taken to cover 1 km. at 12·5 km. per hour.

= $60 \times \frac{2}{25}$ minutes = $\mathbf{\frac{24}{5}}$ **min.**

Time taken to cover 1 km. at 15 km. per hour

$= 60 \times \frac{1}{15}$ min $=$ **4 min**

Difference $\frac{24}{5} - 4 = \frac{4}{5}$ minute

Actual difference $= 3 + 5 = 8$ minutes

Using *Unitary Method*—

If the difference is $\frac{4}{5}$ minute, distance $= 1$ km.

If the difference is 1 minute, distance $= 1 \times \frac{5}{4}$ km.

If the difference is 8 minutes, distance $= 1 \times \frac{5}{4} \times 8$ km.

$=$ **10 km.** Ans.

Example 7. A train 130 metres long is running at a speed of 65 kilometres an hour. How long will it take the train to pass an electric pole ?

Solution : Speed of the train $= 65$ km./hour $= \frac{65000}{60}$ metres per min.

Length of train $= 130$ metres

Clearly, the train will travel its own length to pass the pole

$\therefore$ Reqd. Time. $\frac{\text{Distance}}{\text{Speed}} = 130 \div \frac{65000}{60} = \frac{130 \times 60}{65000}$ min.

$= \frac{3}{25}$ min. $=$ **7·2 second** *Ans.*

PRACTICE EXERCISES 17

A. Complete each formula :

1. *Distance* covered by a moving body = ... × ....

2. *Time* taken to cover a distance by a moving body = ... ÷ ....

3. *Speed* of a moving body = ... ÷ ....

B. Convert the speed to metres per second :

4. 36 kilometres an hour

5. 378 kilometres per hour

6. 450 kilometres per hour

7. 1152 kilometres per hour

C. Convert each speed to kilometres per hour :

8. 15 metres per second

9. 25 metres per second

10. 5 metres per second

11. 200 metres per second

D. 12. Reena walks up to her school at a speed of 4 kilometres an hour. It takes her 45 minutes to reach school. How far is her school from her home ?

13. A train leaves Mumbai at 7:00 p.m. and reaches Delhi at 12:00 a.m. the next day. The average speed of the train was 60 km. an hour. Find the distance between the two cities.

14. A cyclist crosses a bridge in 3·3 minutes. If the bridge be 495 metres long, find his speed.

15. A train is 110 metres long. It is running at a speed of 44 kilometres an hour. How long will it take the train to pass a railway signal ?

16. A man covers 10·2 kilometres in 3 hours. How much distance will he cover in 5 hours ?

17. A traveller walking at 4 kilometres an hour can cover a distance in 2 hours 45 minutes on foot. But on a cycle he covers it in only 40 minutes. Find his speed on the cycle.

18. If I walk up to the station at 5 kilomtres an hour, I miss a train by 7 minutes. But if I cycle to the station at 6 kilometres an hour, I reach the station 5 minutes too early. How far away is the station from my place ?

19. A truck moves at a speed of 36 kilometres an hour. How far will it travel in 15 seconds ?

20. A passenger-plane flies to Mumbai from Delhi in 2 hours. How much time will it take to fly to Hyderabad if Hyderabad is 1285 kilometres away from Delhi while Mumbai is 1542 km. away from Delhi ?

21. Susheel walks up to a nearby station at 3 kilometres an hour. He reaches there 5 minutes late. But if he walks at a speed of 4 kilometres an hour, he reaches 5 minutes too early. How far has Susheel to walk ?

22. A train is 280 metres long and it is running at a speed of 56 kilometres an hour. How much time will it take the train to—

(a) cross a signal-post ? *(b)* cross a 560-metre long platform ?

23. An 150-metre long train is running at 50 kilometres an hour. How much time will it take the train to pass a 600 metre-long platform ?

24. Monika's school is 2 kilometres away from her home. When will she reach her school if she leaves her home at 7·15 a.m. at a speed of 5 kilomtres an hour ?

25. An express train leaves Delhi at 7·00 p.m. and reaches Ahmedabad at 7·00 p.m. the next night. If the distance between Delhi and Ahmedabad is 1440 kilometres, find the speed of the train.

26. A person travelling by a tonga at 15 kilometres an hour goes to a show covering a distance of 18 kilometres. He returns home from the show on a bicycle at 10 kilometres an hour. Find :

(a) his average speed *(b)* the time taken by him for up-journey

(c) The time taken by him for down-journey

(d) the time taken by him to go and return at the average speed.

RESULTANT SPEEDS

Resultant speed comes into play when two objects move in relation to each other. Such movements always lead to a **resultant speed**.

Let us solve some examples :

A. TWO BODIES MOVING TOWARDS EACH OTHER

If two bodies are moving from opposite directions towards each other, they are, in fact, moving with a **resultant speed** that is **equal to the sum of their speeds**.

Example 8. **Two trains are running towards each other on parallel lines. They are 150 metres and 180 metres long respectively and their respective speeds are 30 km./hr. and 24 km./hr. How long will it take them to pass each other ?**

Solution : Speed of the first train = 30 km./hr.

Speed of the second train = 24 km./hr.

$\because$ The trains are running towards each other

$\therefore$ Their **resultant speed** = **sum of their speed**

= (30 + 24) = 54 km/hr.

= **54000 m/hr.**

And they will travel a distance of (150 + 180) = 330 metres to pass each other.

$$\text{Reqd. Time} = \frac{\text{Distance}}{\text{Speed}} = \frac{330 \text{ m}}{54000 \text{ m}} \text{ hrs.} = \frac{11}{1800} \text{ hrs.}$$

$$= \frac{11}{1800} \times 60 \times 60 \text{ seconds}$$

$$= \mathbf{22 \text{ sec.}} \; \textit{Ans.}$$

B. TWO BODIES MOVING IN THE SAME DIRECTION

If two bodies are moving at different speeds in the same direction on parallel lines, their **resultant speed** is equal to the **difference in their speeds**.

Example 9. **Two trains are running on parallel lines in the same direction at 46 km./hr. and 39 km./hr. respectively. If they are 110 metres and 100 metres long respectively, how long will it take the faster train to pass the other train ?**

Solution : Speed of the first train = 46 km./hr.

Speed of the second train = 39 km./hr.

The trains are running in the same direction

Their **resultant speed** = **difference in their speeds**

Now, the faster train will pass the other train at the resultant speed of (46—39) km. = 7 km. per hour after covering (110 + 100) = 210 metres, *i.e.* the sum of their lengths.

$$\therefore \text{Reqd. Time} = \frac{\text{Distance}}{\text{Speed}} = \frac{210 \text{ m}}{7000 \text{ m}} \text{ hrs.} = \frac{3}{100} \text{ hrs.}$$

$$= \frac{3}{100} \times 60 \times 60 \text{ sec} = 108 \text{ sec.}$$

$$= \mathbf{1 \text{ min. } 48 \text{ sec.}} \; \textit{Ans.}$$

PRACTICE EXERCISES 18

A. Complete each statement :

1. If two bodies move towards each other, the resultant speed is equal to the .... of their speeds.

2. If two bodes move in the same direction, their resultant speed is equal to the .... in their speeds.

B. 3. Two trains are 250 metres and 350 metres long respectively. They are moving towards each other at 35 km. per hour and 25 km. per hour respectively. How long will it take them to pass each other ?

4. Two trains are moving in the same direction at 15 km./hr. and 20 km./hr. respectively. If they are 450 metres and 400 metres in length, how long will the faster train take to pass the other train ?

5. A train 315 metres in length is running at a speed of 54 km./hr. It passes another train coming from the opposite direction at 36 km./hr. in 27 seconds. Find the length of the other train.

6. A train 315 metres in length is running at 54 km./hr. It passes another train running in the same direction at 36 km./hr. in 2 minutes 20 seconds. Find the length of the other train.

7. Rahul can run at 5 km./hr. while Roshan at 3 km./hr. Roshan starts running at 9–30 a.m. while Rahul at 10–00 a.m. in the same direction. At what time will Rahul overtake Roshan ?

8. A cyclist moving at a speed of 8 km./hr. starts at 7–30 a.m.. Another cyclist starts from the same point at 8–30 a.m. with a speed of 10 km./hr. When will he overtake the first cyclist ?

9. Two trains 132 metres and 108 metres long respectively are running towards each other on parallel lines. Their speeds are 32 km./hr. and 40 km./hr. respectively. In how much time will they pass each other ?

10. Two trains 125 metres and 175 metres long respectively are running in the same direction at 40 km./hr. and 22 km./hr. respectively. In how much time will the faster train leave the slower train behind ?

11. A bus leaves Delhi for Jammu at 4 p.m. at a speed of 72 km./hr. Another bus leaves for Jammu at 5 p.m. and runs at 80 km./hr. At what time will it catch the former bus ?

12. A 100-metre long train passes another train coming from the opposite direction in 9 seconds. If their speeds are 38 km./hr. and 34 km./hr. respectively, find the length of the other train ?

11 PERCENTAGE

KNOW THESE TERMS :

1. **percentage**—reduction of a quantity to a fraction with 100 as denominator
2. **income tax**—tax imposed by a government on income that exceeds a limit
3. **trade discount**—certain percentage of selling price offered to a customers to attract them for sale of a product

We already know that **per cent** means *per hundred*. We use the sign % to express a percentage.

Thus **14%** means **14 out of every hundred** = $\mathbf{\frac{14}{100}}$

Clearly percentage is a fraction with **numeral for percentage** as its **numerator** and **100 as its denominator**.

Let us now study some examples that show the **application** of **percentage**.

Example 1. Convert : *(a)* **0·75 into per cent form**

(b) **7:12 as per cent** *(c)* **56% into a fraction**

(d) **25% into a ratio** *(e)* **5% into a decimal**

Solution : (a) $0{\cdot}75 = \frac{75}{100} = \mathbf{75\%}$ *Ans.* (∵ *denominator is already 100*)

(b) $7:12 = \frac{7}{12} = \frac{7}{12} \times 100 = \frac{175}{3} = \mathbf{58\frac{1}{3}\%}$ *Ans.*

(c) $56\% = \frac{56}{100} = \mathbf{\frac{14}{25}}$ *Ans.*

(d) $25\% = \frac{25}{100} = \frac{1}{4} = \mathbf{1:4}$ *Ans.*

(e) $5\% = \frac{5}{100} = \mathbf{{\cdot}05}$ *Ans.*

Example 2. 30% of a quantity x is 9. Find the value of x.

Solution : $30\% = \frac{30}{100}$

$\frac{30}{100} \times x = 9$ or $\frac{30x}{100} = 9$

or $30x = 9 \times 100 = 900$ or $x = \frac{900}{30} = \mathbf{30}$ *Ans.*

Example 3. Manish saves $12\frac{1}{2}\%$ of his monthly salary. If he saves Rs. 460 every month, find his salary.

Solution : Suppose Manish's salary = Rs. 100

His saving = Rs. $12\frac{1}{2}$ = Rs. $\frac{25}{2}$

His actual saving = Rs. 460

Using *unitary method*

If the saving is Rs. $\frac{25}{2}$, salary = Rs. 100

If the saving is Rs. 1, salary = Rs. $\frac{100 \times 2}{25}$ = Rs. 8

If the saving is Rs. 460, salary = Rs. 8×460 = **Rs. 3680** *Ans.*

Example 4. A person earned Rs. 12000 a year in 1984. His earning increased by 20% in 1985 and by 10% in 1986. What was his earning in 1986 ?

Solution : Earning in 1984 = Rs. 12000

Increase in 1985 = 20%

$\therefore$ Earning in 1985 = $\frac{120}{100} \times 12000$ = Rs. 14400

Again, increase in 1986 = 10%

$\therefore$ Earning in 1986 = Rs. $\frac{110}{100}$ × Rs. 14400 = **Rs. 15840** *Ans.*

Example 5. In an examination 72% of the candidates passed. If the number of failed candidates be 392, find the total number of candidates.

Solution : Suppose the total number of candidates = 100

No. of passed candidates = 72

$\therefore$ No of failed candidates = 100 – 72 = 28

Actual No. of failed candidates = 392

Using *unitary method*—

If failed candidates are 28, total candidates = 100

If failed candidate is 1, total candidates = $\frac{100}{28}$

If failed candidates are 392, total candidates = $\frac{100}{28} \times 392$

= **1400** *Ans.*

Example 6. A candidate got 540000 votes in an election. These votes were the 54% of the total votes. His rival candidate gets 30% votes. Find—

(*a*) total number of voters

(*b*) votes in favour of the rival candidate

(*c*) votes that were not polled

Solution : (*a*) Votes secured by the candidate = 540000

These votes were 54% of the total votes

$\therefore$ Total votes $= \frac{100}{54} \times 540000 =$ **1000000** *Ans.*

(*b*) Votes secured by the rival candidate $= \frac{30}{100} \times 1000000$

$=$ **300000** *Ans.*

(*c*) Per cent votes not polled $= 100 - 54 - 30 = 16$

Total votes not polled $= \frac{16}{100} \times 1000000$

$=$ **160000** *Ans.*

PRACTICE EXERCISES 19

A. 1. What is meant by x per cent ?

B. Find the value of *a*, if

2. 23% of *a* is 46. **3.** $\frac{1}{2}$% of *a* is 50.

4. 8·4% of *a* is 42. **5.** 34% of *a* is 68.

C. Convert :

6. 68% into a simple fraction. **7.** 14% into a simple ratio.

8. 6% into a decimal fraction. **9.** 0·3% into a simple fraction.

D. Write in per cent form :

10. $\frac{2}{5}$ **11.** 15:16 **12.** 0·18 **13.** 1·003 **14.** $\frac{13}{624}$

E. 15. A house-holder spends 20% of his monthly income on paying house rent and 70% of the rest as household expenditure. His saving is Rs 1800 a month. Find his monthly income.

16. An alloy contains 40% copper, 36% zinc and the rest is nickel. Find the contents of the three constituents in a 1 kg. piece of the alloy.

17. The value of a machine goes down by 5% every year. Its present value is Rs. 100000. What will its value be after three years ?

18. Rohit's salary is 25% more than Rahul's. What per cent is Rahul's Salary less than Rohit's ?

19. The price of kitchen-gas goes up by 20%. How much per cent should a housewife reduce her consumption of the gas so as not to increase her expenditure ?

20. My salary has been increased by 50%. What per cent must the period of work be reduced so that my boss had to pay me the same amount every month ?

21. Pure gold is 24-carat gold. But ornaments are made out of 22-carot gold. What per cent of pure gold is there in the 22-carrot gold ?

22. A buyer has to pay 4% sales tax apart from the price of an article. What is the real price of an article for which he has to pay Rs. 2·60 ?

23. 78·8% of a medicine is alcohol while other three components are 3·3%, 17·2% and 0·7% respectively. If a pack of the medicine weighs 30 milligram, how much of each constituent is there in it ?

24. A person loses 20% of his money when his pocket is picked. He spends 25% of the remainder on personal purchases. Only Rs. 480·00 are left with him. How much money did he have in the beginning ?

25. Ramesh secures 50% marks in English, 60% in Mathematics and 75% in Hindi. These subjects have 50, 70 and 80 marks as total marks respectively. What per cent of the total marks does Ramesh get ?

26. The population of a small village was only 6000 in 1980 but it rose to be 9000 in 1985. The total land of the village was 500 acres out of which 100 acres were used up for public works. Find the decrease per cent per head.

27. In a town, 45% of the population are men while 35% are women. The rest of the population consists of children whose number is 18000. Find the number of men and women.

PROBLEMS ON INCOME TAX

Income tax rates in our country at present are as under :

	Income	*Rate of Income Tax*
1.	Rs. 42000	No tax
2.	Rs. 42001 to 60,000	10%
3.	Rs. 60001 to 1,50000	20% + Rs. 2000
4.	Rs. more than Rs. 1,50000	30% + Rs. 20,000

Let us now solve some examples on income tax.

Example 7. Keeping in view the table of income tax given above calculate the income tax on the following incomes :

(a) **Rs. 56000** *(b)* **69500** *(c)* **1,60000**

Solution : *(a)* We know that the first Rs. 42000 are not taxable.

∴ Taxable income = Rs. (56000 – 42000)= Rs. 14000

Rate of income tax = 10%

∴ Income tax on Rs. 14000 = Rs. $\frac{10}{100} \times 14000$

= **Rs. 1400** *Ans.*

(b) Taxable income = Rs. (69500 – 60,000) = Rs. 9500

Rate of income tax = 20% + 2000

Income tax = Rs. $\left(\frac{20}{100} \times 9500\right)$ + Rs. 2000

= Rs. 1900 + Rs. 2000 = **Rs. 3900** *Ans.*

(c) Taxable income = Rs. 1,60000 – Rs. 1,50000) = Rs. 10000

Rate of income tax = 30% + Rs. 20,000

∴ Income tax = Rs. $\frac{30}{100} \times 10{,}000$ + Rs. 20000

= Rs. 3000 + Rs. 20,000 = **Rs. 23000** *Ans.*

PROBLEMS ON TRADE DISCOUNT

Visit a standard store and observe things there. Every object for sale has a price-card tagged to it. Books have their prices printed on them. This price is called the **marked price.**

For cash payment of an object, a rebate or discount is offered by sellers to their customers. This rebate is called **discount**. It is generally in the form of a **certain percentage of the marked price**. So, **S.P. of the object = Marked Price – Discount.**

Remember that **discount** is always calculated on the *marked price*.

Let us solve some examples :

Example 1. Find the selling price of an object whose marked price is Rs. 64 and discount allowed on it is 12·5%.

Solution : Marked Price = Rs. 64

Discount allowed = 12·5% = $12\frac{1}{2}\%$ = $\frac{25}{2}\%$

$\therefore$ Total discount = Rs. $\frac{25}{2} \times \frac{1}{100} \times 64$ = Rs. 8

$\therefore$ Selling price = Rs. (64 – 8) = **Rs. 56** *Ans.*

Example 2. Find the marked price of a bicycle that was sold for Rs. 1920 after allowing a discount of 4% on the marked price.

Solution : Suppose the marked price = Rs. 100

discount on Rs. 100 = Rs. 4

$\therefore$ selling price = Rs. (100 – 4) = Rs. 96

Actual selling price = Rs. 1920

Using *Unitary Method*

If S.P. is Rs. 96, Marked Price = Rs. 100

If S.P. is Rs. 1, Marked Price = Rs. $\frac{100}{96}$

If S.P. is Rs. 1920, Marked Price = Rs. $\frac{100}{96} \times 1920$

= **Rs. 2000** *Ans.*

Example 3. A shopkeeper allows his customers 10% off his marked price. But he still earns a profit of 25%. If the marked price of an article be Rs. 250, what is its actual cost price ?

Solution : Marked price of the article = Rs. 250

Discount allowed = 10%

$\therefore$ Total discount = Rs. $\frac{10}{100} \times 250$ = Rs. 25

$\therefore$ S.P. of the article = Rs. (250 – 25) = Rs. 225

Gain of the shopkeeper = 25%

$$\therefore \text{C.P.} = \frac{100 \times \text{S.P.}}{100 + \text{Gain\%}} = \text{Rs. } \frac{225 \times 100}{100 + 25}$$

$$= \text{Rs. } \frac{225 \times 100}{125} = \textbf{Rs. 180} \textit{ Ans.}$$

Example 4. A cycle trader marks a cycle much above its cost price and then allows 25% discount to his customers. But he still gains 20% on the cycle. Thus he earns a profit of Rs. 60 on the cycle. Find the cost price as well as the marked price of the cycle.

Solution : Suppose the C.P. of the cycle = Rs. 100

Gain % = 20% = Rs. 20

But actual gain = Rs. 60

$\therefore$ Actual C.P. of the cycle = Rs. $\frac{100}{20} \times 60$ = **Rs. 300**

$\therefore$ S.P. of the cycle = Rs. 300 + Rs. 60 = Rs. 360

But this S.P. is after allowing 25% discount on Marked Price

$\therefore$ Marked Price = Rs. $\frac{100}{75} \times 360$ = **Rs. 480** *Ans.*

Example 5. A shopkeeper allows a discount of 20% on the marked price of his items. How much above the cost must he mark an item so as to gain 20% on it after allowing the discount ?

Solution : Suppose the C.P. of an item = Rs. 100

Required gain = 20%

$\therefore$ S.P. of the item = Rs. (100 + 20) = Rs. 120

Discount to be allowed = 20%

$\therefore$ The Marked Price = Rs. $\frac{100}{80} \times 120$ = Rs. 150

So, Marked Price must be 50% above the C.P. *Ans.*

SUCCESSIVE DISCOUNTS

Successive discounts mean *that after allowing a discount another discount is allowed on the new S.P.*

Let us solve some examples :

Example 6. The marked price of a colour TV is Rs. 12600. The trader allows a festival discount of Rs. 5% and another 2% discount for cash payment. How much will the customer pay for the TV ?

Solution : Marked Price of the TV = Rs. 12600

Festival discount at 5% = Rs. $\frac{5}{100} \times 12600$ = Rs. 630

$\therefore$ Price after the festival discount = Rs. (12600 – 630) = Rs. 11970

$\therefore$ Cash discount at 2% = Rs. $\frac{2}{100} \times 11970$ = Rs. $\frac{1197}{5}$ or 239·40

$\therefore$ Net S.P. = Rs. (11970 – 239·40) = **Rs. 11730·60** *Ans.*

Example 7. Find a single rate of discount that equals two successive discounts of 20% and 5%.

Solution : Suppose the marked price = Rs. 100

Price after the first discount of 20% = Rs. 100 – 20 = Rs. 80

$\therefore$ Second discount of 5% will be on Rs. 80

Net price after the second discount of 5% = Rs. $\frac{95}{100} \times 80$

= Rs. 76

$\therefore$ Total discount allowed = Rs. (100 – 76) = Rs. 24

$\therefore$ Reqd. single discount = **24%** *Ans.*

PRACTICE EXERCISES 20

A. Answer :

1. What is meant *by income tax* ?

2. What is meant by *trade discount* ?

3. What is meant by *successive discounts* ?

B. Find the income tax on the incomes given below :

4. Rs. 53000 **5.** Rs. 80,000 **6.** Rs. 200000

C. 7. Mr Khan works in an office. He earns Rs. 92500 every year. He pays Rs. 7000 as provident fund and Rs. 5500 as the premium of his life insurance policy. Find the amount that he pays as income tax.

(*Hint* : Payments towards Provident Fund and Life Insurance are deducted from the income and then income tax is calculated.)

8. A trader of sewing machines offers 3% discount on cash payments. What cash will a customer pay for a machine with marked price Rs. 650 ?

9. A shopkeeper allows 10% discount on his items. But still he is able to make a profit of 26%. What is the actual price of an article which he has marked to be sold for Rs. 280 ?

10. A shopkeeper marks his goods at such a price that even after allowing a discount of 12·5% for cash payments he is able to make a profit of 10%. How will he mark an article that costs him Rs. 245 ?

11. The marked price of a bicycle is Rs. 750. But 20% discount is allowed for cash payment. What will a customer pay for it in cash ?

12. After allowing a discount of $7\frac{1}{2}$% on the marked price of a water-jug, it was sold for Rs. 555. What was the price marked on it ?

13. A radio is marked with a price 20% more than its real cost. If 10% discount is allowed on it for cash payment, find the gain per cent.

14. A tradesman marks his goods at a price so that after allowing a discount of 15% for cash payments, he may earn a gain of 20%. Find the marked price of an item which costs him Rs. 170.

15. A dealer of cycles allows a discount of 15% on his marked price. How much above the cost must he mark his goods so as to earn a profit of 19% ?

16. A washing-machine is marked to be sold at Rs. 7500. If three successive discounts of 8%, 5% and 2% are allowed on it, find its net selling price.

17. What single discount will be equal to two successive discounts of 8% and 5% ?

18. An article was marked at Rs. 540. But it was sold for Rs. 450 allowing a discount for Diwali Festival. What discount was allowed ?

19. The marked price of a washing powder is Rs. 24. But a soap-case costing Rs. 3·00 is given free with it as a sort of discount. Still the shopkeeper gains 5%. Find the real cost of the washing powder.

20. A dining-table is marked to be sold for Rs. 1500. But three successive discounts of 10%, 5% and 2% are allowed on it. Find the net selling price of the table.

21. What single discount will equal two successive discounts of 20% and 10% ?

12 PROFIT AND LOSS

KNOW THESE TERMS :

1. **cost price**—price at which an article is produced or bought
2. **selling price**—price at which an article is sold
3. **gain**—money earned by selling an article at more than its CP
4. **loss**—money lost in selling an article at less than its cost price

We already know the following facts :

A. 1. *(a)* The amount that is spent to produce an article is its **cost price** (CP).

(b) Also, the price at which an article is bought is its **cost price** (CP).

(c) The amount for which an article (produced or bought) is sold is called its **selling price** (SP).

Remember that CP and SP are relative terms. The same amount is the CP for the buyer and S.P. for the seller.

2. If *SP is larger than CP,* there is a **gain** for the seller.
3. If *SP is lower than CP,* there is a **loss** for the seller.
4. Gain or loss is calculated on CP
5 *Gain or loss calculated on Rs. 100* is called **gain%** or **loss %**

B. We learnt and used the following formulae to solve problems on profit and loss in class VI.

1. Gain = SP – CP
2. Loss = CP – SP
3. $\text{Gain\%} = \dfrac{\text{Gain} \times 100}{\text{CP}}$
4. $\text{Loss\%} = \dfrac{\text{Loss} \times 100}{\text{CP}}$
5. $\text{SP} = \text{CP} \times \left(\dfrac{100 + \text{Gain\%}}{100}\right)$
6. $\text{SP} = \text{CP} \times \left(\dfrac{100 - \text{Loss\%}}{100}\right)$
7. $\text{CP} = \text{SP} \times \left(\dfrac{100}{100 + \text{Gain\%}}\right)$
8. $\text{CP} = \text{SP} \times \left(\dfrac{100}{100 - \text{Loss\%}}\right)$

Let us solve some examples :

Example 1. I purchased a horse for Rs. 3600 and sold it for Rs. 4050. Find my gain and gain %.

Solution : CP of the horse = Rs. 3600

SP of the horse = Rs. 4050

$\because$ SP > CP, so there is a **gain.**

Gain = Rs. (4050 – 3600) = Rs. 450

$\therefore$ Gain% $= \frac{\text{Gain} \times 100}{\text{CP}} = \frac{450 \times 100}{3600}$ %

$= \frac{25}{2}\% = \mathbf{12\frac{1}{2}}$ **%** *Ans.*

Example 2. **Shyam bought a type-writer for Rs. 800 and sold it for Rs. 760. Find his loss and loss %.**

Solution : CP of the type-writer = Rs. 800

SP of the type writer = Rs. 760

SP < CP, so there is a **loss**

Loss = Rs. (800 – 760) = **Rs. 40**

$\therefore$ Loss % $= \frac{\text{Loss} \times 100}{\text{CP}} = \frac{40 \times 100}{800}$ = **5 %** *Ans.*

Example 3. **Amita bougth a washing machine for Rs. 9400. She sold it at a gain of $12\frac{1}{2}$%. Find her SP.**

Solution : CP of the washing machine = Rs. 9400

Gain earned on it $= 12\frac{1}{2}\% = \frac{25}{2}\%$

$\therefore$ SP $= \text{CP} \times \frac{100 + \text{Gain\%}}{100}$ = Rs. $9400 \times \frac{100 + \frac{25}{2}}{100}$

= Rs. $9400 \times \frac{225}{2 \times 100}$ = **Rs. 10575** *Ans.*

Example 4. **Madan bought an old house for Rs. 30,000 and sold it at a loss of $7\frac{1}{2}$ %. Find his SP.**

Solution : CP of the house = Rs. 30000

Loss % $= 7\frac{1}{2}\% = \frac{15}{2}$ %

$\therefore$ SP $= \text{CP} \times \frac{100 - \text{Loss\%}}{100}$ = Rs. $30000 \times \frac{100 - \frac{15}{2}}{100}$

= Rs. $30000 \times \frac{185}{2 \times 100}$ = **Rs. 27750** *Ans.*

Example 5. **By selling a dining-table for Rs. 3852, a man gains 7%. For what price must he sell it in order to gain $12\frac{1}{2}$% ?**

Solution : Given SP = Rs. 3852

Gain = 7%

$$CP = SP \times \frac{100}{100 + \text{Gain\%}} = \text{Rs. } 3852 \times \frac{100}{100 + 7}$$

$$= \text{Rs. } 3852 \times \frac{100}{107} = \text{Rs. } 3600$$

Required Gain % $= 12\frac{1}{2}\% = \frac{25}{2}\%$

$$\therefore \text{Required SP} = CP \times \frac{100 + \text{Gain\%}}{100} = \text{Rs. } 3600 \times \frac{100 + \frac{25}{2}}{100}$$

$$= \text{Rs. } 3600 \times \frac{225}{200} = \textbf{Rs. 4050} \textit{ Ans.}$$

Example 6. A shopkeeper buys eggs at Rs. 7·20 a dozen and sells them at three eggs for Rs. 2. Find his gain or loss %.

Solution : CP of 12 eggs = Rs. 7·20 = Rs. $7\frac{1}{5}$ = Rs. $\frac{36}{5}$

SP of 3 eggs = Rs. 2

SP of 3 × 4 or 12 eggs = Rs. 2 × 4 = Rs. 8.

SP of 12 eggs > CP of 12 eggs

$\therefore$ There is a gain of Rs. $\left(8 - \frac{36}{5}\right)$ = Rs. $\frac{4}{5}$

$$\therefore \text{Gain \%} = \frac{\text{Gain} \times 100}{CP} = \frac{4}{5} \times 100 \times \frac{5}{36}\%$$

$$= \frac{100}{9}\% = \mathbf{11\frac{1}{9}}\% \textit{ Ans.}$$

Example 7. A shopkeeper bought wheat worth Rs. 35000. But due to leakage in the godown, $\frac{1}{7}$ of the wheat was spoiled. The shopkeeper sold the remaining wheat at a gain of 10% and the spoiled wheat at a loss of 25% wheat is his total gain or loss % ?

Solution : CP of the total wheat = Rs. 35,000

Spoiled wheat = $\frac{1}{7}$ and remaining wheat = $1 - \frac{1}{7} = \frac{6}{7}$

CP of the $\frac{1}{7}$ spoiled wheat = $\frac{\text{Rs. } 35000 \times 1}{7}$ = Rs 5000

and CP of the $\frac{6}{7}$ good wheat = Rs. 35000 – 5000 = Rs. 30,000

SP of spoiled wheat at 25% loss $= CP \times \frac{100 - 25}{100}$

$$= \text{Rs. } 5000 \times \frac{75}{100}$$

$$= \text{Rs. } \frac{5000 \times 75}{100} = \textbf{Rs. 3750}$$

SP of good wheat at 10% gain $= \text{CP} \times \frac{100 + \text{Gain\%}}{100}$

$= \text{Rs. } 30000 \times \frac{100 + 10}{100}$

$= \text{Rs. } 30000 \times \frac{110}{100} = \textbf{Rs. 33000}$

Total SP = Rs. (3750 + 33000) = Rs. 36750

$\because$ SP > CP, there is a gain of Rs. (36750 – 35000) = Rs. 1750

$\therefore \text{Gain \%} = \frac{\text{Gain} \times 100}{\text{CP}} = \frac{1750 \times 100}{35000}\% = \textbf{5\%}$ *Ans.*

Example 8. A radio-seller sells two radio-sets at Rs. 1188 each. On one set he gains 10% while on the other he loses 10%. Find his total gain or loss %.

Solution : SP of the first radio-set = Rs. 1188

Gain % = 10 %

$\therefore \text{CP} = \text{SP} \times \frac{100}{\text{Gain\%} + 100} = \text{Rs. } 1188 \times \frac{100}{100+10}$

$= \text{Rs. } 1188 \times \frac{100}{110} = \textbf{Rs. 1080}$

SP of the second radio-set = Rs. 1188

Loss % = 10 %

$\therefore \text{CP} = \text{SP} \frac{100}{100 - \text{Loss\%}} = \text{Rs. } 1188 \times \frac{100}{100 - 10}$

$= \text{Rs. } 1188 \times \frac{100}{90} = \textbf{Rs. 1320}$

Total CP = Rs. (1080 + 1320) = Rs. 2400

Total SP = Rs. 1188 × 2 = Rs. 2376

$\because$ SP < CP, so there is a loss of Rs. (2400 – 2376) = Rs. 24

$\therefore \text{Loss \%} = \frac{\text{Loss} \times 100}{\text{CP}} = \frac{24 \times 100}{2400} = \textbf{1 \%}$ *Ans.*

Example 9. A cloth-seller sold a saree for Rs. 330 and gained $\frac{1}{10}$ of its cost price. Find the CP of the saree.

Solution : SP of the saree = Rs. 330

This SP $= \text{CP} + \frac{1}{10}$ CP of the saree $= \frac{11}{10}$ CP

$\therefore$ CP of the saree $= \text{Rs. } \frac{330 \times 10}{11} = \textbf{Rs. 300}$ *Ans.*

Example 10. The selling price of 10 articles is equal to the cost price of 11 articles. Find the gain %.

Solution : Suppose the CP of 1 article = Re. 1

CP of 10 articles = Rs. 10 and CP of 11 articles = Rs. 11

$\therefore$ SP of 10 articles = Rs. 11

$\because$ SP > CP, so there is a gain of Rs. (11 – 10) = Re. 1

$\therefore$ Gain % $= \dfrac{\text{Gain} \times 100}{\text{CP}} = \dfrac{1 \times 100}{10} =$ **10%** *Ans.*

Example 11. A shopkeeper sells a fan at a gain of 10%. Had he sold it for Rs. 15 more, he would have gained 12%. Find the CP of the fan.

Solution : Suppose the CP of the fan = Rs. 100

First SP = Rs. 110

Second possible SP = Rs. 112

$\therefore$ Difference = Rs. (112 – 110) = Rs. 2

Actual Difference = Rs. 15

Using *unitary method*—

CP of the fan = Rs. $\dfrac{100}{2} \times 15 =$ **Rs. 750** *Ans.*

PRACTICE EXERCISES 21

A. Complete each statement :

1. Gain = ... – ....

2. Loss = ... – ....

3. Gain% $= \dfrac{\rule{3cm}{0.4pt}}{\text{CP}}$

4. Loss% $= \dfrac{\rule{3cm}{0.4pt}}{\text{CP}}$

5. SP = CP × $\dfrac{100 + \text{......}\%}{100}$

6. SP = CP × $\dfrac{100 - \text{.........}\%}{100}$

7. CP = SP × $\dfrac{100}{100 + \text{........}}$

8. SP = CP × $\dfrac{100}{100 - \text{........}}$

9. There is a gain if .... > ....

10. There is a loss if .... > ....

B. 11. A person buys a table for Rs. 300 and sells it for Rs. 330. What is his gain or loss % ?

12. A person buys a bull for Rs. 8500 and sell it at a gain of 10%. Find his selling price.

13. A person buys an old type-writer for 760 and spends Rs. 120 on its repairs. Then he sells it for Rs. 990. Find his gain or loss %.

14. Aman bought an old car and an old jeep for Rs. 35500 and 24500 respectivily. He sold the car at a loss of 10 % and the jeep at a gain of 10%. What is his overall gain or loss % ?

15. Prakesh bought an old building for Rs. 50,000 and spent Rs. 10,000 on its repairs. Then he sold it to a friend at a gain of 15 %. His friend sold it further to Naseem gaining 10 %. What did Naseem pay for it ?

16. A cycle was bought for Rs. 645. What should be its selling price so that there may be a gain of $13\frac{1}{3}$ % ?

17. A radio-set was sold for Rs. 655·50 at a loss of 5 %. Find its cost price.

18. A rickshaw was sold for Rs. 2640 losing 12 %. For what should it be sold so as to gain 12 % ?

C. 19. Toffees are bought at 6 for a rupee and sold at 4 for a rupee. Find the gain or loss %.

20. A dealer buys 100 hockey-sticks at Rs. 50 each. He sells 25 of them gaining 5 %. At what price per stick should he sell the remaining 75 hockey-sticks so as to earn an overall gain of 20 % ?

21. A man sells two similar radio-sets at Rs. 924 each. He sells one of them at a profit of 20 % while the other at a loss of 20 %. What does he gain or lose in the whole bargain ?

22. By selling 144 hens a poultry-farmer loses equal to the selling price of 6 hens. Find his loss per cent.

23. A person sells 144 hens for Rs. 6912 and loses 4 %. For what price should he sell each hen so as to gain 10 % ?

24. By selling a hand-cart for Rs. 720, the seller loses 25 %. For what should it be sold to earn a profit of 10 % ?

25. A bicycle was sold at a profit of 16 %. Had it been sold for Rs. 10 more, there would have been a gain of 20 %. Find its CP.

26. Some marbles are bought at 11 for a rupee and the same number of them at 9 for a rupee. If the whole lot is sold at 10 for a rupee, what will be the gain or loss % ?

27. 40 kg. of wheat is sold for Rs. 308 earning a profit of 12%. But 40 kg. of rice sold for the same amount bring in a loss of 12 %. Find the CP of wheat and rice per kg. Find the total loss or gain % also.

28. Three sheep were bought at Rs. 500 each. One was sold at a loss of 10 %. For what price should the other two sheep be sold together so as to gain 20% on the entire bargain ? Also find the gain % on these two sheep.

D. 29. The selling price of 4 tables is the same as the cost price of 5 tables. What is the gain or loss per cent ?

30. A man sells an ox at a gain of 5 %. Had he sold it for Rs. 490 less, he would have lost 2 %. Find the CP of the ox.

31. By selling 100 oranges, a fruiterer gains equal to the selling price of 20 oranges. Find the gain %.

32. Anil sells a pen to Atul gaining 10 % and Atul sells it to Vimal at a gain of 20 %. If Vimal buys it for Rs. 19·80, find its CP.

33. A cycle dealer sells a bicycle at a gain of 8%. Had he sold it for Rs. 75 less, he would have lost 2 %. What is the cost price of the bicycle ?

34. A scooter was bought for Rs. 7500 and 500 rupees were spent on its repairs. then it was sold for Rs. 7750. Find the loss %.

35. 20 dozen bananas were bought at Rs. 6 per dozen. Out of the lot 20 bananas went bad. The remaining lot was sold at a profit of 10 %. At what rate per dozen were they sold ?

36. 15 blankets were bought for Rs. 3750 and sold to a retailer at a gain of 20 %. The retailer sold them to his customers at a gain of 25 %. What did the customer pay for a blanket ?

37. A farmer bought a cow for Rs. 2500 and an ox for Rs. 3500. The cow was sold at a gain of 12 % but the ox was sold at a loss of 10 %. Find the farmer's overall gain or loss.

38. A sells an article to B at a gain of 10 %. While B sells it to C at a gain of $7\frac{1}{2}$ % C has to sell it at a loss of 20 % for some reason. The CP of the article was Rs. 6·37 P. Find the selling price of C.

39. A man buys a house for Rs. 11500. Its ground floor brings a yearly rent of Rs. 250. Also annual repairs amount to 1 per cent of the CP. At what yearly rent should the entire house be given to earn 8% of the CP every year ?

40. A man buys 300 eggs at 15 for 75 paisa and sells them at 65 paise per dozen. Find his loss or gain %.

13 SIMPLE INTEREST

KNOW THESE TERMS :

1. **principal**—money borrowed from a person or bank
2. **interest**—money paid at a certain rate % for using borrowed money
3. **amount**—total amount including principal + interest
4. **rate** %—the rate fixed per hundred for calculating interest

We studied simple interest in class VI and we know the following facts :

A. 1. Money borrowed from a person or bank etc. is called **principal (P).**

2. Money is always borrowed for a certain period called **time (T).**

3. Money is always borrowed with a promise to pay something for its use at a certain **rate (R)**. This rate is often expressed as **rate % per annum**, *i.e. money to be paid for using Rs. 100 for one year.*

4. The extra money paid for using the principal is called **simple interest (S. I.)**

5. The total money returned after the fixed period to the lender is called **amount (A)**. It includes the **principal** and the **interest**.

B. We also know the following :

1. **Simple Interest (S.I.)** $= \dfrac{P \times R \times T}{100}$

2. **Amount** = **Principal + Simple Interest**

3. **Principal** $= \dfrac{S.I. \times 100}{T \times R}$

4. **Rate %** $= \dfrac{S.I. \times 100}{P \times T}$

5. **Time** $= \dfrac{S.I. \times 100}{P \times R}$

Let us now solve some examples :

Example 1. Find the simple interest on Rs. 3750 for $2\frac{1}{4}$ years at the rate of 8 per cent per annum.

Solution : Principal = Rs. 3750

Rate = 8% ; Time = $2\frac{1}{4}$ yrs = $\frac{9}{4}$ yrs.

$$\therefore \text{S.I.} = \frac{P \times T \times R}{100} = \text{Rs. } \frac{3750 \times 8 \times 9}{4 \times 100}$$

= **Rs. 675** *Ans.*

Example 2. **Mohan borrowed a sum of Rs. 8500 from a bank on 8th November 1996 at 12% per cent per annum. He cleared off the loan on 3rd April, 1997. What did he pay to the bank in all ?**

Solution : Principal borrowed from the bank = Rs. 8500

Rate = 12% ; Time = 146 days = $\frac{146}{365}$ yr. = $\frac{2}{5}$yr.

$\therefore$ S.I. = $\frac{P \times T \times R}{100} = \frac{\text{Rs. } 8500 \times 12 \times 2}{5 \times 100}$ = Rs. 408

$\therefore$ Mohan will return to the bank = Rs. (8500 + 408)

= **Rs. 8908** *Ans.*

DAYS		
Nov.	=	22
Dec.	=	31
Jan.	=	31
Feb.	=	29
Mar.	=	31
Apr.	=	3
		146

Example 3. **The simple interest on a certain sum for 3 years at 14% is Rs. 235·20. Find the sum.**

Solution : S.I. = Rs. 235·20 = Rs. $235\frac{1}{5}$ = Rs. $\frac{1176}{5}$

Time = 3 yrs ; Rate = 14%

$\therefore$ Principal = $\frac{\text{S.I.} \times 100}{T \times R}$ = Rs. $\frac{1176 \times 100}{5 \times 3 \times 14}$ = **Rs. 560** *Ans.*

Example 4. **The simple interest on Rs. 450 for a certain period of time at 8% per annum is Rs. 126. Find the time.**

Solution : S.I. = Rs. 126 ; R = 8%

Principal = Rs. 450

$\therefore$ Time = $\frac{\text{S.I.} \times 100}{P \times R} = \frac{126 \times 100}{450 \times 8}$ yrs.

= $\frac{7}{2}$ yrs. = $\mathbf{3\frac{1}{2}}$ **yrs.** *Ans.*

Example 5. **A what rate per cent will a sum of Rs. 6740 yield Rs. 2426·40 as simple interest in $4\frac{1}{2}$ years ?**

Solution : Principal = Rs. 6740 ; Time = $4\frac{1}{2}$yrs.= $\frac{9}{2}$ yrs.

S.I. = Rs. 2426·40 = Rs. $2426\frac{2}{5}$ = Rs. $\frac{12132}{5}$

$\therefore$ Rate = $\frac{\text{S.I.} \times 100}{P \times R} = \frac{12132 \times 100 \times 2}{5 \times 9 \times 6740}$ %

= $\frac{12132 \times 4}{674 \times 9}$% = $\frac{1348 \times 4}{674}$% = **8 %** *Ans.*

SOME MISCELLANEOUS EXAMPLES

Example 6. The simple interest on a principal for 5 years at 8% is Rs. 200 less than the simple interest on this very principal for 3 years and 4 months at 18%. Find the principal.

Solution : Suppose the principal is Rs. 100

Int. in the I case $= \text{Rs. } 100 \times 5 \times 8 \times \frac{1}{100} = \text{Rs. } 40$

$\therefore$ Int. in the II case $= \text{Rs. } 100 \times 18 \times \frac{10}{3} \times \frac{1}{100} = \text{Rs. } 60$

Difference = Rs. (60 – 40) = Rs. 20

Actual Difference = Rs. 200

$\therefore$ Using *unitary method*—

Principal $= \text{Rs. } 100 \times \frac{1}{20} \times 200 =$ **Rs. 1000** *Ans.*

Example 7. Divide Rs. 1550 into two parts such that the interest on one part lent out at 15% and the other at 24% may bring in a total yearly interest of Rs. 300.

Solution : Suppose one part = Rs. x Time = 1 yr

$\therefore$ Other part = Rs. $1550 - x$ Rates = 15%, 24%

Int on Rs. x at 15% $= \text{Rs. } \frac{x \times 15 \times 1}{100} = \text{Rs. } \frac{15x}{100}$

Int on R. $(1550 - x)$ at 24% $= \text{Rs. } \frac{(1550 - x) \times 24 \times 1}{100}$

$= \text{Rs. } \frac{24\,(1550 - x)}{100}$

According to the expression :

$$\frac{15x}{100} + \frac{24\,(1550 - x)}{100} = \text{Rs. } 300$$

or $15x + 37200 - 24x = 30000$

or $15x - 24x = 30000 - 37200$

or $-9x = -7200$

or $x = 800$

Hence one part = **Rs. 800** and the other = (1550 – 800)

= **750** *Ans.*

Alternative method

Int on Rs. 1550 at 15% for I year $= \text{Rs. } \frac{1550 \times 15 \times 1}{100} = \text{Rs. } \frac{465}{2}$

But the total interest = R.s 300

Difference = Rs. $\left(300 - \frac{465}{2}\right)$ = Rs. $\frac{135}{2}$

This interest of Rs. $\frac{135}{2}$ is to be there at (24 – 15) = 9%

on the second part for 1 year.

$\therefore$ Second Part = $\frac{\text{Int.} \times 100}{T \times R}$ = Rs. $\frac{135 \times 100}{2 \times 1 \times 9}$ = **Rs. 750** *Ans.*

$\therefore$ First Part = Rs. (1550 – 750) = **Rs. 800** *Ans.*

Example 8. A sum of money lent out at simple interest amounts to Rs. 2200 in 1 year and to Rs. 2800 in 4 years. Find the sum and the rate per cent.

Solution : Amount (P + S.I.) in 4 years = Rs. 2800

Amount (P + S.I.) in 1 year = Rs. 2200

Subtracting, S.I. in 3 years = Rs. 600

$\therefore$ S.I. for 1 year = Rs. 600 × $\frac{1}{3}$ = Rs. 200

Amount for 1 year = Rs. 2200

$\therefore$ Principal = Rs. (2200 –200) = **Rs. 2000**

Now Rate % = $\frac{\text{S.I.} \times 100}{P \times T}$ = $\frac{200 \times 100}{2000 \times 1}$ = **10%**] *Ans.*

Example 9. Divide Rs. 6000 into two parts so that the S.I. on one part for 9 months at 16% may be equal to the S.I. on the other part for 1·5 years at 12% per annum.

Solution : Let the equal S.I. be = Rs. 100

$\therefore$ Principal in the first case = $\frac{\text{S.I.} \times 100}{R \times T}$

= Rs. $\frac{100 \times 100 \times 4}{16 \times 3}$ = Rs. $\frac{2500}{3}$

and Principal in the second case = Rs. $\frac{100 \times 100 \times 2}{12 \times 3}$ = Rs. $\frac{5000}{9}$

$\therefore$ Ratio between the two parts = $\frac{2500}{3} : \frac{5000}{9}$

= 7500 : 5000 = 3 : 2

$\therefore$ First part = Rs. $\frac{6000}{3+2}$ × 3 = Rs. $\frac{6000}{5}$ × 3= **Rs. 3600**

$\therefore$ Second part = Rs. $\frac{6000}{3+2}$ × 2 = Rs. $\frac{6000}{5}$ × 2 = **Rs. 2400**] *Ans.*

PRACTICE EXERCISES 22

A. Complete each formula :

1. $\text{S.I.} = \dfrac{\text{Principal} \times \text{.........} \times \text{.........}}{100}$

2. $\text{Time} = \dfrac{\text{S.I.} \times \text{............}}{\text{P} \times \text{..........}}$

3. $\text{Principal} = \dfrac{\text{S.I.} \times \text{............}}{\text{R} \times \text{T}}$

4. $\text{Rate} = \dfrac{\text{..........} \times 100}{\text{..........} \times \text{T}}$

5. Amount = ... + ...

6. S.I. = ... – Principal

B. Find the simple interest and amount on—

7. Rs. 2276 for $2\frac{1}{2}$ years at $12\frac{1}{2}$ % per annum.

8. Rs. 8600 at 15% per annum from October 12 to March 7.

9. Rs. 3600 for 3 years at 9% per annum.

10. Rs. 500 for 3 years at 6% per annum.

11. Rs. x for y years at z% per annum.

C. Find the principal if—

12. the S.I. is Rs. 90, time is $2\frac{1}{2}$ years and rate is 4·5%.

13. the S.I. is Rs. 123, time is 123 days and rate is 5%.

14. S.I. is Rs. 37·50, time is 8 months and rate is 6·25%.

15. amount is Rs. 4572, time is 3 years and rate is 9%.

16. amount is Rs. 12402, time is 3 years and rate is 10%.

D. Find the time, if—

17. S.I. is Rs. 781·20, rate is 12% and principal is Rs. 1860.

18. S.I. is Rs. 2426·40, rate is 8% and principal is Rs. 6740.

19. amount Rs. 750, rate is 12% and principal is Rs. 500.

20. amount Rs. 10440, rate is 8% and principal is Rs. 9000.

E. Find the rate %, if—

21. Principal is Rs. 1600, S.I. is Rs. 1232 and time is $5\frac{1}{2}$ years.

22. Principal is Rs. 110, S.I. is Rs. 27·50 and time $2\frac{1}{2}$ years.

23. a sum of money at simple interest doubles itself in 8 years.

24. a sum of money trebles itself in 15 years at simple interest.

25. a sum of Rs 25 yields Re 0·125 as S.I. in 1·25 years.

F. **26.** The simple interest on a certain sum for 2·5 years at 12% per annum is Rs. 40 less than the simple interest on the same sum for $3\frac{1}{2}$ years at 10%. Find the sum.

27. A sum of money lent out at simple interest amounts to Rs. 3224 in 2 years and to Rs. 4160 in 5 years. Find the sum and the rate per cent.

28. Divide Rs. 6000 into two parts so that the S.I. on one part for 3 years at 12% per annum may be equal to the simple interest on the second part for $4\frac{1}{2}$ years at 16%.

29. The simple interest on a certain sum for $3\frac{1}{2}$ years at 12% per annum is Rs. 98 more than the simple interest on the same sum for $2\frac{1}{2}$ years at 14% per annum. Find the sum.

30. A sum of money amounts to Rs. 2880 in 2 years and to Rs. 3600 in 5 years. Find the sum of money and the rate per cent.

31. Divide Rs. 12000 into two parts so that the simple interest on one part for 3 years at 12% may be equal to the simple interest on the other part for $4\frac{1}{2}$ years at 16%.

32. Divide Rs. 1750 into two parts such that the S.I. on one part for 2 years at 15% and on the second part for 3 years at 16% may be Rs. 624 in all.

33. Mohan and Sohan borrow Rs. 2500 and 2250 from a bank respectively for $3\frac{1}{2}$ years at the same rate of interest. Mohan pays Rs. 140 more as simple interest than Sohan does. Find the rate of interest.

34. A person deposits Rs. 9000 in a bank. After 2 years he withdraws Rs. 4000 and at the end of 5 years, he receives Rs. 8300 in all. Find the rate %.

35. A and B borrow Rs. 750 each from C at the same rate of interest. A paid back Rs. 930 after 3 years and cleared the account. B was able to pay the loan after 5 years only. How much money will he pay to C to clear the account ?

36. A lady deposits Rs. 7000 in a bank. After one year, she withdraws Rs. 1000 and after another one year, she withdrew another Rs. 2500. After 6 years of her deposit, she got Rs. 5930 in all. Find the rate % of interest paid by the bank.

37. A man borrowed Rs. 2500 and Rs. 4500 from two persons. He repaid both the loans after 3 years 3 months. He had to pay Rs. 520 more as interest on the second sum. Find the rate % which was equal for both the loans.

MISCELLANEOUS EXERCISES II

A. Answer *yes* **or** *no* **:**

1. Every natural number is a rational number too. ....

2. 0 is not a rational number. ....

3. There is an integer between two consecutive integers. ....

4. There are infinite rational numbers between two rational numbrs. ....

5. The reciprocal of 5 is –5. ....

6. The additive inverse of $\frac{-3}{4} = \frac{3}{4}$ ....

7. $a^{-1} = \frac{1}{a}$ and $a^0 = 1$ ....

8. $29 = 2{\cdot}9 \times 10$ ....

9. $0{\cdot}29\overline{56} = \frac{2956 - 29}{9900} = \frac{2927}{9900}$ ....

10. $\frac{19}{51}$ is a terminating decimal. ....

B. 11. Represent the following numbers on number lines :

(a) $\frac{-3}{4}$ (b) $\frac{4}{3}$ (c) $1\frac{2}{3}$ (d) $-1\frac{2}{3}$

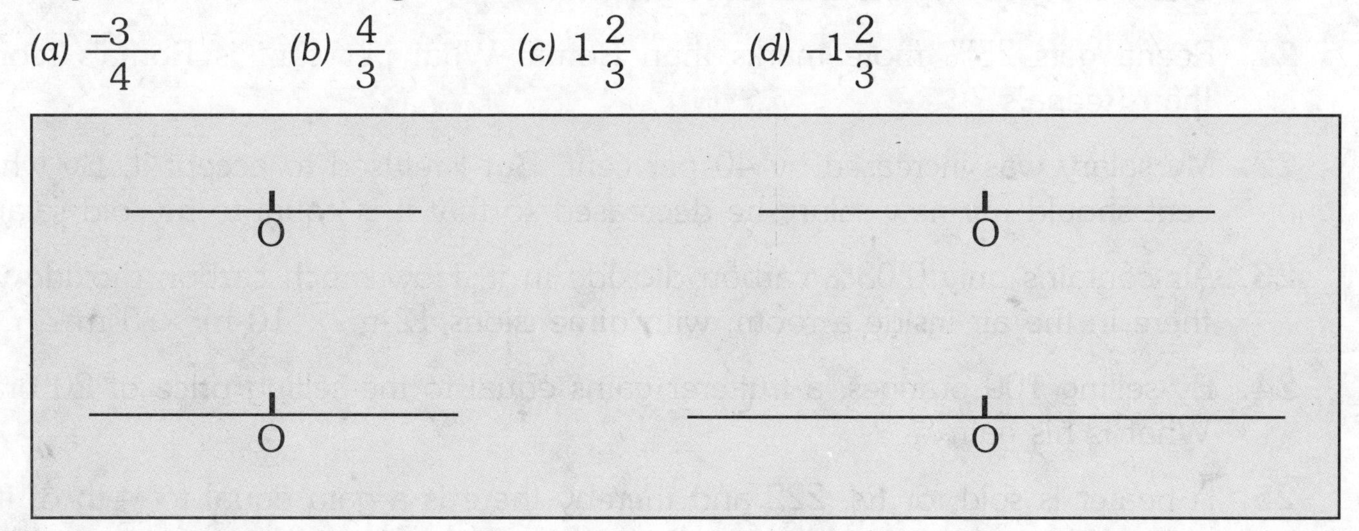

C. Solve :

12. (i) $(x^a)^{b-c} \times (x^b)^{c-a} \times (x^c)^{a-b}$

(ii) $(a^x)^{y+z} \times (a^y)^{z+x} \times (a^z)^{x+y}$

13. A 3 kg. weight when hung from a spring produces an extension of 0·4 cm. in it. What weight will produce an extension of 6 cm. in it ?

14. A working girls's hostel has food-stuffs for 40 days for 50 girls. But 30 more girls join the hostel. How long will the food-stuffs last now ?

15. 30 workers working 7 hours a day finish a job in 18 days. How many labourers working 6 hours a day will finish the same job in 30 days ?

16. Two taps A and B can fill a tank in 6 and 4 hours respectively. A third tap can empty the full tank in 8 hours. If the tank is empty and all the three taps are opened together, how long will it take the tank to get filled ?

17. A and B can do a job in 12 days while B and C can do it in 15 days. C and A can do it together in 20 days. In how many days will each of them do the job separately ?

18. A tank can be filled by a pipe in 4 hours. If full, it can be empted in 6 hours by another pipe. If both the pipes are opened, how long will it take the tank to be full of water ?

19. If I walk at 5 km. per hour, I miss a train by 7 minutes. But if I walk at 6 km. per hour, I reach the station 5 minutes too early. How far is the station from my place ?

20. A train is 220 metres long and it is running at a speed of 60 km. per hour. A man is running at 6 km. per hour in the same direction as the train. In how many seconds will the train pass the man ?

21. Reena gets 25% more marks than Roma. What per cent is Roma's score less than Reena's ?

22. My salary was increased by 40 per cent. But I refused to accept it. By what per cent should my new salary be decreased so that it is equal to my old salary ?

23. Air contains only 0·03% carbon dioxide in it. How much carbon dioxide will be there in the air inside a room, with dimensions 12 m × 10 m × 5 m ?

24. By selling 100 oranges, a fruiterer gains equal to the selling price of 20 oranges. What is his gain % ?

25. A heater is sold for Rs. 222 and thereby there is a gain equal to $\frac{1}{6}$th of its cost price. What is the gain per cent ?

26. A clock yields Rs. 95 more when sold at a gain of 6·25% instead of at a loss of 6·25%. What is its cost price ?

27. A trader marks his goods at such a price that after allowing a discount of 15%, he is able to gain 20%. What is the marked price of an article that costs him Rs. 170 ?

28. Divide Rs. 2600 in two parts so that one part lent at 15% per annum and the other at 12·5% per annum may bring in a total simple interest of Rs. 356.

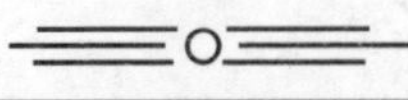

UNIT III
ALGEBRA

IN THIS UNIT—

14 MULTIPLICATION

KNOW THESE TERMS :

1. **monomial**—an algebraic term is called monomial expression
2. **binomial**—an algebraic expression consisting of two terms
3. **trinomial**—an algebraic expression consisting of three terms
4. **polynomial**—an algebraic expression with more than three terms

WHAT IS AN ALGEBRAIC EXPRESSION ?

We know what an algebraic expression is. We can define it as under :

An *algebraic expression* **is a group of two or more algebraic terms connected together by operation-signs of** *plus* **or** *minus*.

Remember that algebraic terms connected by operation-signs of × and ÷ do not have the status of an expression because they can be given the form of one term. They remain **terms** only but sign of + and – change a group of terms into an expression because they cannot take the form of one single term ; as—

$a \times b \times c$ = ***abc*** is a term only.

$abc \div bc$ = ***a*** is also a term only.

But $a + b + c = a + b + c$ is an expression consisting of three terms. So, terms are separated by signs of + and – only, not by signs of × and ÷.

MONOMIALS, BINOMIALS, TRINOMIALS

1. *An algebraic term standing alone is called a* **monomial** ; as $5x$; ab ; lmn etc.
2. *An algebraic expression consisting of two terms connected by + or – is called a* **binomial** ; as : $x + y$; $l - m$ etc.
3. *An algebraic expression consisting of three terms connected by + or – is called a* **trinomial** ; as : $a + b + c$; $x - y - z$ etc.
4. *Similarly an algebraic expression with more than three terms is called a* **polynomial** *or* **multinomial** ; as : $a + b + c - ab + bc$ is a polynomial.

VARIABLE, CONSTANT

1. An algebraic literal number (*a* letter) that can be replaced by any numerical value is called a **variable** ; as : x, a, l, y, z etc.
2. A number or variable that has a fixed unchanging value in an algebraic expression is called a **constant**.

MULTIPLICATION

A. MULTIPLYING A MONOMIAL BY A MONOMIAL

In order to multiply monomials together, we proceed as under :

1. First of all, we observe the **signs** before the monomials to be multiplied. If they are **like**, the product has a *plus* (+) before it. But if they are **unlike,** the product has a *minus* (–) before it.
2. Next, we multiply the **co-efficients** of the monomials to be multiplied and put their product as the *co-efficient of the product.*
3. Finally, we multiply the *variables* one by one and write them side by side in the product after the co-efficient.
4. If a variable occurs in both the multiplying monomials, we add its powers to get that variable in the product.

Let us now solve some examples :

Example 1. Multiply :

(a) $\mathbf{3x}$ **by** $\mathbf{2x}$ (b) $\mathbf{-2ab}$ **by** $\mathbf{7b}$ (c) $\mathbf{-5x}$ **by** $\mathbf{3yz}$

Solution : (a) $3x \times 2x = 3 \times 2 \times x \times x$

$= 6 \times x \times x = 6x^{1+1} = \mathbf{6x^2}$ *Ans.*

(b) $-2ab \times 7b = (-2) \times 7 \times a \times b \times b$

$= -14 \times a \times b^1 \times b^1 = \mathbf{-14ab^2}$ *Ans.*

(c) $-5x \times -3yz = (-5) \times (-3) \times x \times y \times z$

$= 15 \times x \times y \times z = \mathbf{15xyz}$ *Ans.*

Example 2. Find the product of $\mathbf{\frac{-18}{25}x^2yz \times \frac{35}{-54}xy^2z \times \frac{-45}{72}xyz^2}$

Solution : $\frac{-18}{25}x^2yz \times \frac{35}{-54}xy^2z \times \frac{-45}{72}xyz^2$

$= \frac{-18}{25} \times \frac{35}{-54} \times \frac{-45}{72} \times (x^2 \times x \times x) \times (y \times y^2 \times y) \times (z \times z \times z^2)$

$= -\frac{7}{24} \times (x^2 \times x^1 \times x^1) \times (y^1 \times y^2 \times y^1) \times (z^1 \times z^1 \times z^2)$

$= \frac{-7}{24}x^{2+1+1}\ y^{1+2+1}\ z^{1+1+2} = \frac{-7}{24}x^4 \times y^4 \times z^4 = \mathbf{\frac{-7}{24}x^4y^4z^4}$ *Ans.*

Example 3. **Multiply $x^3 \times 5x^5 \left(\frac{1}{5}x^2\right)\left(-6x^4\right)$**

Solution : $x^3 \times 5x^5 \left(\frac{1}{5}x^2\right)(-6x^4)$

$$= \left(1 \times 5 \times \frac{1}{5} \times (-6)\right) \times x^3 \times x^5 \times x^2 \times x^4$$

$$= -6 \times x^{3+5+2+4} = \mathbf{-6x^{14}} \text{ Ans.}$$

PRACTICE EXERCISES 23

A. Find the product :

1. $\frac{-1}{4} \times 2a^2b \times -6a^2bc$
2. $-4 \times 5xyz^2 \times 6xy \times \left(-\frac{3}{2}x^2\right)$
3. $\frac{-3}{4}p^2r \times \frac{2}{3}pq$
4. $3xyz \times 4x^2yz$
5. $(-4a^2b) \times (ab^2) \times 2abc^4$
6. $5x^2y \times \frac{-1}{10}xy^2 \times 3xyz \times 2yz^4$
7. $3{\cdot}5xy \times \frac{1}{10}yz \times \frac{2}{7}zx$
8. $\frac{-2}{3}x^2y \times \frac{9}{14}xy^3 \times -7xz^4$

B. Find the product and evaluate :

9. $7xy^2 \times \frac{-3}{7}x^2z \times \frac{-2}{5}yz^3 \times \frac{-4}{9}xyz \times (-5z^2x)$, if $x = 3$, $y = 2$, $z = 1$
10. $\frac{5}{2}xy^3 \times \frac{2}{3}x^2y^2 \times 3x^2y \times 2xy^2 \times \frac{1}{5}x^3y$, if $x = 1$, $y = 2$
11. $-7x^2yz \times \frac{2}{7}xy^3z^2$, if $x = 2$, $y = 3$, $z = \frac{1}{2}$
12. $\frac{-4}{3}x^2y^3 \times \frac{6}{7}x^2y$, if $x = 2$, $y = 1$
13. $\frac{-8}{15}a^2bc^3 \times \frac{-3}{4}ab^2$, if $a = 1$, $b = 2$, $c = 5$
14. $\left(-5x^2y\right) \times \left(\frac{-2}{3}xy^2z\right) \times \frac{-8}{15}xyz^2 \times \left(\frac{-9}{16}\right)$, if $x = \frac{1}{2}$, $y = \frac{1}{3}$, $z = \frac{1}{4}$

C. 15. Show that $7sqr \times \left(\frac{3}{4}r^2\right) = \left(\frac{3}{4}r^2\right) \times 7sqr$

16. Simplify $(-2x^2)\ (7a^2x^7) \times (16a^5x^5)$

D. Answer *yes* **or** *no* **:**

17. While multiplying two quantities, their bases are added. ....
18. The product of two negative monomials is also negative. ....

B. MULTIPLICATION OF A BINOMIAL BY A MONOMIAL

Example 4. Multiply $(3y^2 - 4y)$ by $2y^2$

Solution : $(3y^2 - 4y) \times 2y^2 = 2y^2\ (3y^2 - 4y)$

$= (2y^2 \times 3y^2) + \left(2y^2 \times (-4y)\right) = 6y^{2+2} - 8y^{2+1}$

$= \mathbf{6y^4 - 8y^3}$ *Ans.*

Example 5. Multiply $\frac{4}{7}xyz + \frac{-2}{5}y^2z$ by 35xyz

Solution : $\left(\frac{4}{7}xyz + \frac{-2}{5}y^2z\right) \times 35xyz = 35xyz\left(\frac{4}{7}xyz + \frac{-2}{5}y^2z\right)$

$= \left(35xyz \times \frac{4}{7}xyz\right) + \left(35xyz \times \frac{-2}{5}y^2z\right)$

$= \left(35 \times \frac{4}{7} \times xyz \times xyz\right) + 35 \times \frac{-2}{5} \times xyz \times y^2z$

$= \mathbf{20x^2y^2z^2 - 14xy^3z^2}$ *Ans.*

C. MULTIPLICATION OF BINOMIALS

Example 6. Multiply $x^2 + y^2$ by $3x + 2y$

Solution :

$$
\begin{array}{r}
x^2 + y^2 \\
\times\ 3x + 2y \\
\hline
2x^2y + 2y^3 \\
3x^3 + 3xy^2 \qquad\qquad \\
\hline
\mathbf{3x^3 + 3xy^2 + 2x^2y + 2y^2}
\end{array}
$$

Ans.

Other Method

$(x^2 + y^2)(3x + 2y) = (x^2 \times 3x) + (x^2 \times 2y) + (y^2 \times 3x) + (y^2 \times 2y)$

$= \mathbf{3x^3 + 2x^2y + 3xy^2 + 2y^3}$ *Ans.*

Example 7. Simplify : $2a^2(a^3 - a) - 3a(a^4 - 2a) - 2(a^4 - 3a^2)$

Solution : $2a^2(a^3 - a) - 3a(a^4 - 2a) - 2(a^4 - 3a^2)$

$= \left((2a^2 \times a^3 + 2a^2 \times (-a)\right) - \left(3a \times a^4 - 3a \times (-2a)\right) - \left(2 \times a^4 - 2 \times (-3a^2)\right)$

$= 2a^5 - 2a^3 - 3a^5 + 6a^2 - 2a^4 + 6a^2$

$= \mathbf{-a^5 - 2a^4 - 2a^3 + 12a^2}$ *Ans.*

Example 8. Solve : $(4a + 3b)(2a + 3b)$

Solution : To solve such a multiplication, we multiply the second set of terms by the terms of the first set one by one :

$(4a + 3b)(2a + 3b)$

$= 4a(2a + 3b) + 3b(2a + 3b)$

$= 8a^2 + 12ab + 6ab + 9b^2$

$= \mathbf{8a^2 + 18ab + 9b^2}$ *Ans.*

Example 9. Simplify : (a) $\mathbf{x^2y^2z^2(3x^2 - 4y^2 + 5z^2)}$

(b) $\left(\frac{1}{2}a^2 - \frac{1}{3}b^2\right) \times \left(\frac{1}{3}a + \frac{1}{2}b\right)$

Solution : (a) $x^2y^2z^2(3x^2 - 4y^2 + 5z^2)$

$= 3x^2(x^2y^2z^2) - 4y^2(x^2y^2z^2) + 5z^2(x^2y^2z^2)$

$= \mathbf{3x^4y^2z^2 - 4x^2y^4z^2 + 5x^2y^2z^4}$ *Ans.*

(b) $\left(\frac{1}{2}a^2 - \frac{1}{3}b^2\right) \times \left(\frac{1}{3}a + \frac{1}{2}b\right)$

$= \frac{1}{2}a^2\left(\frac{1}{3}a + \frac{1}{2}b\right) - \frac{1}{3}b^2\left(\frac{1}{3}a + \frac{1}{2}b\right)$

$= \mathbf{\frac{1}{6}a^3 + \frac{1}{4}a^2b - \frac{1}{9}ab^2 - \frac{1}{6}b^3}$ *Ans.*

Example 10. Multiply $\left(y + \frac{2}{7}y^2\right)$ and $(7y - y^2)$ and verify the result for $y = 3$.

Solution : $\left(y + \frac{2}{7}y^2\right)(7y - y^2) = y(7y - y^2) + \frac{2}{7}y^2(7y - y^2)$

$= 7y^2 - y^3 + 2y^3 - \frac{2}{7}y^4 = \mathbf{-\frac{2}{7}y^4 + y^3 + 7y^2}$ *Ans.*

D. MULTIPLICATION OF A TRINOMIAL BY A BINOMIAL

Example 11. Multiply $(x^2 - 3x + 7)$ and $(2x + 3)$

Solution : $(2x + 3)(x^2 - 3x + 7)$

$= 2x(x^2 - 3x + 7) + 3(x^2 - 3x + 7)$

$= (2x \times x^2) + \left(2x \times (-3x)\right) + (2x \times 7) + (3 \times x^2) - (3 \times 3x) + (3 \times 7)$

$= 2x^3 - 6x^2 + 14x + 3x^2 - 9x + 21$

$= \mathbf{2x^3 - 3x^2 + 5x + 21}$ *Ans.*

PRACTICE EXERCISES 24

A. Multiply :

1. $(3x + 5y)$ and $(5x - 7y)$

2. $(3x^2 + y^2)$ and $(2x^2 + 3y^2)$

3. $\left(\frac{x}{5} - \frac{y}{4}\right)$ and $(5x^2 - 4y^2)$

4. $(7l - 3m)$ and $(4l + 5m)$

5. $(3m^2 + mn)$ and $(m + 2n)$

6. $(3a + 2b)$ and $(2a + 3b)$

7. $(a - 3b)$ and $(2a + 5b)$

8. $(3x^3 - 2x^2)$ and $(2x^2 - x)$

9. $(3x^2y - 5xy^2)$ and $\left(\frac{x^2}{5} - \frac{y^2}{3}\right)$ and verify the answer for $x = 1$, $y = 2$

B. Find the product of :

10. $(5x^2 - 6x + 9)$ and $(2x - 3)$

11. $(2x^2 - 5x + 4)$ and $(2x + 3)$

12. $(x^2 + 7x - 8)$ and $(3x - 2)$

13. $(9x^2 - x + 15)$ and $(x^2 - 4)$

14. $(x^3 - 2x^2 - 7)$ and $(5x - 7)$

15. $(x + y)$ and $(x^2 - xy + y^2)$

C. Multiply :

16. $(2x^2 - 5x + 4)$ and $(x^2 + 7x - 8)$

17. $(x^2 - 4x - 3)$ and $(x^2 - 5x + 8)$

18. $(3x^2 - 3x + 4)$ and $(2x^2 + 5x - 7)$

19. $(2x + 3y - 5)$ and $(x - y + 6)$

20. $(x^3 - 2x^2 + 5x - 7)$ and $(5x - 6)$

D. Simplify :

21. $(2x + 3)(3x + 4)(4x - 5)$

22. $(a + b)(a + c)(b + c)$

23. $(5x^2 - 6x + 9)(2x - 3) - (2x^2 - 5x + 4)(5x + 1)$

24. $(2x^2 - 5x + 4)(x + 2) - (x^2 + 7x - 8)(2x - 3)$

E. Find the value of :

25. $(0{\cdot}5x - y)(3x + y)$ if $x = 2$ and $y = 3$

26. $(x^3 - y^3)(x - y)$ if $x = 1$ and $y = 2$

27. $\frac{1}{3}(6x^2 + 15y^2)(2x + 3y)$ if $x = 2$, $y = 3$

15 IDENTITIES AND FACTORISATION

KNOW THESE TERMS :

1. **identity**—equation of two expressions which is true for all values of the variables used in them.
2. **factorisation**—process of writing a numeral or expression as the product of two or more quantities
3. **multiple**—the product of more-than-one quantities is called the multiple of each of those quantities

A. IDENTITIES

What is an *identity* ?

In algebra, **an** *identity* **is the equality of two expressions true for all values of their variables.**

There are a number of identities in Algebra. But we shall study only three of them in this chapter. Remember that an identity is also called a **formula**.

IDENTITY 1

This identity holds that—

The square of a binomial of the form $(a + b)$ **is equal to the square of the first term + square of the second term + twice the product of both the terms.** We can generalise it as under :

$$(a + b)^2 = a^2 + b^2 + 2ab$$

We can prove it through multiplication and with the help of a diagram.

$$\begin{aligned}(a + b)^2 &= (a + b)(a + b)\\ &= a(a + b) + b(a + b)\\ &= a^2 + ab + ab + b^2\\ &= a^2 + b^2 + 2ab\end{aligned}$$

a b
ab b^2
a^2 ab
a b

IDENTITY 2

This identity holds that

The square of *a binomial of the form* $a - b$ **is equal to the square of the first term + square of the second term – twice the product of the both the terms.** We can generalise it as under :

$$(a - b)^2 = a^2 + b^2 - 2ab$$

We can prove this identity by actual multiplication and also through a diagram.

$$\mathbf{(a - b)^2} = (a - b)\,(a - b)$$
$$= a\,(a - b) - b\,(a - b)$$
$$= a^2 - ab - ab + b^2$$
$$= \mathbf{a^2 + b^2 - 2ab}$$

Otherwise—

$$(a - b)^2 = [a + (-b)]^2$$
$$= [a + (-b)]\,[a + (-b)]$$
$$= a[a + (-b)] + (-b)\,[a + (-b)]$$
$$= a^2 + (-ab) + (-ab) + (-b \times -b)$$
$$= a^2 - ab - ab + b^2 = \mathbf{a^2 - 2ab + b^2}$$

IDENTITY 3

This identity holds that—

The product of the *sum* **and** *difference* **of two quantities is equal to the** *difference in their squares*.

We can generalise it as under :

$$\mathbf{a^2 - b^2 = (a + b)\,(a - b)}$$

We can prove this identity by actual multiplication and also through a diagram.

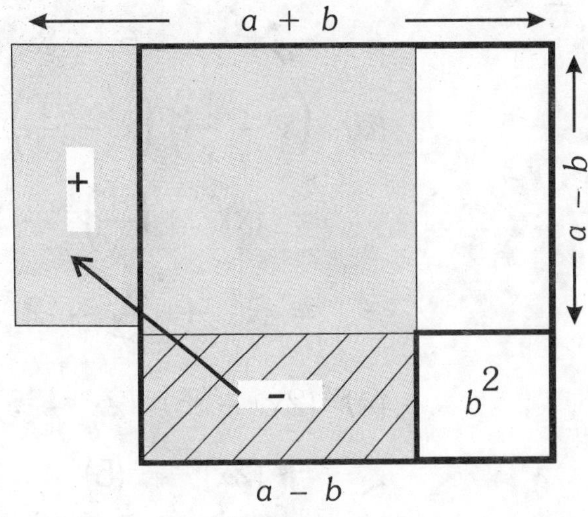

$$\mathbf{(a + b)\,(a - b)} = a(a - b) + b\,(a - b)$$
$$= a^2 - ab + ab - b^2$$
$$= \mathbf{a^2 - b^2}$$

The diagram on the right also proves this identity. The rectangle with (–) in it has been transferred to a new place with (+) in it.

APPLICATION OF THE THREE IDENTITIES

We have studied the following three identities :

1. $\mathbf{(a + b)^2 = a^2 + b^2 + 2ab}$
2. $\mathbf{(a - b)^2 = a^2 + b^2 - 2ab}$
3. $\mathbf{(a + b)\,(a - b) = a^2 - b^2}$

Let us now solve some examples :

Example 1. Solve : *(a)* $(a + 7)(a + 7)$ *(b)* $\left(x + \frac{1}{x}\right)\left(x + \frac{1}{x}\right)$

(c) $(x - 4)(x - 4)$ *(d)* $\left(x - \frac{1}{x}\right)\left(x - \frac{1}{x}\right)$

(e) $(2x + 5)(2x - 5)$ *(f)* $\left(x + \frac{1}{3}\right)\left(x - \frac{1}{3}\right)$

Solution : *(a)* $(a + 7)(a + 7) = (a + 7)^2$ ..... *identity* $(a+b)^2$

$= a^2 + (7)^2 + (2 \times a \times 7)$

$= a^2 + 49 + 14a = \mathbf{a^2 + 14a + 49}$ *Ans.*

(b) $\left(x + \frac{1}{x}\right)\left(x + \frac{1}{x}\right) = \left(x + \frac{1}{x}\right)^2$ .... *identity* $(a+b)^2$

$= (x)^2 + \left(\frac{1}{x}\right)^2 + 2 \times x \times \frac{1}{x}$

$= \mathbf{x^2 + \frac{1}{x^2} + 2}$ *Ans.*

(c) $(x - 4)(x - 4) = (x - 4)^2$ .... *identity* $(a-b)^2$

$= x^2 + (4)^2 - (2 \times x \times 4)$

$= x^2 + 16 - 8x = \mathbf{x^2 - 8x + 16}$ *Ans.*

(d) $\left(x - \frac{1}{x}\right)\left(x - \frac{1}{x}\right) = \left(x - \frac{1}{x}\right)^2$ .... *identity* $(a-b)^2$

$= (x)^2 + \left(\frac{1}{x}\right)^2 - 2 \times x \times \frac{1}{x}$

$= \mathbf{x^2 + \frac{1}{x^2} - 2}$ *Ans.*

(e) $(2x + 5)(2x - 5)$ .... *identity* $a^2 - b^2)$

$= (2x)^2 - (5)^2$

$= \mathbf{4x^2 - 25}$ *Ans.*

(f) $\left(x + \frac{1}{3}\right)\left(x - \frac{1}{3}\right)$ .... *identity* $a^2 - b^2)$

$= (x)^2 - \left(\frac{1}{3}\right)^2$

$= \mathbf{x^2 - \frac{1}{9}}$ *Ans.*

Example 2. Evaluate (*a*) $\mathbf{16x^2 - 40xy + 25y^2}$ **if** $\mathbf{x = 2,\ y = 3}$

(*b*) $\mathbf{81a^2 + 90ab + 25b^2}$ **if** $\mathbf{a = 1,\ b = 2}$

(*c*) $\mathbf{169a^2 - 144b^2}$ **when** $\mathbf{a = 1,\ b = -1}$

Solution : (*a*) $16x^2 - 40xy + 25y^2$

$= (4x)^2 - (2 \times 4x \times 5y) + (5y)^2$

$= (4x - 5y)^2$ .... *identity* $(a - b)^2$

Putting the values of x, y

$(4x - 5y)^2 = [(4 \times 2) - (5 \times 3)]^2$

$= (8 - 15)^2 = (-7)^2 =$ **49** *Ans.*

(*b*) $81a^2 + 90ab + 25b^2$

$= (9a)^2 + (2 \times 9a \times 5b) + (5b)^2$

$= (9a + 5b)^2$ .... *identity* $(a+b)^2$

Putting the values of a, b

$(9a + 5b)^2 = [(9 \times 1) + (5 \times 2)]^2$

$= (9 + 10)^2 = 19^2 =$ **361** *Ans.*

(*c*) $169a^2 - 144b^2$

$= (13a)^2 - (12b)^2$ .... *identity* $a^2 - b^2)$

$= (13a + 12b)\ (13a - 12b)$

Putting the values of a, b

$(13a + 12b)\ (13a - 12b)$

$= [(13 \times 1) + (12 \times -1)]\ [(13 \times 1) - (12 \times -1)$

$= [13 + (-12)]\ [13 - (-12)]$

$= (13 - 12)\ (13 + 12)$

$= 1 \times 25 =$ **25** *Ans.*

Example 3. (*a*) **Find** $\mathbf{(85)^2}$ **without actual multiplication.**

(*b*) **Simplify** : $\dfrac{\mathbf{2{\cdot}734 \times 2{\cdot}734 - 1{\cdot}266 \times 1{\cdot}266}}{\mathbf{2{\cdot}734 + 1{\cdot}266}}$

Solution : (a) $(85)^2 = (80 + 5)^2$ .... ($\because$ 85 = 80 + 5)

$= (80)^2 + (5)^2 + 2 \times 80 \times 5$ .... *using* $(a+b)^2$

$= 6400 + 25 + 800 = \mathbf{7225}$ *Ans.*

(b) $$\frac{2{\cdot}734 \times 2{\cdot}734 - 1{\cdot}266 \times 1{\cdot}266}{2{\cdot}734 + 1{\cdot}266}$$

$$= \frac{(2{\cdot}734)^2 - (1{\cdot}266)^2}{(2{\cdot}734 + 1{\cdot}266)}$$

$$= \frac{(2{\cdot}734 + 1{\cdot}266)\,(2{\cdot}734 - 1{\cdot}266)}{(2{\cdot}734 + 1{\cdot}266)}$$

$= 2{\cdot}734 - 1{\cdot}266 = \mathbf{1{\cdot}468}$ *Ans.*

PRACTICE EXERCISES 25

A. Complete each identity :

1. $(x + y)^2 = x^2 + y^2$ .... **2.** $(x - y)^2 = x^2 + y^2$.......

3. $x^2 - y^2 = (x + y)$ (........ – ....)

B. Find the value of :

4. $(2x + 3y)^2$ **5.** $\left(\frac{3x}{2} - 6y\right)^2$ **6.** $x^2 - y^2$

7. $\left(a + \frac{1}{a}\right)^2$ **8.** $\left(a - \frac{1}{a}\right)^2$ **9.** $a^2 - \frac{1}{a^2}$

10. $\left(\frac{x}{2} + y\right)^2$ **11.** $\left(\frac{x}{2} - y\right)^2$ **12.** $\frac{x^2}{4} - \frac{y^2}{9}$

13. $(4a + 3b)^2$ **14.** $(3x - 7y)^2$ **15.** $4a^2 - 25b^2$

16. $(100 + 8)^2$ **17.** $(100 - 8)^2$ **18.** $(56)^2 - (44)^2$

C. Find the products :

19. $(3x + 4y)\,(3x + 4y)$ **20.** $(2p - 5q)\,(2p - 5q)$

21. $(3c + 4d)\,(3c + 4d)$ **22.** $(5m - 6n)\,(5m - 6n)$

23. $\left(\frac{a}{5} + \frac{b}{2}\right)\left(\frac{a}{5} + \frac{b}{2}\right)$ **24.** $\left(m - \frac{1}{m}\right)\left(m - \frac{1}{m}\right)$

25. $\left(m + \frac{1}{m}\right)\left(m - \frac{1}{m}\right)$ **26.** $(x + 5)\,(x - 5)$

27. $\left(\frac{x}{y} + \frac{y}{x}\right)\left(\frac{x}{y} - \frac{y}{x}\right)$ **28.** $\left(\frac{3x}{4} + \frac{2y}{3}\right)\left(\frac{3x}{4} - \frac{2y}{3}\right)$

29. $(3x - 2y)\,(3x + 2y)$ **30.** $\left(z + \frac{1}{z}\right)\left(z - \frac{1}{z}\right)$

D. Evaluate :

31. $9x^2 - 30xy + 25y^2$ if $x = 12$, $y = -10$

32. $16x^2 - 72xy + 81y^2$ if $x = 9$, $y = 6$

33. $25a^2 + 30ab + 9b^2$ if $a = 8$, $b = 10$

34. $9x^2 + 24x + 16$ when $x = 17$

35. $64a^2 + 144ab + 81b^2$ if $a = 1$, $b = 1\frac{1}{3}$

36. $x^2 + \frac{1}{x^2}$, if $x + \frac{1}{x} = 5$

37. $x^4 + \frac{1}{x^4}$ if $x + \frac{1}{x} = 5$

38. $a^2 + \frac{1}{a^2}$ and $a^4 + \frac{1}{a^4}$ if $a + \frac{1}{a} = 9$

39. $x^2 + \frac{1}{x^2}$ and $x^4 + \frac{1}{x^4}$ if $x - \frac{1}{x} = 5$

40. $a^2 + \frac{1}{a^2}$ and $a^4 + \frac{1}{a^4}$ if $a - \frac{1}{a} = 3$

41. $9b^2 - \frac{1}{9b^2}$ if $b = 7$

42. $5x - \frac{1}{5x} = a$, find $25x^2 - \frac{1}{25x^2}$

E. Simplify :

43. $(82)^2 - (18)^2$

44. 113×87

45. 43×57

46. $(79)^2 - (69)^2$

47. $(105)^2 - (95)^2$

48. Find the value of $9x^2 + 4y^2$ if $xy = 20$, $3x - 2y = 7$

49. Evaluate $\frac{9}{25} a^2 \times \frac{4}{9} b^2$, if $ab = 20$ and $\frac{2}{5} b = 11$

B (FACTORISATION)

Factorisation **is the process of writing a numeral or expression as the product of two or more numbers/expressions**.

The given expression is called the **multiple** while the two or more expressions are called its **factors**.

Example : *(a)* **3 × 5 = 15 or 15 = 3 × 5**

In it, 15 is the multiple while 3 and 5 are its factors

(b) ***ab* = *a* × *b***

In it, *ab* is the multiple while *a* and *b* are its factors.

Let us now study how to factorise different types of expressions.

A. FACTORISATION OF MONOMIALS

Example 1. Factorise $5x^2y$

Solution : Given monomial $= 5x^2y = 5 \times x^2 \times y$

$= 5 \times x \times x \times y$; so factors are 5, x, x and y

B. COMMON FACTORS

Example 2. Factorise *(a)* **$3x + 6$** *(b)* **$16m - 4m^2$**

Solution : *(a)* $3x + 6$

Clearly 3 is a common factor of both the terms of $3x$ and 6

We take out 3 and divide each term by it

So, $3x + 6 =$ **$3(x + 2)$** *Ans.*

(b) $16m - 4m^2$

$4m$ is the greatest common factor of both the terms

$\therefore$ $16m - 4m^2 =$ **$4m(4 - m)$** *Ans.*

C. FACTORISATION OF POLYNOMIALS

Example 3. Factorise $a^3b^4 - a^3b^5 + a^2b^5$

Solution : $a^3b^4 - a^3b^5 + a^2b^5$

Clearly, a^2b^4 is the greatest common factor among the terms.

$\therefore$ $a^3b^4 - a^3b^5 + a^2b^5 =$ **$a^2b^4(a - ab + b)$** *Ans.*

Example 4. Factorise $a(x + 2) + b(x + 2)$

Solution : $a(x + 2) + b(x + 2)$

Clearly $(x + 2)$ is the common factor

$\therefore$ $a(x + 2) + b(x + 2) =$ **$(x + 2)(a + b)$** *Ans.*

D. FACTORS OF IDENTITY EXPRESSIONS

Example 5. Factorise $a^2 + 2ab + b^2$

Solution : $a^2 + 2ab + b^2 = a + ab + ab + b$

$= a(a + b) + b(a + b) =$ **$(a + b)(a + b)$** *Ans.*

Example 6. Factorise $p^2 - 4pq + 4q^2$

Solution : $p^2 - 4pq + 4q^2 = p - 2pq - 2pq + 4q^2$

$= p(p - 2q) - 2q(p - 2q) = \mathbf{(p - 2q)(p - 2q)}$ *Ans.*

Example 7. Factorise $a^2 - b^2$

Solution : $a^2 - b^2 = a^2 + ab - ab - b^2$

$= a(a + b) - b(a + b) = \mathbf{(a + b)(a - b)}$ *Ans.*

PRACTICE EXERCISES 26

A. Define—

1. a multiple **2.** a factor **3.** factorisation

4. a common factor **5.** the greatest common factor

B. Factorise the following monomials :

6. $2x^2y$ **7.** $3x^2y$ **8.** $5xy^2$ **9.** $6a^3b^5$

10. $7x^2y^2$ **11.** $-30m^2n^3$ **12.** $15y^4z^3$ **13.** $14a^2b^4$

14. $-16a^3b^2c^3$ **15.** $110m^2n^2$ **16.** $-25l^3m^4$ **17.** $-12y^4z^3$

C. Factorise the following binomials :

18. $5x + 15$ **19.** $2n^2 - 3n$ **20.** $5x^2y + 10xy^2$

21. $6x^2 - 8x^3y$ **22.** $2x^5 + 12x^3$ **23.** $4a^3 - 2a$

24. $14m^7 - 7m^3$ **25.** $-14x^2y^2z - 8xyz^2$ **26.** $15m^6 - 5m^4$

D. Factorise the following polynomials :

27. $9x^2 - x - y^2x$ **28.** $a^2 + bc + ab + ca$

29. $ax^2 + by^2 + ay^2 + bx^2$ **30.** $m^2 + 14m + 49$

31. $am + bm + an + bn$ **32.** $px + py + qx + qy$

33. $ax^2 + by^2 + bx^2 + ay^2$ **34.** $4x - ay + 4y - ax$

35. $a^3 - b^2 + a - a^2b^2$ **36.** $- mn^2 + lm^2 + n^2 - lm$

E. Factorise the following using identities :

37. $4x^2 - 9y^2$ **38.** $16a^2 - 9b^2$ **39.** $9m^2 - (m - n)^2$

40. $32x^4y^2 - 8x^2$ **41.** $4x^2 - 9$ **42.** $25a^2 - 16b^2$

43. $36x^2 - (a - b)^2$ **44.** $x^4 - y^4$ **45.** $x^4 + 2x^2 + 1$

46. $4m^2 - 4m + 1$ **47.** $x^2 - (y + z)^2$ **48.** $a^4 - 16$

49. $a^2 - 2ab + b^2 - 9$ **50.** $4x^2 + 12xy + 9y^2 - 25$

16 LINEAR EQUATIONS (ONE VARIABLE)

KNOW THESE TERMS :

1. **equation**—a statement of equality that contains an *unknown* quantity/quantities
2. **linear equation**—an equation that has a variable/variables of the *first degree*
3. **additive inverse**—the negative form of a quantity
4. **multiplicative inverse**—the reciprocal of a quantity

An *equation* **is a statement of equality that contains an unknown quantity or quantities (variables).**

A *linear equation* **is an equation that has a variable/variables of the first degree,** *i.e.* **with exponent 1** ; as—

(a) $3x + 5 = 8$ (b) $x + \frac{1}{2} = 2$ (c) $2a + 3 = 7$

In this chapter, we shall study how to solve linear equations with only one variable. Solving an equation means to find a numerical value of the variable that proves the equation to be true. This value is called the **root** of the equation.

We learnt the rules for solving linear equations in class VI.

Let us recall them.

1. If one and the same quantity is added to or subtracted from each side of an equation, its value does not change.
2. If one and the same quantity multiplies or divides each side of an equation, its value does not change.
3. Any quantity transposed from one side of an equation to the other side becomes its *additive inverse* or *multiplicative inverse* as the case may be.

Let us now solve some examples :

Example 1. **Solve : $5x - 5 = 0$**

Solution : $5x - 5 = 0$

or $5x = 0 + 5 = 5$ *(Transposing –5)*

or $x = 5 \times \frac{1}{5} = 1$ *(Transposing 5)*

Hence $\boldsymbol{x} = \mathbf{1}$ *Ans.*

Example 2. **Solve : $7 - 5x = 5 - 7x$**

Solution : $7 - 5x = 5 - 7x$

or $-5x = 5 - 7x - 7$ *(Transposing 7)*

or $-5x + 7x = 5 - 7$ *(Transposing –7x)*

or $2x = -2$

or $x = -2 \times \frac{1}{2} = -1$ *(Transposing 2)*

Hence $\mathbf{x = -1}$ *Ans.*

Example 3. **Solve : $2x - \frac{1}{3} = \frac{1}{5} - x$**

Solution : $2x - \frac{1}{3} = \frac{1}{5} - x$

or $2x + x = \frac{1}{5} + \frac{1}{3}$ *(Transposing x, $\frac{1}{3}$)*

or $3x = \frac{3 + 5}{15} = \frac{8}{15}$

or $3x \times 15 = 8$ *(Transposing $\frac{1}{15}$)*

or $45x = 8$ or $\mathbf{x = \frac{8}{45}}$ *Ans.*

Example 4. **Solve : $\frac{y - 1}{3} - \frac{y - 2}{4} = 1$**

Solution : $\frac{y - 1}{3} - \frac{y - 2}{4} = 1$

or $\frac{4(y - 1) - 3(y - 2)}{12} = 1$

or $\frac{(4y - 4) - (3y - 6)}{12} = 1$

or $\frac{4y - 4 - 3y + 6}{12} = 1$

or $\frac{y + 2}{12} = 1$

or $y + 2 = 1 \times 12 = 12$ *(Transposing $\frac{1}{12}$)*

or $y = 12 - 2 = 10$ *(Transposing 2)*

$\therefore$ $y = \mathbf{10}$ *Ans.*

Example 5. $\mathbf{\frac{2}{3} x = \frac{3}{8} x + \frac{7}{12}}$

Solution : $\frac{2}{3} x = \frac{3}{8} x + \frac{7}{12}$

or $\frac{2x}{3} - \frac{3x}{8} = \frac{7}{12}$ (*Transposing* $\frac{3x}{8}$)

or $\frac{16x - 9x}{24} = \frac{7}{12}$

or $\frac{7x}{24} = \frac{7}{12}$ or $7x = \frac{7}{12} \times 24$ (*Transposing* $\frac{1}{24}$)

or $7x = 14$

or $\boldsymbol{x = 2}$ *Ans.*

Example 6. **Solve : $\cdot 5x + \frac{x}{5} = 0{\cdot}25x + 7$**

Solution : $\cdot 5x + \frac{x}{5} = 0{\cdot}25x + 7$

or $\frac{5x}{10} + \frac{x}{5} = \frac{25x}{100} + 7$

or $\frac{5x + 2x}{10} = \frac{25x}{100} + 7$

or $\frac{7x}{10} = \frac{25x}{100} + 7$

or $\frac{7x}{10} - \frac{25x}{100} = 7$ (*Transposing* $\frac{25x}{100}$)

or $\frac{70x - 25x}{100} = 7$

or $\frac{45x}{100} = 7$

or $45x = 7 \times 100 = 700$ (*Transposing* $\frac{1}{100}$)

or $x = 700 \times \frac{1}{45} = \frac{140}{9}$ (*Transposing* 45)

or $\boldsymbol{x = 15\frac{5}{9}}$ *Ans.*

PRACTICE EXERCISES 27

A. Define :

1. an equation
2. a linear equation
3. transposition
4. root of an equation

B. Solve the following equation :

5. $3x - 2 = 16$
6. $2x - 3 = 7$
7. $4x - 3 = 2x - 7$
8. $5x - 6 = 4x - 2$

9. $3x + \frac{1}{2} = 5$

10. $4x + \frac{3}{5} = 5$

11. $\frac{1}{3}x - \frac{1}{2} = 6$

12. $3x + \frac{1}{5} = 2 - x$

13. $\frac{1}{4}x + 5 = 2x + \frac{3}{4}$

14. $\frac{x}{4} + \frac{x}{6} = \frac{x}{2} + \frac{3}{4}$

15. $\frac{y}{3} + 2 = 2y + \frac{15}{4}$

16. $\frac{5x-4}{8} - \frac{x-3}{5} = \frac{x+4}{4}$

17. $x - (3x - \frac{2x-5}{10}) = \frac{2x-57}{6} - \frac{5}{3}$

18. $x - (2x - \frac{3x-4}{7}) = \frac{4x-27}{3} - 3$

19. $2y + \frac{11}{4} + \frac{1}{3}y + 2$

20. $\frac{2}{3}(x-5) - \frac{1}{4}(x-2) = \frac{-3}{2}$

21. $0{\cdot}3x + 0{\cdot}4 = {\cdot}28x + 1{\cdot}16$

22. $0{\cdot}6x + \frac{4}{5} = 0{\cdot}28x + 1{\cdot}16$

23. $2{\cdot}4x + 1{\cdot}35 - 0{\cdot}04x = 3{\cdot}71x + 13{\cdot}5$

24. $0{\cdot}4x + 12 = 11{\cdot}4x - 4{\cdot}5$

25. $3(x-4) - 4(2x+3) = 2(x+5) + 4$

26. $2(x-2) - 3(x-3) = 5(x-5) - 4(x-8)$

27. $3x - 2(2x-5) = 2(x+3) - 8$

PROBLEMS INVOLVING LINEAR EQUATIONS

Example 7. If a number is doubled and then increased by 7, it becomes 13. Find the number.

Solution : Suppose the reqd. no. $= x$

When doubled, x becomes $2x$

When increased by 7, $2x$ becomes $2x + 7$

According to the expression—

$2x + 7 = 13$

or $2x = 13 - 7 = 6$

$x = 3$

$\therefore$ **Reqd. No. = 3** *Ans.*

Example 8. **The length of a rectangle is 6 metres larger than three times its breadth. If its perimeter is 148 metres, find its length and breadth.**

Solution : Suppose the breadth of the rectangle = x metres

$\therefore$ its length = $3x + 6$ metres

and its perimeter = 2(length + breadth)

= $2(3x + 6 + x)$ metres

So, $2(3x + 6 + x) = 148$

or $6x + 12 + 2x = 148$ or $8x + 12 = 148$

or $8x = 148 - 12 = 136$

or $x = 136 \div 8 = 17$

Hence the breadth of the rectangle = **17*m*.**

And its length = $17 \times 3 + 6$ = **57*m*** *Ans.*

Example 9. **Reena is heavier than Roma by 2 kg. while Reeta is lighter than Roma by 1 kg. The sum of the weights of the three is 115 kg. Find their weights.**

Solution : Suppose the weight of Roma = x kg.

Reema's weight = $(x + 2)$ kg.

and Reeta's weight = $(x - 1)$ kg.

$\therefore$ Sum of their weights = $(x + x + 2 + x - 1)$ kg.

So, $x + x + 2 + x - 1 = 115$

or $3x + 1 = 115$

or $3x = 115 - 1 = 114$

or $x = 38$

Hence Roma's weight = **38 kg.**

Reena's weight = $38 + 2$ = **40 kg.**

Reeta's weight = $38 - 1$ = **37 kg.** *Ans.*

Example 10. **$\frac{4}{5}$ of a number is larger than its $\frac{3}{4}$ by 4. Find the number.**

Solution : Suppose the number = x

$\frac{4}{5}$ of $x = \frac{4x}{5}$ and its $\frac{3}{4} = \frac{3x}{4}$

So, $\frac{4x}{5} > \frac{3x}{4}$ by 4

or $\frac{4x}{5} = \frac{3x}{4} + 4$

or $16x = 15x + 80$ *(Multiplying both sides by 20)*

or $16x - 15x = 80$; *i.e.* $x = 80$

Hence the number is **80** *Ans.*

Example 11. The ages of Mohan and Manoj are in the ratio of 7 : 5. Ten years hence, the ratio will become 9 : 7. Find their present ages.

Solution : Suppose Mohan's age = $7x$ yrs.

$\therefore$ Manoj's age = $5x$ yrs.

After 10 years—

Mohan's Age = $(7x + 10)$ yrs.

and Manoj's Age = $(5x + 10)$ years.

New Ratio = $(7x + 10) : (5x + 10) = \frac{7x + 10}{5x + 10}$

So, $\frac{7x + 10}{5x + 10} = \frac{9}{7}$

or $49x + 70 = 45x + 90$ *(By cross multiplication)*

or $49x - 45x = 90 - 70$

or $4x = 20$ or $x = 5$

Mohan's Age = $7x = 7 \times 5 =$ **35** *yrs.*

Manoj's Age = $5x = 5 \times 5 =$ **25** *yrs.*

Example 12. The sum of four consecutive numbers is 266. Find the numbers.

Solution : Suppose the number are x, $x + 1$, $x + 2$, $x + 3$

Their sum = $x + x + 1 + x + 2 + x + 3 = 4x + 6$

$4x + 6 = 266$

or $4x = 266 - 6 = 260$

or $x = 260 \div 4 = 65$

$\therefore$ Reqd. Numbers are **65, 66, 67, 68** *Ans.*

PRACTICE EXERCISES 28

1. A man's present age is x years. What was his age 7 years ago and what will his age be after 9 years ?

2. Number x is larger than number y. How much larger is it than y ?

3. A number has a as its unit's digit and b as its ten's digit. What is the number ?

4. Divide 60 into two parts so that one part is 3 times the other. Find the parts.

5. An isosceles triangle has either of its equal sides shorter than thrice its third side by 4 metres. Its perimeter 55 m. Find its sides.

6. Three times a number added to 3 makes 9. Find the number.

7. Amita is older than Anita by 3 years. Six years ago, Amita's age was 4 times that of Anita. Find their present ages.

8. The numerator of a fraction is larger than its denominator by 4. It we add 1 to its denominator, the fraction becomes $\frac{3}{2}$. Find the fraction.

9. Sohan's father is three times as old as Sohan. After 10 years, he will he twice as old as Sohan. Find their present ages.

10. If 9 is added to thrice a number, it become 45. Find the number.

11. The sum of two consecutive multiples of 3 is 69. Find them.

12. The breadth of a rectangular park is shorter than its length by 5 metres. Find the dimensions of the park, if its perimeter is 142 metres.

13. The price of 2 tables is Rs. 340. If the cost of a table is Rs. 20 higher than that of the chair. Find the price of each table.

14. A number when added to *its half*, *its two-thirds* and *its one-seventh* amounts to 97. Find the number.

15. A number has two digits whose sum is 8. If 36 be added to the number, the digits interchange their places. Find the number.

16. A number consist of two digits whose difference is 3. If 27 be added to the number, its digits get interchanged. Find the number.

17. If a radio is sold for Rs. 684, there is a loss of 5%. Find the CP of the radio.

18. The perimeter of a rectangle is 50 metres. Its length is larger than its breadth by 5 metres. Find the length and breadth of the rectangle.

19. Renu's Age is four times that of her younger brother. Five years back her age was 9 times the age of her brother. Find their present ages.

20. 50 kg. of a mixture of two types of tea contains 60% of superior tea. How much more superior tea be mixed into it to make it 75% in the mixture ?

MISCELLANEOUS EXERCISES III

A. Answer *yes* **or** *no* **:**

1. When two monomials with the same base but different exponents are multiplied, their exponents add up. ....

2. $a^7 \times a^5 \times a^{-3} \times a^2 \times a^{-4} = a^6$ ....

3. A binomial is an expression with two monomials connected by + or – ....

4. If two quantities with like signs are multiplied their product is negative. ....

5. If two quantities with unlike signs are multiplied, their product is positive. ....

B. Simplify :

6. $\frac{2}{3} x^2y \times \frac{-3}{4} xy^3 \times \frac{-2}{5} x^2y^2z^2$

7. $\left(\frac{5}{6} x^2y - \frac{2}{3} xy^2\right) \times - 2x^2y^2$

8. $- 3xy^2 \left(\frac{5}{2} xy^3 - \frac{2}{3} x^2y^2\right)$

9. $a^3 (a - 2) + 2a^2 (a + 3) - 6a (a - 4)$

C. Find the product of :

10. $(4x - 5) (10 - 3x)$

11. $(4x^2 - 5y^2) (x^2 + 2y^2)$

D. Find the squares of :

12. $3m + 4n$

13. $y - z$

14. $z - \frac{1}{z}$

E. Solve :

15. $(x + 14) (x - 14)$

16. $(x^2 + yz) (x^2 - yz)$

17. $\left(\frac{x}{3} + \frac{y}{5}\right)\left(\frac{x}{3} - \frac{y}{5}\right)$

18. 84×76

F. Factorise :

19. $ax^2 + by^2 + bx^2 + ay^2$

20. $4(x - 3y)^2 - 6(x - 3y)$

G. Find the value of y :

21. $\frac{1}{3}y + 2 = 2y + 3\frac{3}{4}$

22. $\frac{y+1}{3} - \frac{y+2}{4} + \frac{y+3}{5} = 1$

23. The sum of two consecutive multiples of 4 is 68. Find them.

MEMORABLE FACTS

1. A. combination of terms connected by signs of + and – is called an **algebraic expression**.

2. A **monomial** is another name for a term.

3. A **binomial** is made up of two monomials and a **trinomial** is made up of three monomials connected by + or –.

4. A **polynomial** is made up of more than three terms/monomials linked by + and – signs.

5. $(a + b)^2 = a^2 + b^2 + 2ab$

6. $(a - b)^2 = a^2 + b^2 - 2ab$

7. $a^2 - b^2 = (a + b)(a - b)$

8. A **linear equation** is a statement of equality between two expression of the first degree.

9. The value of a variable in an equation is called its **root**.

UNIT IV

GEOMETRY

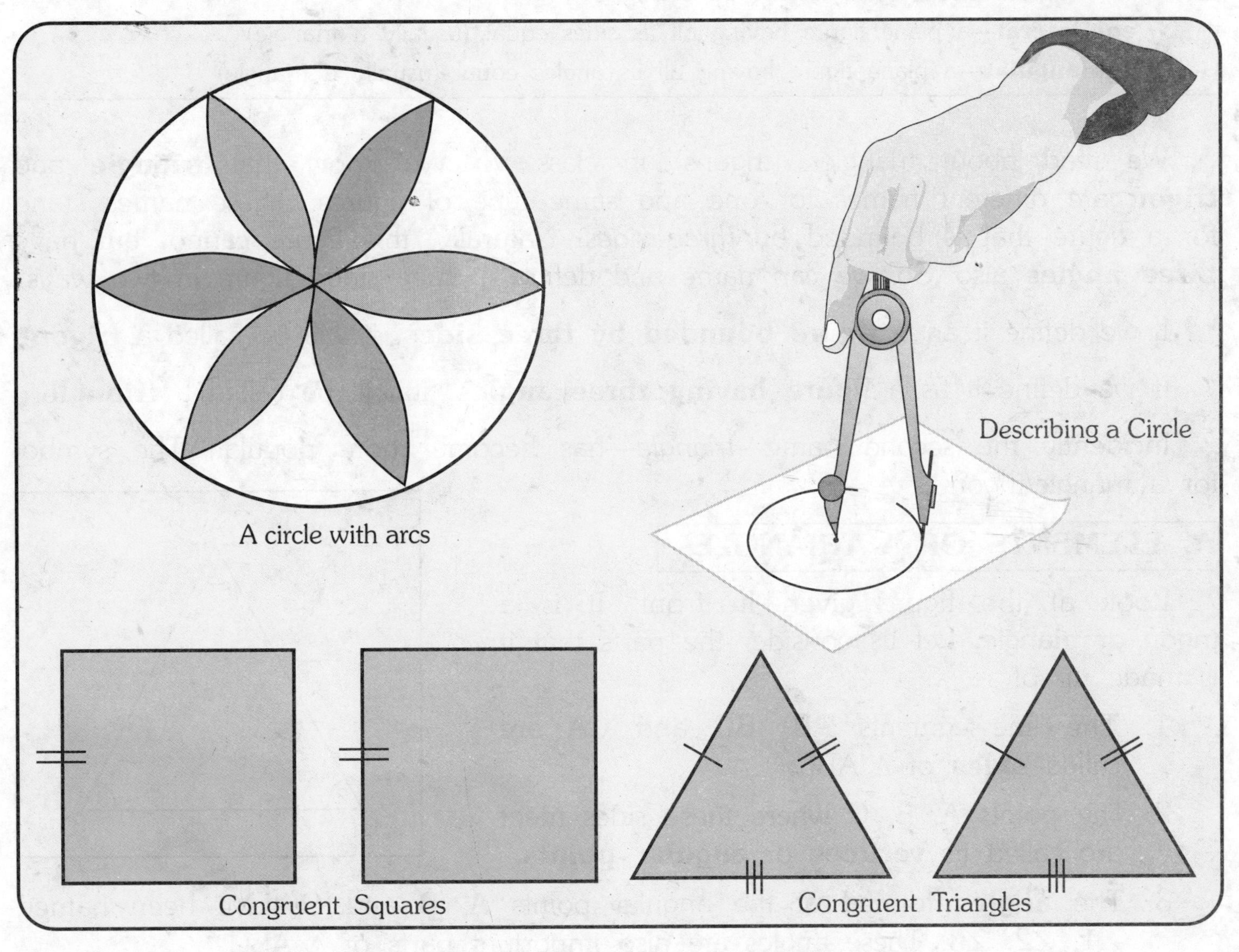

IN THIS UNIT—

17 TRIANGLES—I

KNOW THESE TERMS :

1. **trigon**—a plane figure bounded by three sides
2. **triangle**—a plane figure having three angles
3. **equilateral**—a plane figure having all its sides equal (usually a triangle)
4. **equiangular**—a plane figure having all its angles equal (usually a triangle)

We read about triangles (trigons) in class VI. We know that **triangle** and **trigon** are different names for one and same type of figures. These names stand for a figure that is bounded by *three sides*. Naturally, this figure cannot but have **three angles** also. So, we can name and define a three sided figure in two ways.

If we define it **as a figure bounded by three sides**, it will be called a **trigon**.

If we define it as a **figure having three angles**, it will be called a **triangle**.

Incidently the second name—*triangle*—has become more popular. The symbol for a triangle/trigon is Δ.

A. ELEMENTS OF A TRIANGLE

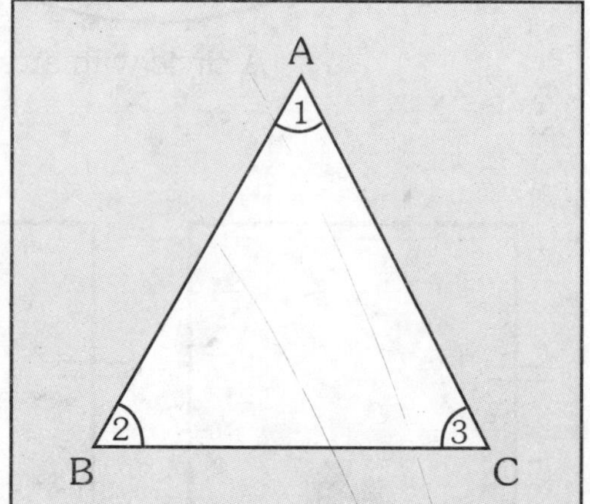

Look at the figure given in front. It is a trigon or triangle. Let us consider the parts that it is made up of :

1. The line-segments AB, BC and CA are called **sides** of Δ ABC.
2. The points A, B, C where these sides meet are called its **vertices** or **angular points**.
3. The **angles** formed at the angular points A, B and C have been named ∠1, ∠2, ∠3. These angles are also important parts of Δ ABC.

So, **three sides** *and* **three angles** *of a triangle are called its six* elements.

B. TYPES OF TRIANGLES

A. IN TERMS OF SIDES

Considering the *measurement of sides,* triangles are of three types as under :

(a) A triangle whose all the three sides are of different lengths is called a **scalene triangle**.

(b) *A triangle with any two of its sides equal to each other* is called an **isosceles triangle.** Clearly, two angles of such a triangle are also equal. These angles are located opposite to the equal sides.

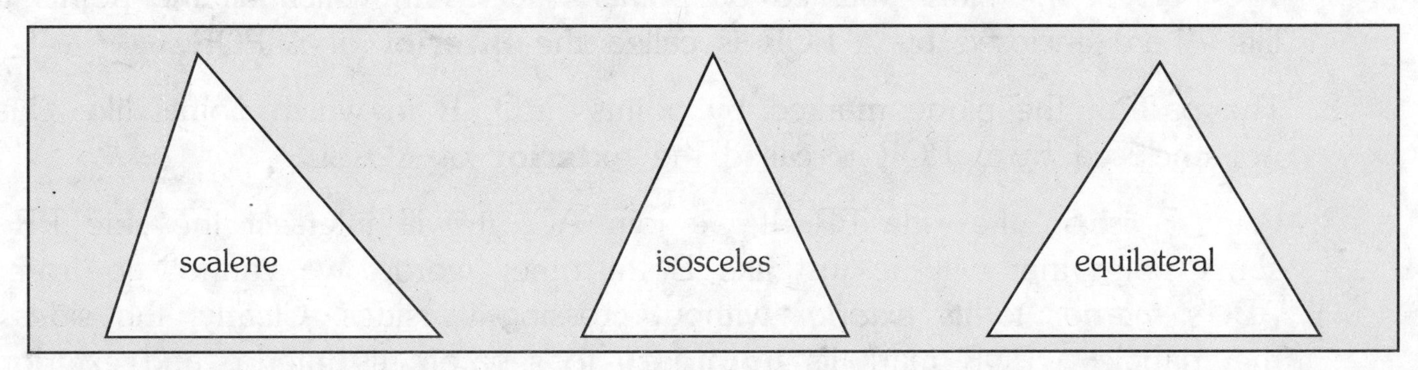

(c) A triangle with all its three sides equal to one another is called an **equilateral triangle**. Clearly, each of its angles will also be equal. So, another name for an equilateral triangle is **equiangular triangle**.

B. IN TERMS OF ANGLES

In terms of the *measurement of angles*, triangles are of the following three types :

(a) A triangle with all its angles smaller than 90°, *i.e.* **acute angles** is called an **acute-angled triangle** or **acute triangle**.

(b) A triangle with one of its angles equal to 90°, *i.e.* a **right angle** is called a **right-angled triangle** or **right triangle**.

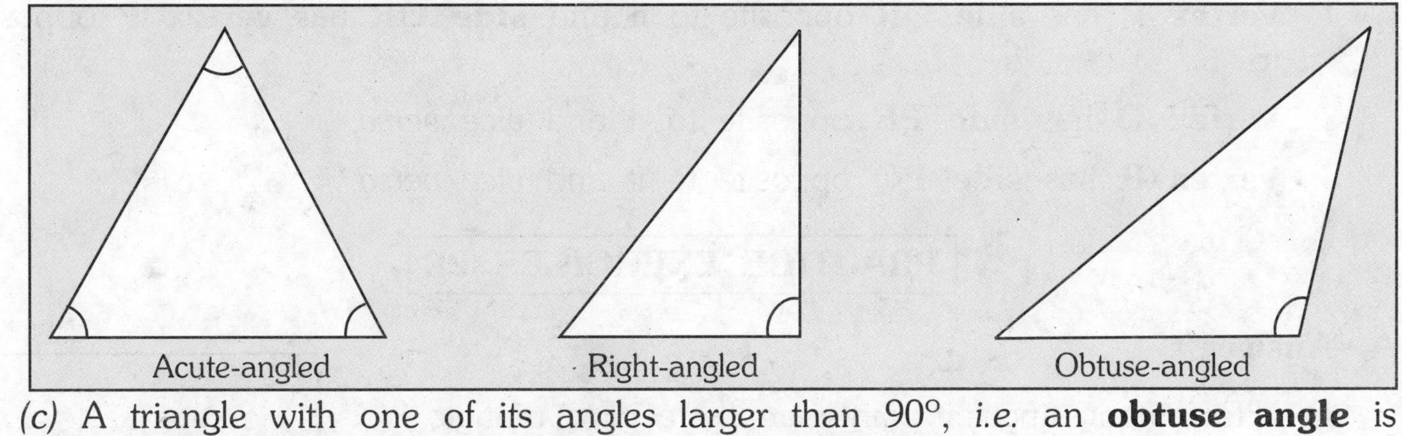

(c) A triangle with one of its angles larger than 90°, *i.e.* an **obtuse angle** is called an **obtuse-angled triangle** or **obtuse triangle.**

C. TRIANGULAR REGION, INTERIOR, EXTERIOR

A triangle is a plane figure with all its points lying in the plane marked by its three angular points.

Observe the points A, B and C in the diagram given in front. Point A is inside the triangle PQR while point B is on the side PR. As for point C, it is outside the Δ PQR.

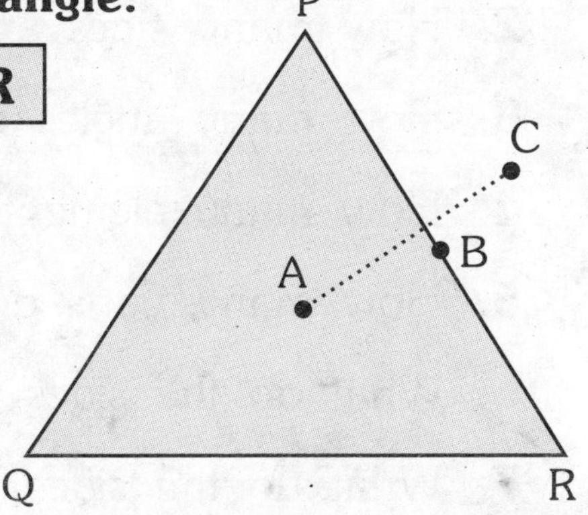

These three points A, B and C fall into three parts of the plane marked by P, Q, R as under :

1. The part of the plane marked by points P, Q, R in which all the points just like A are enclosed by Δ PQR is called the **interior** of Δ PQR.

2. The part of the plane marked by points P, Q, R in which points like C are not enclosed by Δ PQR is called the **exterior** of Δ ABC.

3. Point B is on the side PR. If we join AC, it will intersect the side PR at some point that will be just like B. In other words, we cannot go from Δ ABC's *interior* to its *exterior* without crossing its sides. Clearly, the sides of the triangle Δ PQR mark its **boundary** to separate its interior and exterior.

☞ **Note that Δ PQR's interior along with Δ PQR itself is called the triangular region PQR.**

D. MUTUALLY OPPOSITE

Observe Δ PQR given in front. Its vertices are P, Q, R. Each of these three vertices has a side opposite to it. Inversely, each side of this triangle has a vertex opposite to it. Thus in the given triangle PQR.

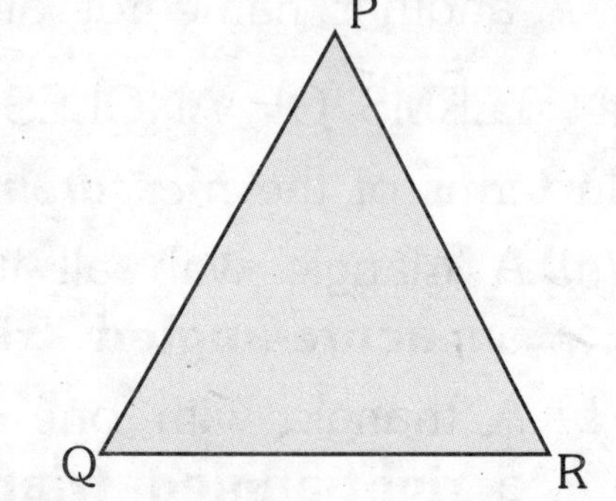

1. **Vertex P** has **side QR** opposite to it and **side QR** has **vertex P** opposite to it.
2. **Vertex Q** has **side PR** opposite to it and *vice versa*.
3. **Vertex R** has **side PQ** opposite to it and *vice versa*.

PRACTICE EXERCISES 28

A. Answer :

1. How many angular points are there of a triangle ? ....
2. How many sides are there of a triangle ? ....
3. How many angles does a triangle have ? ....
4. How many elements does a triangle have ? ....
5. How many parts does a triangle's plane have ? ....
6. What do the sides of a triangle enclose ? ....
7. What do the sides of a triangle mark ? ....

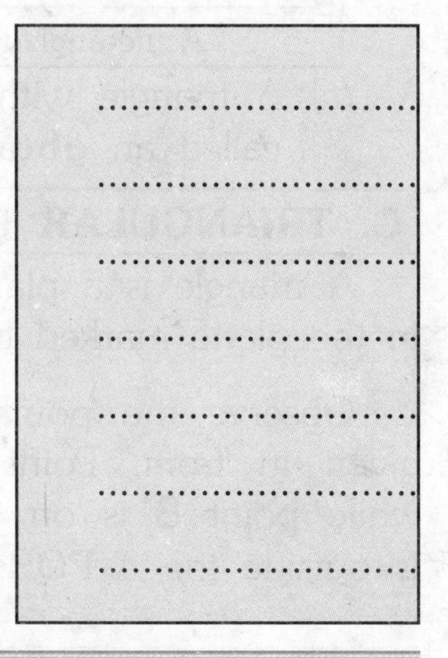

8. What does a *triangular region* include ? ....

9. Which part of a triangle's plane is outside its sides ? ....

B. 10. Take a sheet of paper and mark three collinear points A, B, C on it. Join the points to form line-segments AB, BC, CA. What figure do you get ?

11. Take three non-collinear points L, M, N on a sheet of paper. Join them to get line-segments LM, MN, LN. What figure do you get ? Name—

(*a*) the figure itself (*b*) its sides and angles

(*c*) the side opposite to ∠M (*d*) the side opposite to ∠L

12. Define—

(*a*) a triangle (*b*) a triangular region (*c*) a vertex

(*d*) interior of a Δ (*e*) exterior of a Δ (*f*) boundary of a Δ

13. Take four points P, Q, R, S and join them in pairs. Also, join PR and QS and let them intersect at O. Locate and name the eight triangles in the figure.

14. Given below are three triangles with measurements of their sides. Write below each triangle its type—*scalene, isosceles* or *equilateral.*

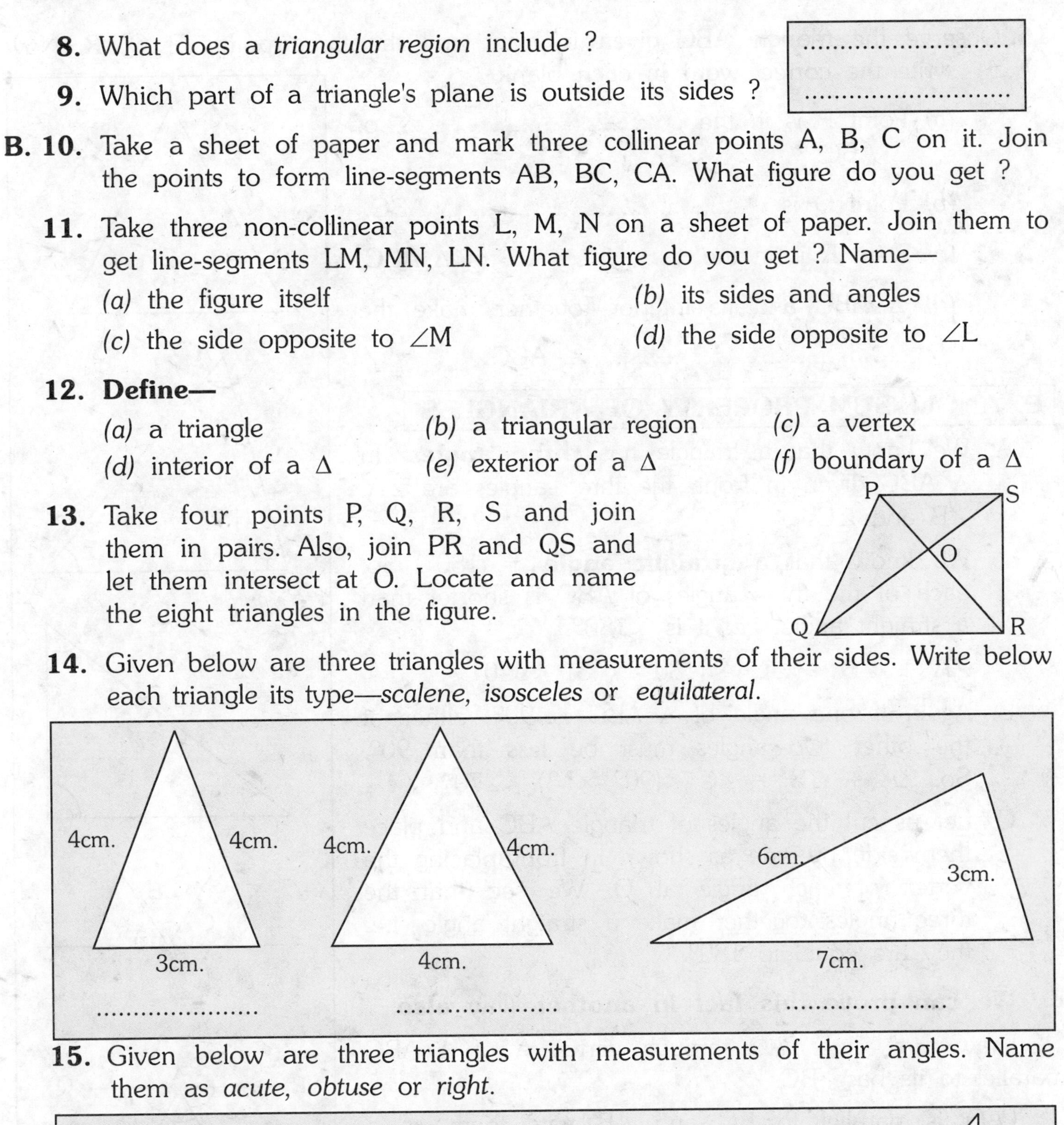

15. Given below are three triangles with measurements of their angles. Name them as *acute, obtuse* or *right.*

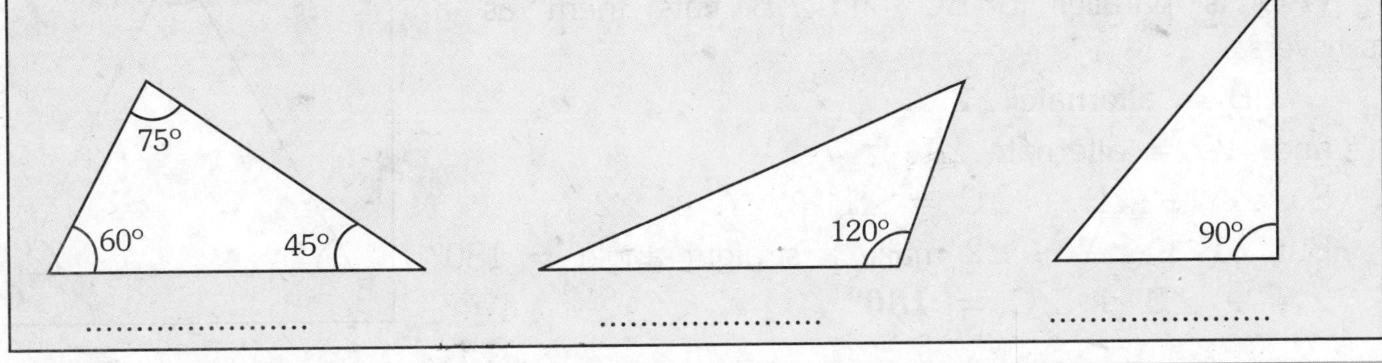

16. Observe the triangle ABC given in front and the three points P, Q, R. Now write the correct word in each blank :

(*a*) Point P is in the .... of Δ ABC.

(*b*) Point Q is .... Δ ABC.

(*c*) Point R is in the .... of Δ ABC.

(*d*) Δ ABC and its interior together make the .... ABC.

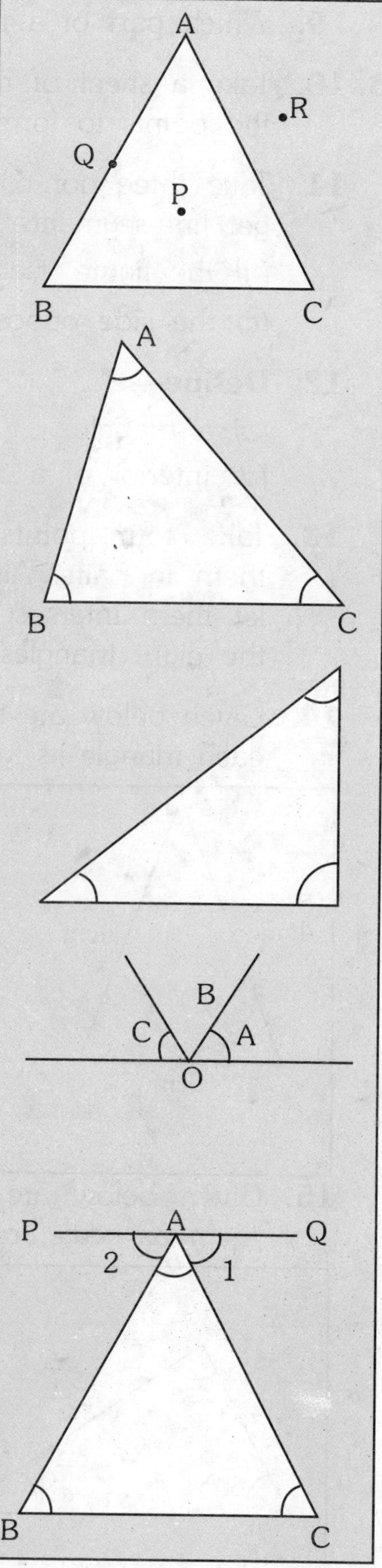

E. ANGLE-SUM PROPERTY OF TRIANGLES

A. We know that a triangle has **three angles**. In Δ ABC given in front, the three angles are $\angle A$, $\angle B$ and $\angle C$.

We know that a **straight angle** = 180°. So, each of the three angles of ABC is shorter than a straight angle, i.e. it is <180°.

$\angle A + \angle B + \angle C < (180^\circ \times 3) < 540^\circ$

B. Again if one angle of Δ ABC is 90°, either of the other two angles must be less than 90°. So, $\angle A + \angle B + \angle C < (90^\circ \times 3) < 270^\circ$

C. Let us cut the angles of triangle ABC and place them side by side as shown in front placing the vertex of each angle at O. We see that the three angles together make a straight angle, i.e. they are equal to 180°.

We can prove this fact in another way also.

Draw a st. line PAQ through vertex A of Δ ABC parallel to its base BC.

PAQ is parallel to BC and AB cuts them as a transversal.

$\therefore \angle B$ = alternate $\angle 2$

and $\angle C$ = alternate $\angle 1$

So, $\angle A + \angle B + \angle C = \angle 1 + \angle A + \angle 2$

But $\angle 1 + \angle A + \angle 2$ make a straight angle = 180°

$\mathbf{\angle A + \angle B + \angle C = 180^\circ}$

Let us now solve same examples :

Example 1. Two angles of a triangle measure 75° and 45°. Find its third angle.

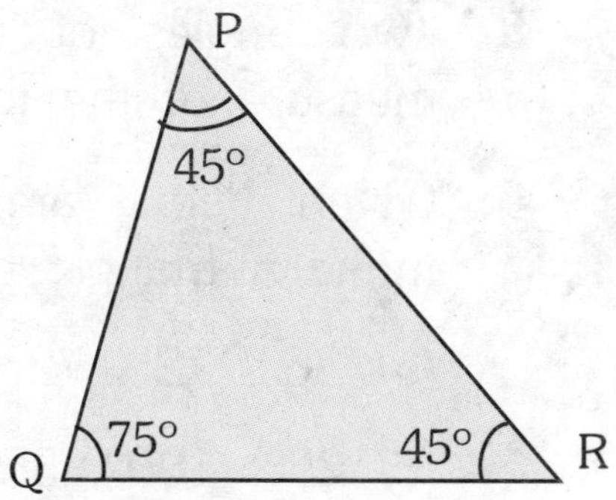

Solution : Let PQR be a triangle with its

$\angle Q = 75^\circ$ and $\angle R = 45^\circ$

But $\angle P + \angle Q + \angle R = 180^\circ$ .... (*angle-sum property*)

or $\angle P + 75^\circ + 45^\circ = 180^\circ$

or $\angle P = 180^\circ - 75^\circ - 45^\circ = \mathbf{60^\circ}$ *Ans.*

Example 2. In an isosceles triangle ABC either of the equal angles is half the third angle. Find all the angles of the triangle.

Solution : Let the triangle be Δ ABC as shown in front

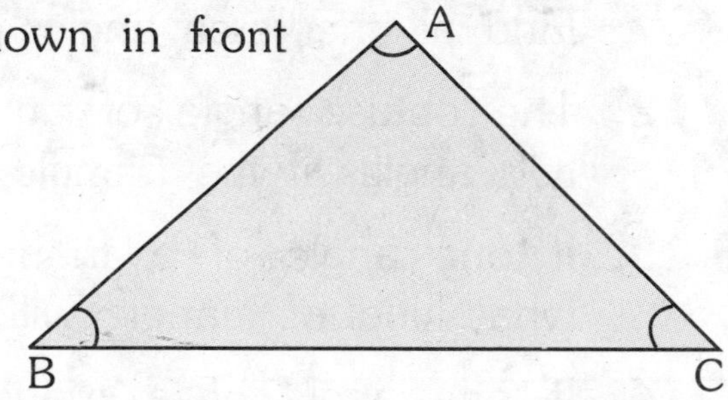

Now $\angle B = \frac{1}{2} \angle A$

Also, $\angle C = \frac{1}{2} \angle A$

But $\angle A + \angle B + \angle C = 180^\circ$

or $\angle A + (\frac{1}{2} \angle A + \frac{1}{2} \angle A) = 180^\circ$ .... (*angle-sum property*)

or $\angle A + \angle A = 180^\circ$ ....($\angle B = \angle C = \frac{1}{2} \angle A$)

$\therefore$ $\mathbf{\angle A = 90^\circ}$

Hence $\mathbf{\angle B = 45^\circ}$ and $\mathbf{\angle C = 45^\circ}$ *Ans.*

PRACTICE EXERCISES 30

A. Answer :

1. How many degrees are there in a *straight angle* ? ....
2. How many degrees are there in a *right angle* ? ....
3. What is the *total measure* of the angles of a triangle ? ....
4. Is it possible to have a triangle with *two right angles* ? ....
5. Is it possible to have a triangle with *two acute angles* ? ....
6. Is it possible to have a triangle with *two obtuse angles* ? ....
7. Is it possible to have a triangle with *three acute angles* ? ....

B. 8. Two angles of a triangle measure 75° and 45° respectively. Find the measure of the third angle.

9. Given below are some sets of measures of three angles. Which set can make a triangle possible ?

(a) 36°, 72°, 72° *(b)* 100°, 40°, 35°

(c) 25°, 100°, 55° *(d)* 30°, 105°, 45°

(e) 70°, 75°, 35° *(f)* 80°, 63°, 39°

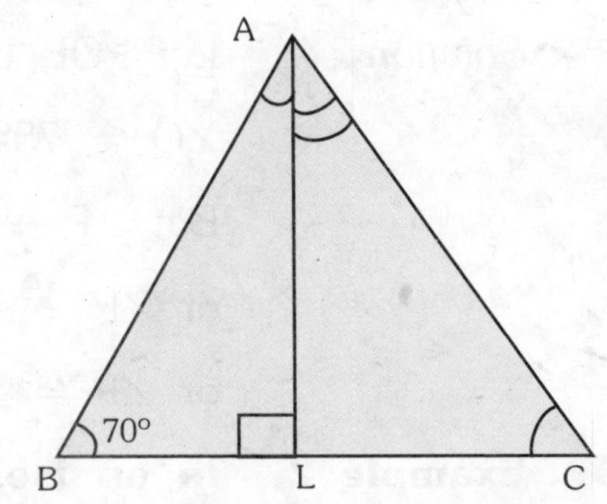

10. Observe the figure given in front. AL is drawn perpendicular from vertex A to the base BC. $\angle B = 70°$ and $\angle A = 90°$. Find $\angle ACL$, $\angle CAL$ and $\angle BAL$.

11. Each of the equal angles of an isosceles triangle is twice its third angle. Find all the three angles.

12. The obtuse angle of an obtuse triangle is equal to 120°. Find the other two angles if the triangle is isosceles also.

13. If one angle of a triangle is equal to the sum of its other two angles, what kind of triangle will it be ? Find its angles also.

14. If one angle of a triangle is four times either of the other two angles, what kind of triangle will it be ? Find its angles also.

15. The angles of a triangle are in the ratio of 3 : 4 : 5. Find them.

16. You are given a triangle ABC. PQ is drawn paralled to BC, $\angle C = 110°$ and $\angle A = 40°$ find $\angle B$, $\angle 1$, $\angle 2$.

17. A figure PQRS is made up of four sides. Find the sum of its angles.
(**Hint** : *Join PR. The figure will be divided into two triangles*)

18. The figure in front is like a star. Find the sum of $\angle A + \angle B + \angle C + \angle P + \angle Q + \angle R$
(**Hint** : *The figure is made up two Δs = ABC, PQR.*

19. In the adjoining five-sided figure, find the sum of $\angle A + \angle B + \angle C + \angle D + \angle E$.
(**Hint** : *Divide the figure into triangles*)

20. The adjoining figure is a figure with six sides. Find $\angle A + \angle B + \angle C + \angle D + \angle E + \angle F$.

F. EXTERIOR ANGLES, INTERIOR OPPOSITE ANGLES

Suppose we have a triangle PQR whose side QR is produced to S. As a result, an angle is formed outside the triangle. It is ∠PRS. This angle is called an **exterior angle** of Δ PQR at R. We can have such angles at P and Q also.

What is the relation of the exterior ∠PRS with the interior angles of the Δ PQR :

1. ∠PRQ is **adjacent** to ∠PRS. So, it is called the **adjacent interior angle** to ∠PRS. We have named it ∠1.
2. ∠Q is called the **interior opposite angle.**
3. ∠P is also the **interior opposite angle**.

Now, ∠PRS + ∠1 make a straight angle

∴ ∠PRS + ∠1 = 180° .... (i)

Also, ∠P + ∠Q + ∠1 = 180° ....(ii)

From (i) and (ii)

∠PRS + ∠1 = ∠P + ∠Q + ∠1 (*∠s of a Δ*)

Therefore—

4. **∠PRS = ∠P + ∠Q** which are interior opposite angles
5. **∠PRS greater than ∠P**. It is also **greater than ∠Q**.

So, we get the following two results :

1. **An exterior angle of a triangle is equal to the sum of the two interior opposite angles.**
2. **An exterior angle of a triangle is greater than either of the two interior opposite angles.**

Example. Given in front is a triangle ABC whose all the three sides have been produced. The measures of its two angles have also been given. Find the values of its three exterior angles *x*, *y*, *z*. Find their sum also.

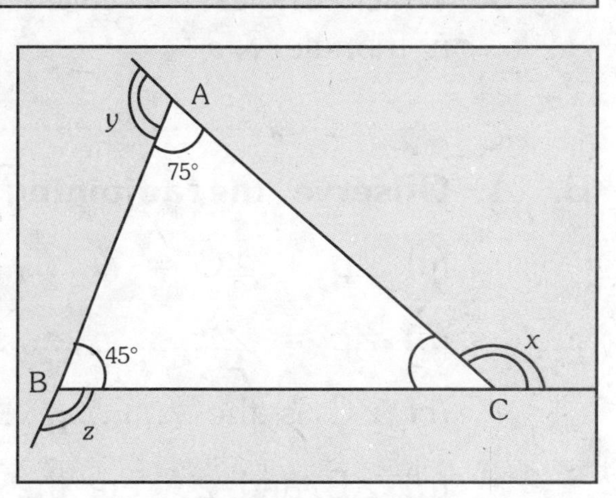

Solution : ∠B = 45° and ∠A = 75°

But ∠A + ∠B + ∠C = 180°

or $75^\circ + 45^\circ + \angle C = 180^\circ$

or $\angle C = 180^\circ - 75^\circ - 45^\circ = \mathbf{60^\circ}$

Now ext. $\angle x$ = int. opp. $\angle B$ + int. opp $\angle A$

$= 45^\circ + 75^\circ = \mathbf{120^\circ}$ *Ans.*

Ext. $\angle y$ = int. opp. $\angle B$ + int. $\angle C$

$= 45^\circ + 60^\circ = \mathbf{105^\circ}$ *Ans.*

Ext. $\angle z$ = int. opp. $\angle A$ + int. opp $\angle C$

$= 75^\circ + 60^\circ = \mathbf{135^\circ}$ *Ans.*

$\therefore \angle x + \angle y + \angle z = 120^\circ + 105^\circ + 135^\circ = \mathbf{360^\circ}$ *Ans.*

So, remember that if the three sides of a triangle are produced in order the sum of the three exterior angles so formed is always equal to 360° or 4° rt. ∠s.

PRACTICE EXERCISES 31

A. Answer :

1. *When* and *where* is an *exterior angle* of a triangle formed ?

(a) ....

(b) ....

2. What is the *interior angle just touching an exterior angle* of a triangle called ?

....

3. Which angles are called the *interior opposite angles* of an exterior angle of a triangle ?

....

B. 4. Observe the adjoining figure and fill up each blank :

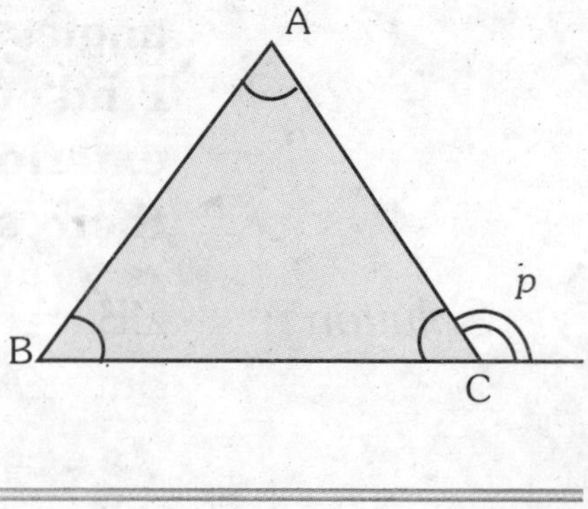

(a) $\angle p + \angle C$ = ...

(b) $\angle p = \angle$ .... + $\angle$ ....

(c) $\angle C$ is the .... angle to $\angle$p.

(d) $\angle B$ and $\angle A$ are the .... angles $\angle$p.

A

B

C

p

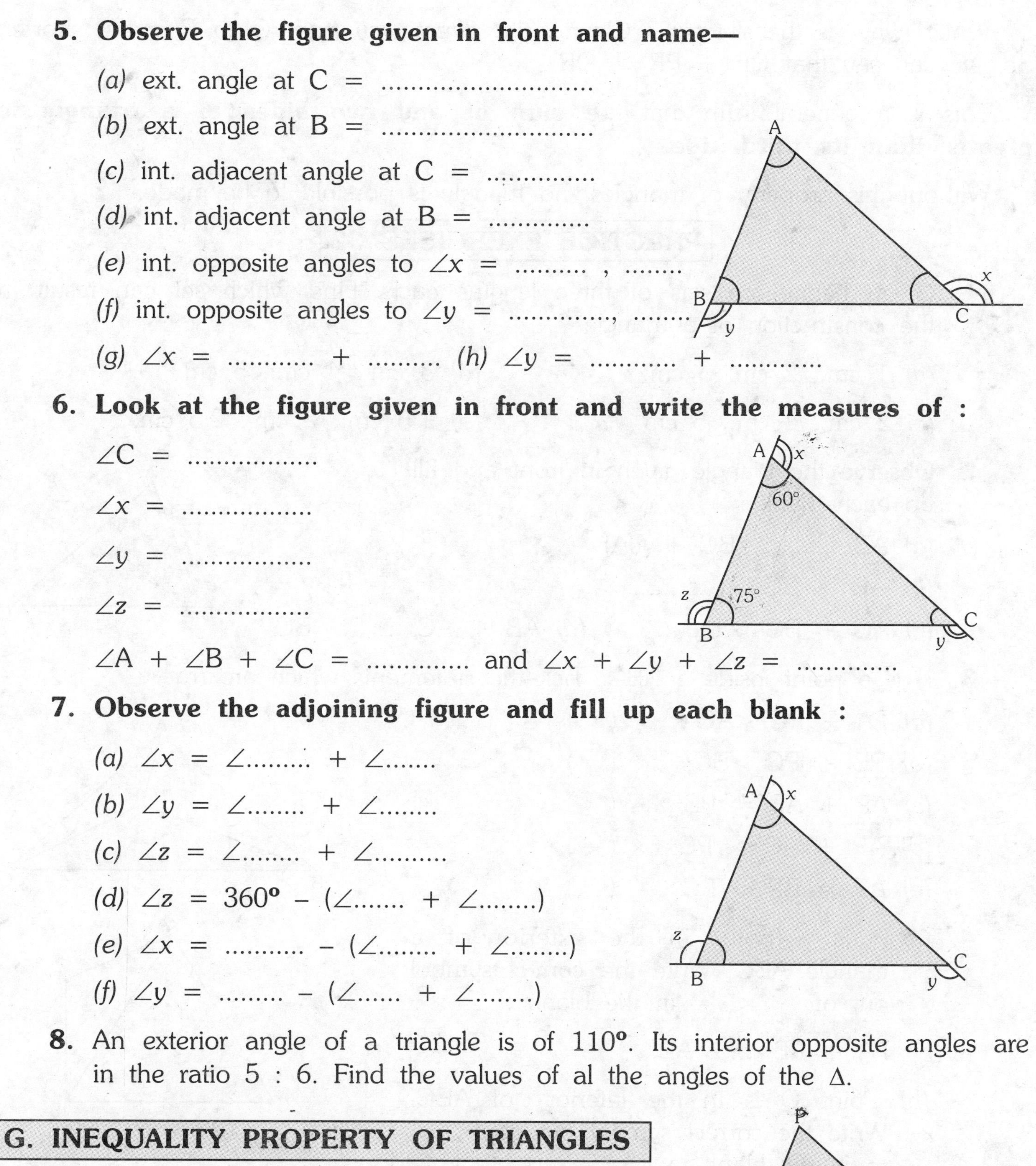

5. Observe the figure given in front and name—

(a) ext. angle at C = ...

(b) ext. angle at B = ...

(c) int. adjacent angle at C = ...

(d) int. adjacent angle at B = ...

(e) int. opposite angles to $\angle x$ = ... , ...

(f) int. opposite angles to $\angle y$ = ..., ...

(g) $\angle x$ = ... + ... *(h)* $\angle y$ = ... + ...

6. Look at the figure given in front and write the measures of :

$\angle C$ = ...

$\angle x$ = ...

$\angle y$ = ...

$\angle z$ = ...

$\angle A + \angle B + \angle C$ = ... and $\angle x + \angle y + \angle z$ = ...

7. Observe the adjoining figure and fill up each blank :

(a) $\angle x = \angle$........ + $\angle$.......

(b) $\angle y = \angle$........ + $\angle$........

(c) $\angle z = \angle$........ + $\angle$..........

(d) $\angle z = 360^\circ - (\angle$....... + $\angle$........)

(e) $\angle x$ = ... $- (\angle$........ + $\angle$........)

(f) $\angle y$ = ... $- (\angle$...... + $\angle$........)

8. An exterior angle of a triangle is of 110°. Its interior opposite angles are in the ratio 5 : 6. Find the values of al the angles of the Δ.

G. INEQUALITY PROPERTY OF TRIANGLES

Here is a triangle PQR. A boy wants to go from Q to R. He can do so in two ways.

1. *to go direct from Q to R*
2. *to first go from Q to P and then from P to R.*

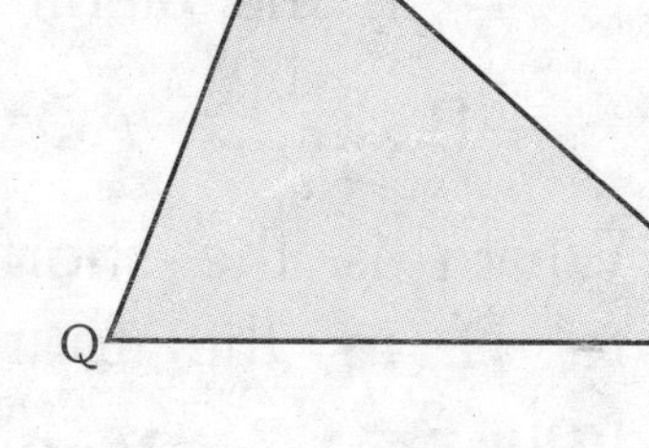

Which way is the shorter ? Clearly, the *direct way from Q to R* is the shorter. So, we can say that QP + PR > QR.

This is a general truth that **the sum of any two sides of a triangle is greater than its third side**.

Without this property of triangles, no triangle is possible to be made.

PRACTICE EXERCISES 32

1. Given below are sets of three lengths each. Find which set can result in the construction of a triangle ?

(a) 1 cm., 2 cm. 3 cm. *(b)* 3 cm., 4 cm., 5 cm.

(c) 2 cm., 4 cm., 5 cm. *(d)* 1·5 cm., 2 cm., 2·5 cm.

2. Observe the triangle given in front and fill up each blank :

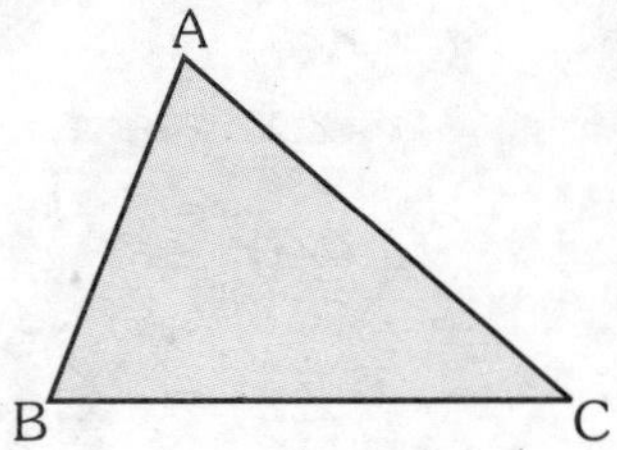

(a) AB .... (BC + CA)

(b) AB + BC >..............

(c) AC + BC >............ *(d)* AB + AC .... BC

3. P is a point inside a ABC. Tick the statements which are *true.*

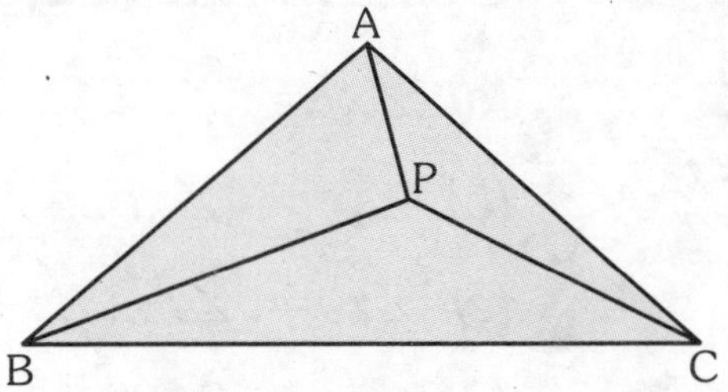

(a) PA + PC <AC ( )

(b) PB + PC >BC ( )

(c) AP + AB = PB ( )

(d) AP + AC > PC ( )

(e) AP = BP + PC ( )

4. *(a)* P is a point in the exterior of a triangle ABC. Write the correct symbol out of >, <, = in the blank :

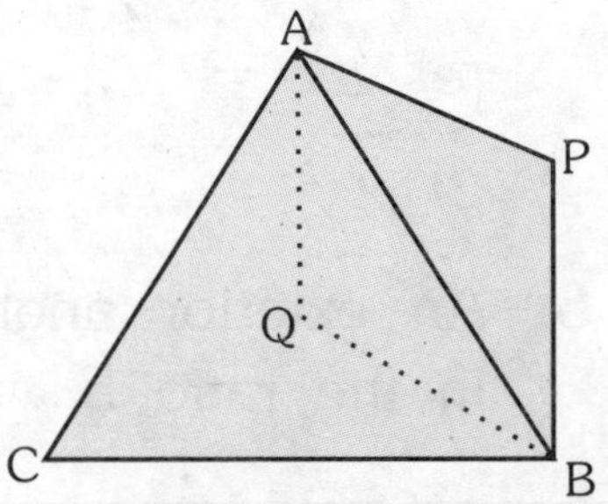

PA + PB .... AB

(b) Point Q is in the interior of ABC. Write the correct symbol out of >, <, = in the blank :

AB .... AQ + BQ

5. Which is the shorter way to go from A to D in the four-sided figure given in front ? ....

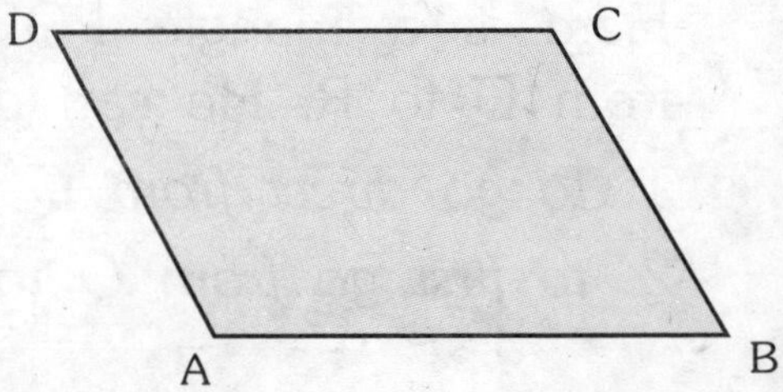

18 TRIANGLES—II

KNOW THESE TERMS :

1. **bisector**—line-segment that bisects a side or angle of a figure
2. **symmetry**—sameness of shape, size and position
3. **hypotenuse**—the longest side in a right-angled triangle opposite to the right angle
4. **converse**—just the opposite of a theory or theorem

We studied three very important facts about triangles in the previous lesson. These facts are :

1. *The sum of the angles of a triangle is 180°, i.e. 2rt. ∠s.*
2. *The sum of any two sides of a triangle is greater than its third side.*
3. *If any side of a triangle be produced, the exterior angle so formed is equal to the sum of the two interior opposite angles.*

SOME OTHER PROPERTIES OF TRIANGLES

1. ISOSCELES TRIANGLES

We know that **an isosceles triangle has two of its sides equal**. Also, *it has the angles opposite to these equal sides equal* to each other.

Let us verify these two facts. We take a triangle ABC with sides AB = AC = 5cm. while its third side BC = 6cm. Measure ∠B and ∠C with a *protractor* and calculate their difference. It will be **zero.** Repeat this experiment with two or three isosceles triangles and check the difference of ∠B and ∠C. Every time, the result will be zero. *So, we can conclude :*

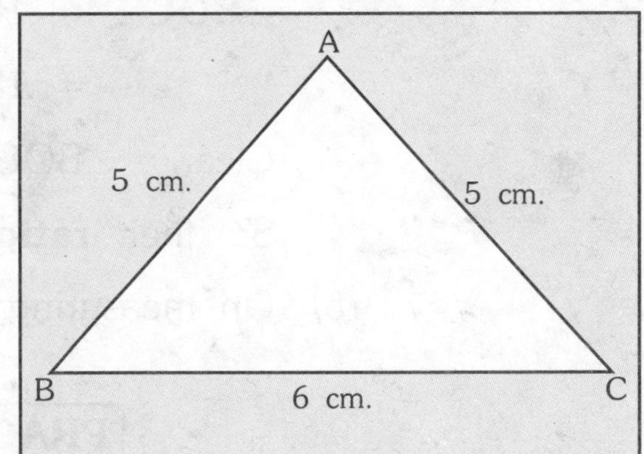

If a triangle has two of its sides equal, the angles opposite to these side are also equal.

Conversely—

If a triangle has two of its angles equal, the sides opposite to these angles are also equal.

We can check both the facts by folding the tracing paper on which an isosceles triangle is drawn.

Let us now solve some examples.

Example 1. **A Δ ABC has its side AC equal to AB. The bisectors of the base angles B and C meet at O. If $\angle A = 60^\circ$ find :**

(a) **$\angle BOC$. What is its ratio with $\angle BAC$?**

(b) **Measure the lengths of OB and OC. Are they equal ?**

Solution : *(a)* $AB = AC$

$\therefore$ $\angle B = \angle C$

But $\angle A + \angle B + \angle C = 180^\circ$ (*Angle-sum property*)

or $60^\circ + \angle B + \angle C = 180^\circ$ $(\because \angle A = 60^\circ)$

or $\angle B + \angle C = 180^\circ - 60^\circ = 120^\circ$

or $2\angle B = 120^\circ$ or $\angle \mathbf{B} = \mathbf{60^\circ}$ $(\because \angle B = \angle C)$

$\therefore$ $\angle \mathbf{C} = \mathbf{60^\circ}$ too

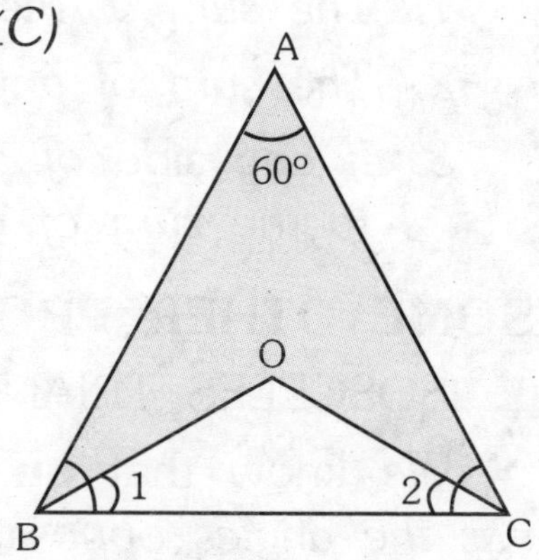

Now In Δ OBC—

$\angle 1 = \frac{1}{2}\angle B = 60^\circ \times \frac{1}{2} = 30^\circ$

Also $\angle 2 = \frac{1}{2}\angle C = 60^\circ \times \frac{1}{2} = 30^\circ$

$\therefore$ $\angle \mathbf{BOC} = 180^\circ - \angle 1 - \angle 2$

$= 180^\circ - 30^\circ - 30^\circ = \mathbf{120^\circ}$ *Ans.*

Clearly, $\angle BOC = 2\angle A$

So, their **ratio** $=$ **2 : 1**

(b) On measuring, it is found that $OB = OC$

PRACTICE EXERCISES 33

1. PQR is an isosceles triangle with $PQ = PR$. If $\angle P = 100^\circ$. Find $\angle Q$ and $\angle R$.
2. ABC is an isosceles triangle with $AC = AB$. If $\angle A = 48^\circ$, find $\angle B$ and $\angle C$?
3. DEF is an equilateral triangle. What is the measure of each of its angles ?
4. ABC is an isosceles triangle with $AB = AC$. If $\angle A = 40^\circ$ and the sides AB and AC have been produced. Find the measures of the exterior angles a and b. Are they equal ?

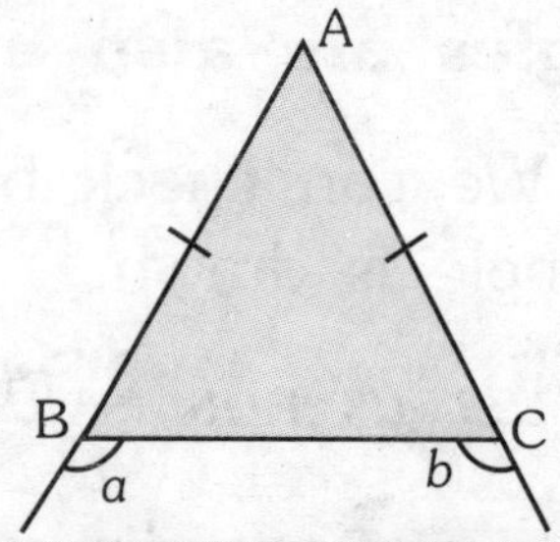

5. Side QR of a triangle PQR is produced. The exterior angle so formed measures 120° while angle $\angle P = 60°$. What type of triangle is PQR ?

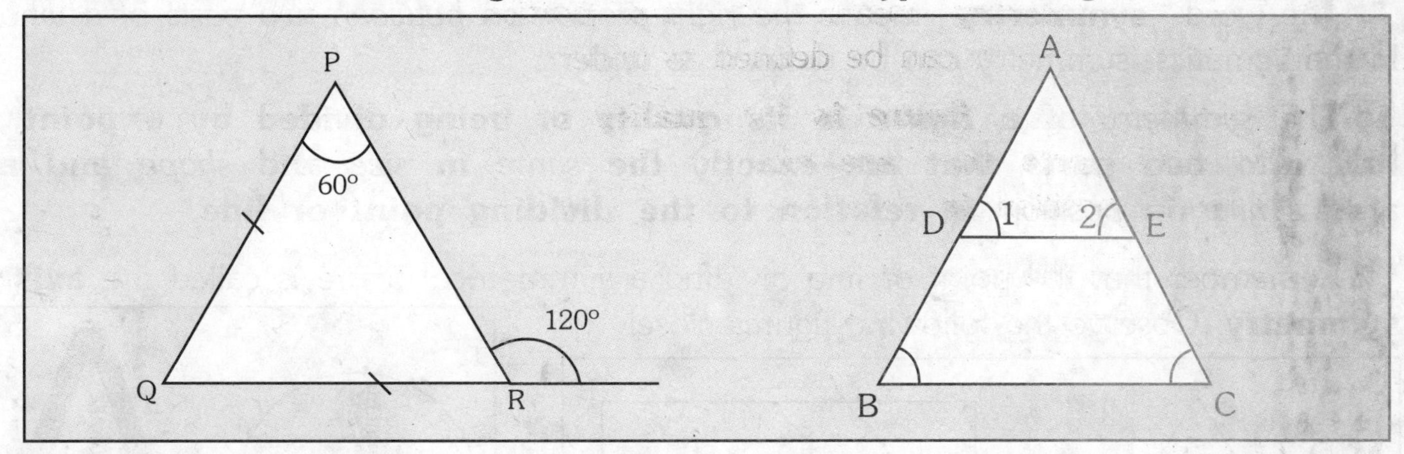

6. ABC is an isosceles triangle in which AB and AC are equal. DE is drawn parallel to BC. Explain the following :

(a) $\angle B = \angle C$ *(b)* $\angle 1 = \angle B$ *(c)* $\angle 2 = \angle C$

(d) $\angle 1 = \angle 2$ *(e)* AD = AE *(f)* BD = CE

7. Given a triangle PQR such that QR = 6 cm., PR = 5 cm. and PQ = 4 cm. Measure $\angle Q$ and $\angle R$. Which of them is the larger ? Is the side opposite to the larger angle also larger than the side opposite to the smaller angle ? What do you infer from it ?

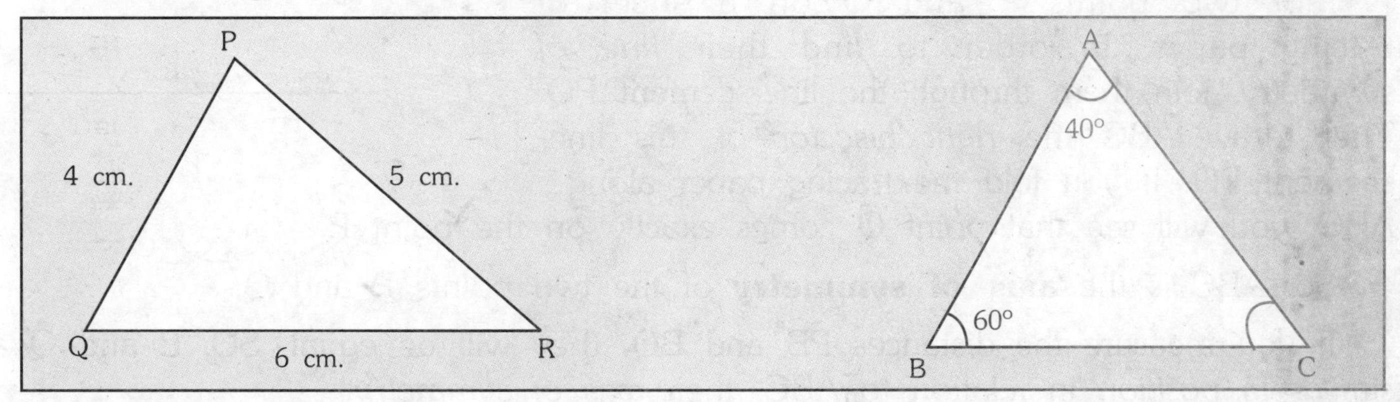

8. Draw a triangle ABC such that $\angle B = 60$ and $\angle A = 40$. Find $\angle C$ and measure the sides BC and AC. Which of them is the larger ? Is it opposite to the larger angle or the smaller one. What do you infer from it ?

9. Two isosceles triangles ABC and DBC have a common base BC. Is—

(a) $\angle 1 = \angle 2$? If yes, why ?

(b) $\angle 3 = \angle 4$? If yes, why ?

(c) $\angle ABD = \angle ACD$? If yes, why ?

(d) If $\angle A = \angle D$? If not, why ?

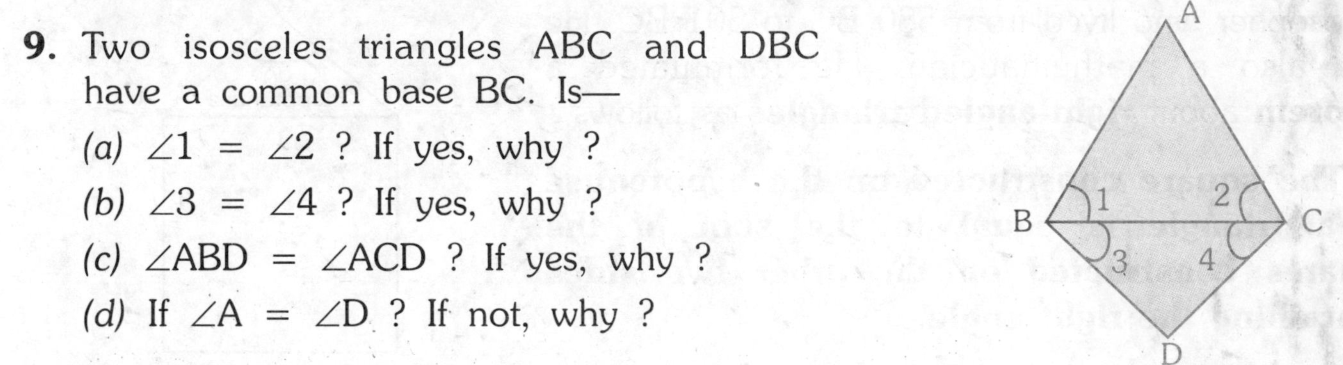

SYMMETRY

The word—**symmertry**—means *the right proportion between two parts of a whole.* In mathematics, symmetry can be defined as under :

The *symmetry* **of a figure is its quality of being divided by a point or line into two parts that are exactly the** *same* **in** *size* **and** *shape* **and are also** *similar* **in** *position* **in relation to the dividing point or line.**

Remember that the point or line dividing a symmetrical figure is called the **axis of symmetry**. Observe the following figures closely :

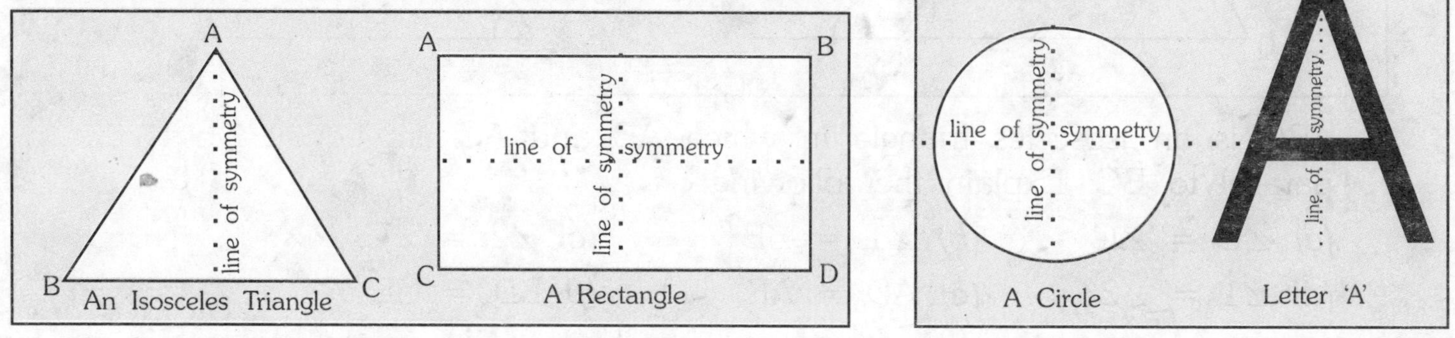

If you observe the above figures, you will come to know that a symmetrical figure **may have more than one** lines/points of symmetry.

LINE OF SYMMETRY OF TWO POINTS

Plot two points P and Q on a sheet of tracing paper. In order to find their *line of* symmetry, join them through the line-sgement PQ. Then draw ABC the *right bisector* of this line-segment PQ. If you fold the tracing paper along ABC, you will see that point Q comes exactly on the point P.

So, ABC is the **axis of symmetry** of the two points P and Q.

If you measure the distances PB and BQ, they will be equal. SO, P and Q are *similar in position* in relation to ABC, their *axis of symmetry*.

PYTHAGOREAN THEOREM

Pythagoras has been a famous Greek philosopher who lived from 580 BC to 501 BC. He was also a mathematician. He formulated a **theorem** about **right-angled triangles** as follows :

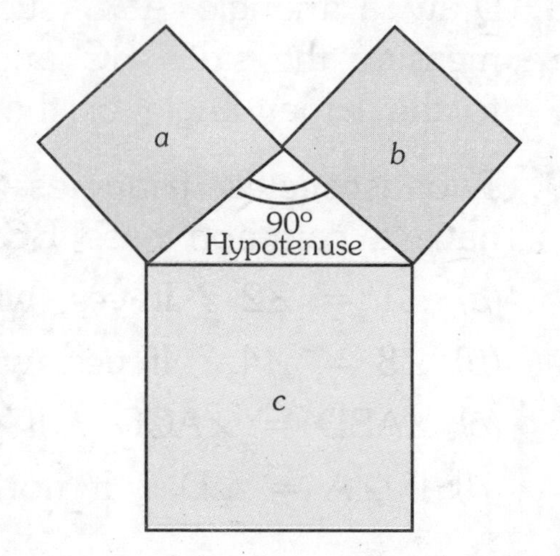

The square constructed on the hypotenuse of a triangle is equal to the sum of the squares constructed on the other two sides containing the right angle.

This theorem was proved by **Euclid,** another mathematician in his book—*The Elements*. He lived around 300 BC in Greece. Anyhow, Pythagorean Theorem is a very useful proposition in mathematics. Let us know more about certain *other facts* that follow from this theorem. Such facts are called **corollaries**.

COROLLARY 1

In the figure on page 160

$c = a + b$

$c > a$ and also $c > b$

or $\boldsymbol{c > a}$ or $\boldsymbol{b}$

Clearly, **the hypotenuse is the longest side in a rt. triangle.**

COROLLARY 2

1. Take a line and a pt. P outside it.
2. Draw a perpendicular from P to the line.
3. Let the perpendicular meet the line at R.
4. Now, take any other point Q on the line and join PQ.

   Clearly, PQR is a rt. triangle and PQ is .... its hypotenuse

$\therefore$ PR < PQ *(corollary 1)*

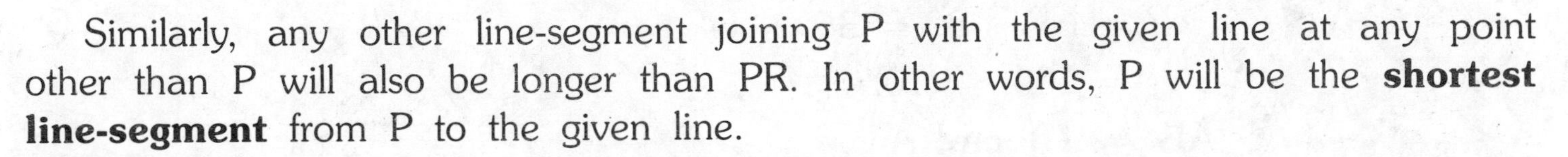

Similarly, any other line-segment joining P with the given line at any point other than P will also be longer than PR. In other words, P will be the **shortest line-segment** from P to the given line.

So, **perpendicular is the shortest distance between a line and a point outside it.**

CONVERSE OF PYTHAGOREAN THEOREM

Let the sides of a triangle ABC be **3 cm., 4 cm.** and **5 cm.** as shown in front.

We know that—

$3^2 = 9$; $4^2 = 16$ and $5^2 = 25$

and $9 + 16 = 25$ or $\mathbf{3^2 + 4^2 = 5^2}$

or $\mathbf{AC^2 + AB^2 = BC^2}$

If we measure ∠A of this triangle, we shall find it to be 90°. In other words, ABC is a rt. triangle.

This experiment can be repeated by drawing triangles with the following sets of sides :

(*a*) 1·5 cm., 2 cm., 2·5 cm. (*b*) 6 cm., 8 cm., 10 cm.

(*c*) 4·5 cm., 6 cm., 7·5 cm. (*d*) 9 cm., 12 cm., 15 cm.

In each case, the triangle will be right angled.

So, **if the square on one side of a triangle is equal to the sum of the squares on the other two sides, the triangle is rt. angled.**

Also remember that—

Numerical values of the sides of a right triangle are called a **Pythagorean Triplet** ; as—

(*a*) 3, 4, 5 (*b*) 1·5, 2, 2·5 (*c*) 6, 8, 10 are such triplets

Let us now solve some examples :

Example 1. A rt. triangle ABC has it base = 6 cm. and altitude = 8 cm. Find the length of its hypotenuse :

Solution : Let the triangle ABC be as shown in front.

BC = 6 cm. and AC = 8 cm.

$\because$ AB is a rt Δ.

$\therefore AB^2 = BC^2 + AC^2$

$= 6^2 + 8^2 = 36 + 64$

$= 100 = (10)^2$

$\therefore$ **AB = 10 cm.** *Ans.*

Example 2. The hypotenuse QR of a right triangle PQR is 15 cm. and its altitude PR is 9 cm. Find its third side.

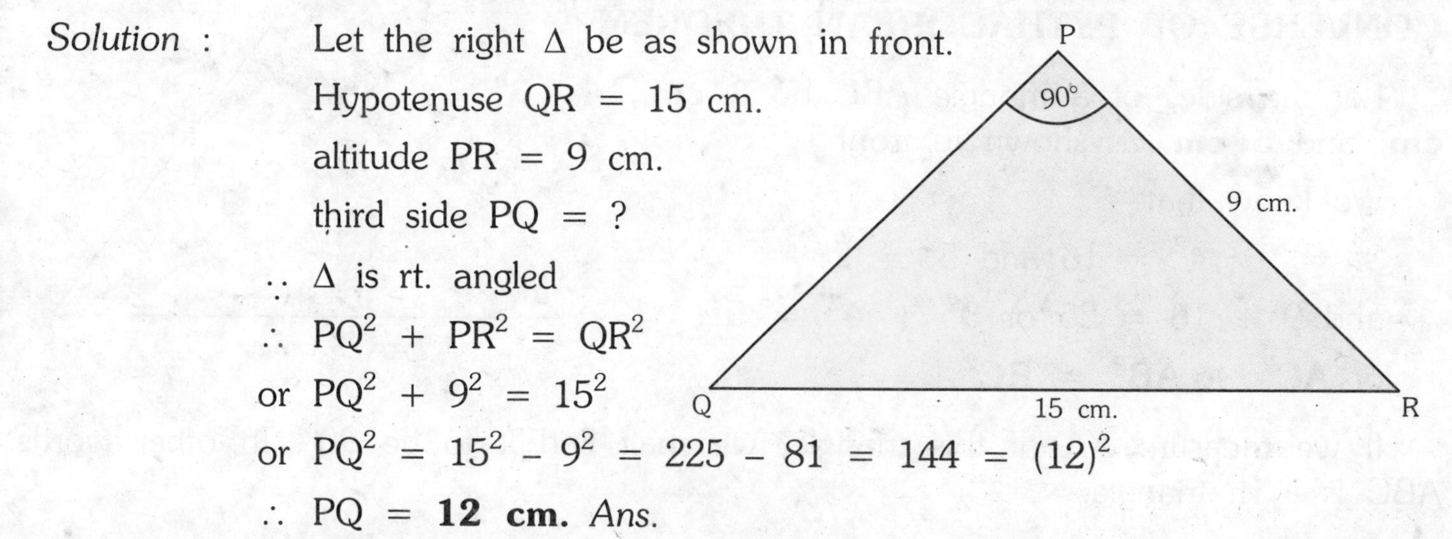

Solution : Let the right Δ be as shown in front.

Hypotenuse QR = 15 cm.

altitude PR = 9 cm.

third side PQ = ?

$\because \Delta$ is rt. angled

$\therefore PQ^2 + PR^2 = QR^2$

or $PQ^2 + 9^2 = 15^2$

or $PQ^2 = 15^2 - 9^2 = 225 - 81 = 144 = (12)^2$

$\therefore$ PQ = **12 cm.** *Ans.*

PRACTICE EXERCISES 34

A. Name—

1. three objects that you see around with symmetrical figures.

....

2. three letters of the English Alphabet with symmetrical bodies.

....

3. two types of triangles that have symmetry about a vertical axis.

....

4. three geometrical figures that have symmetry about a horizontal axis.

....

B. 5. Draw an angle ABC and bisect it. Is ∠ABC symmetrical ? If yes, name its axis of symmetry.

6. Take two points P and Q. How will you find its *axis of symmetry* ?

7. AB is a chord of a circle with centre O. A diameter meets chord AB at right angles at E. Trace the figure on a tracing paper. Find by folding whether :

(a) the circle is symmetrical about the diameter.

(b) chord AB is symmetrical about the diameter.

(c) Is AE = BE

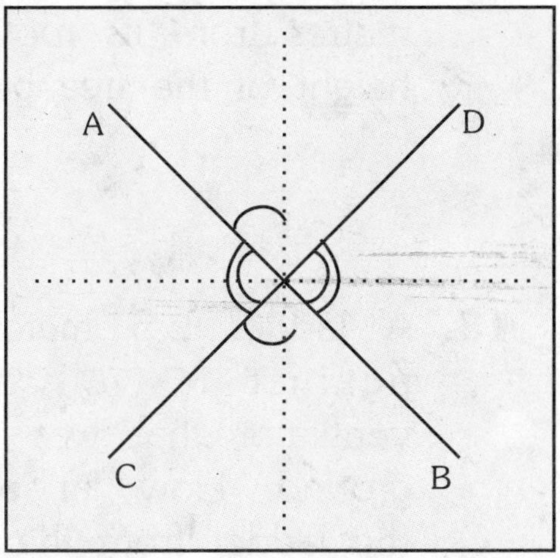

8. Draw two intersecting straight lines so that they may make two pairs of vertically opposite angles. Now answer :

(a) Whether the figure is symmetrical.

(b) How many axes of symmetry does it have ?

A D C B

9. Draw a line PQ and draw BA the perpendicular bisector of PQ. Is it correct that—

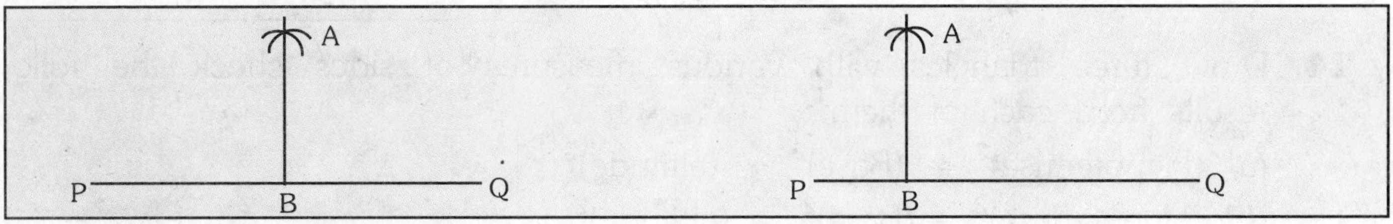

A P B Q A P B Q

(a) BA is an axis of symmetry of line PQ ?

(b) Any line perpendicular to PQ is an axis of symmetry of line PQ.

10. Draw two intersecting circles with the same radius. Is the figure symmetrical ? If yes, which is its axis of symmetry.

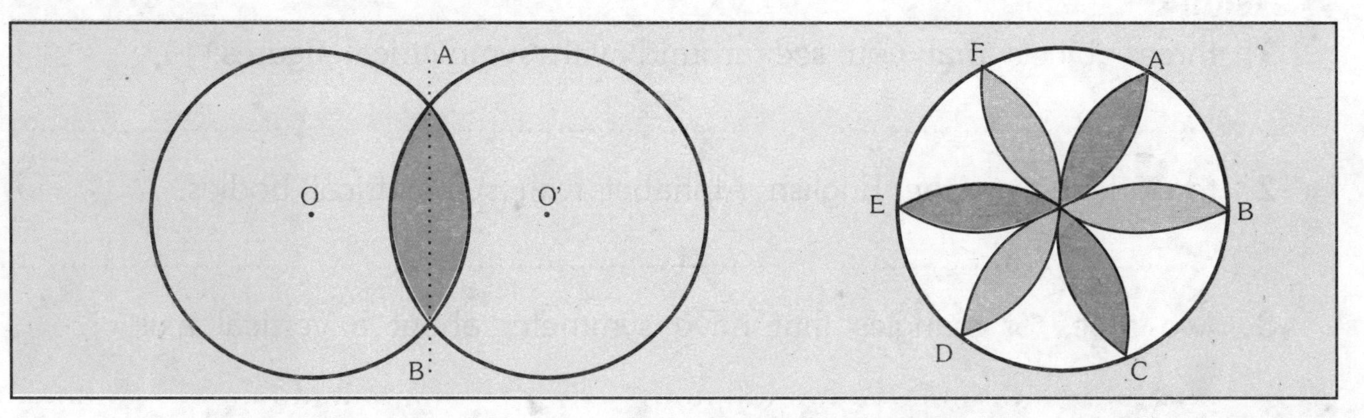

11. Draw a circle and then draw arcs AC, AE, BD, BF, CE and DF. How many axes of symmetry does this figure have. Draw them in dotted lines.

12. A tree broke in a storm at a point 3 metres above the ground but its parts did not get separated. Instead its *top* touched the ground at distance of 4 metres from its *root-base*. Find the total height of the tree before it broke.

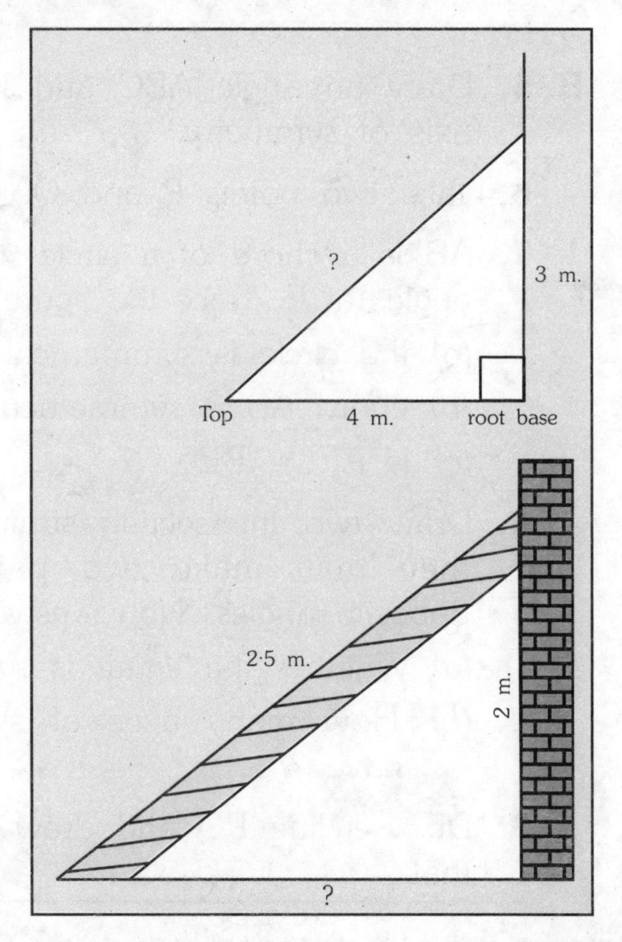

13. A ladder 2·5 meters long was placed against a wall and it reached a ventilator that was 2 metres above the ground. How far away is the foot of the ladder from the wall ?

14. Draw three triangles with various measures of sides check the following results from each of them.

(a) $(\text{Hypotenuse})^2 = (\text{Base})^2 + (\text{altitude})^2$

(b) $(\text{Hypotenuse})^2 - (\text{Base})^2 = (\text{altitude})^2$

(c) $(\text{Hypotenuse})^2 - (\text{altitude})^2 = (\text{Base})^2$

19 MEDIANS, ALTITUDES, BISECTORS

KNOW THESE TERMS :

1. **median**—line-segment that joins a vertex of a triangle with the middle point of the opposite side
2. **altitude**—line-segment drawn from the vertex of a triangle meeting the opposite side at an angle of 90°
3. **right-bisector**—line-segment bisecting another line-segment at right angles

A. MEDIANS OF A TRIANGLE

A *median* **is a line-segment that joins the mid-point of the side of a triangle to the vertex opposite to it.**

Clearly, a triangle has three medians because it has three sides and three vertices.

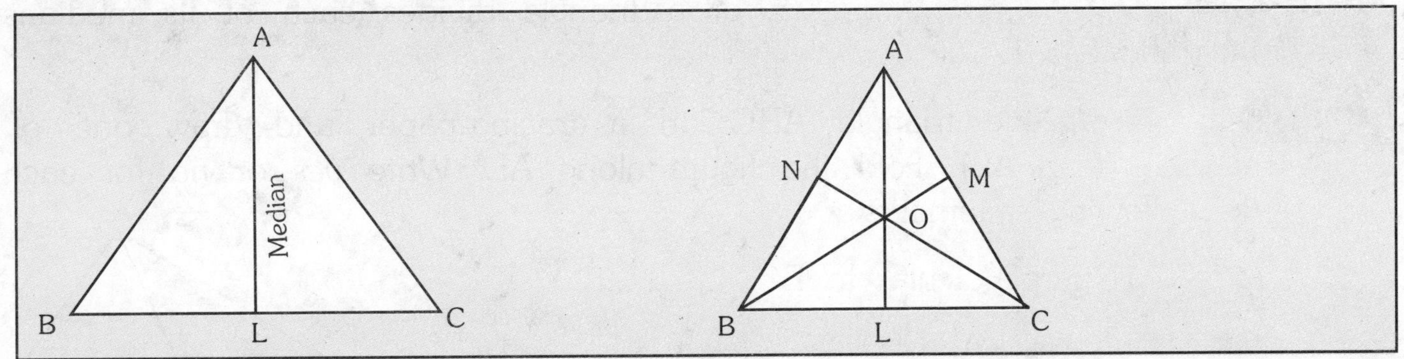

Observe the figures given above. The figure on the left shows one median **AL**. It joins the vertex A with L, the middle-point of the side BC.

In the figure on the right, three medians **AL, BM** and **CN** have been drawn. Each median joins a vertex with the middle-point of the side opposite to it.

SOME FACTS ABOUT MEDIANS OF A TRIANGLE

1. Each median lies in the **interior of its triangle**.
2. Each median lies in the **interior of the angle** whose vertex it joins with the middle point of the opposite side.
3. All the three medians of a triangle *pass through one and the same point*. In other words, they are **concurrent**.
4. The point where the medians of a triangle intersect is called the **centroid** of the triangle.
5. The centroid of a triangle divides each of its medians in the ratio 2 : 1. It can be proved by measuring the two parts of each median.

PRACTICE EXERCISES 35

A. complete each sentence :

1. A median of a triangle is the line-segment that joins one of its .... to the mid-point of the opposite side.

2. Medians of a triangle .... through one and the same point, *i.e.* they are ....

3. The point of intersection of the medians of a triangle is called its ....

4. The centroid of a triangle lies in the—

   (a) .... of the triangle

   (b) .... of the angle formed at the joined vertex.

5. The .... of a triangle divides each of its medians in the ratio 2 : 1.

6. Draw a scalene triangle ABC on a tracing-paper and draw one of its medians (say AL). Fold the figure along AL. Write *yes* or *no* for each of the following statements :

   (a) AL is perpendicular to BC. ....

   (b) AL bisects ∠A. ....

   (c) AL bisects BC at L ....

7. Draw an isosceles triangle PQR and draw its medians RA and BQ bisecting its equal sides and interesting at O. Answer *yes* or *no* for each statement :

   (a) RA = PQ and BQ = PR ....

   (b) AQ = BR and PA = PB ....

   (c) If PO is joined and produced to meet QR at C. It will bisect QR at C. ....

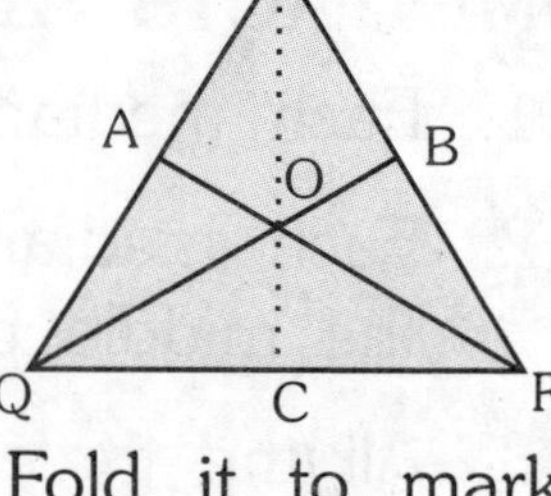

8. Draw an equilateral triangle ABC on a tracing paper. Fold it to mark its medians and then find its centroid.

9. In an isosceles triangle, a median is drawn to bisect the side other than the equal sides. Can the median serve as an axis of symmetry of the triangle ?

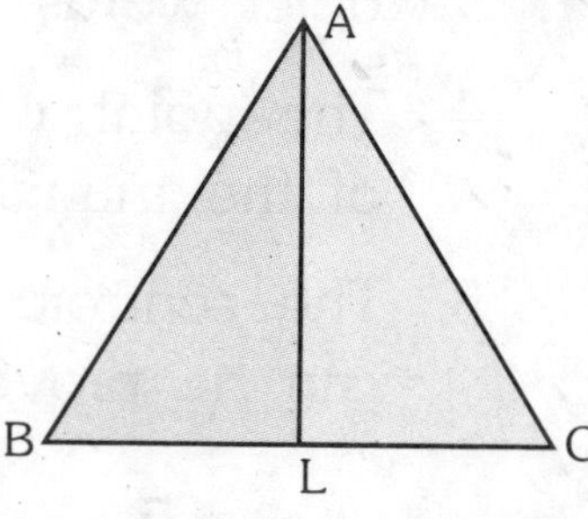

B. ALTITUDES OF A TRIANGLE

The word—**altitude**—means *height*. And we know that a perpendicular is the shortest distance between a line and a point outside it.

An *altitude* of a triangle is the perpendicular drawn from any of its vertices to the side opposite to that vertex.

As a triangle has three vertices and three sides. So, a triangle can have three altitudes.

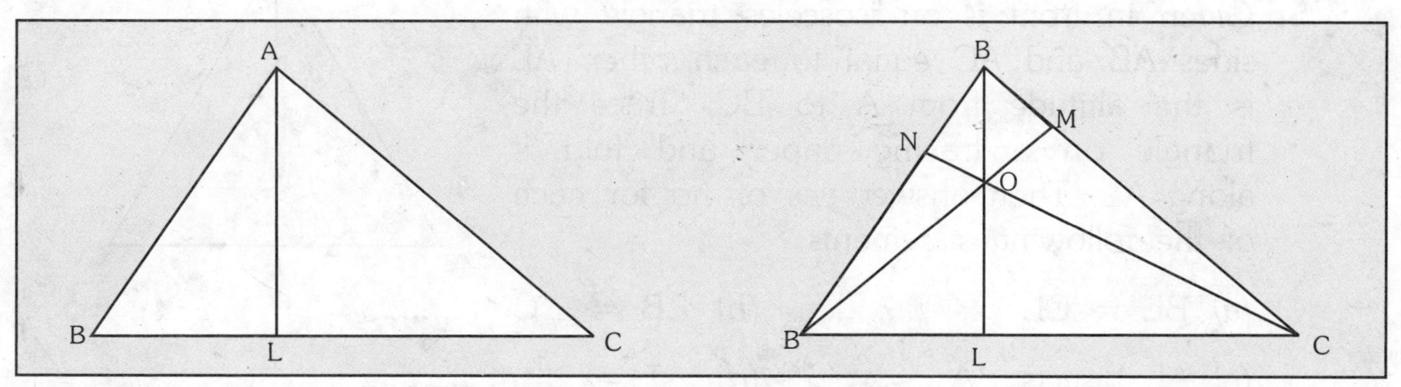

Observe the figure given above on the left. It shows a triangle ABC in which AL, one of the altitudes, has been drawn.

In the figure on the right above, all the three altitudes have been drawn. They are AL, BM and CN. It is quite clear that the altitudes of a triangle pass through *one and the same point*. In other words, they are **concurrent**.

SOME FACTS ABOUT ALTITUDES OF A TRIANGLE

1. Each altitude of a triangle meets the opposite side at an angle of 90°.
2. The three altitudes of a triangle pass through a common point, i.e. they are **concurrent**.
3. The point of concurrence of the altitudes of a triangle is called the **orthocentre** of the triangle.
4. In order to find the point of concurrence of the three altitudes of a triangle, it is sufficient to draw two altitudes only.
5. The orthocentre of a triangle can fall into its exterior or at one of the vertices also.

PRACTICE EXERCISES 36

A. Complete each statement :

1. An altitude of a triangle is a perpendicular drawn from any of its .... to the .... side.

2. The common point where the altitudes of a triangle intersect is called its ....

3. If a triangle is a right-angled, only .... of the altitudes can be drawn.

4. The altitudes of a triangle may sometimes intersect .... the triangle on being produced.

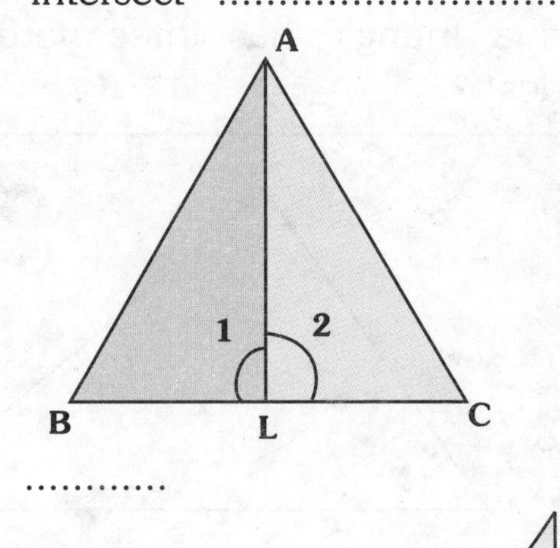

5. Given in front is an isosceles triangle with sides AB and AC equal to each other. AL is the altitude from A to BC. Trace the triangle on a tracing paper and fold it along AL. Then answer *yes* or *no* for each of the following statements

   (a) BL = CL .... *(b)* ∠B = ∠C ....

   (c) AL bisects ∠A .... *(d)* ∠1 = ∠2 ....

6. Δ PQR is a rt. triangle at R. How will you find its orthocentre without drawing any latitude.
   Is it correct to say that R is the orthocentre of Δ PQR ?

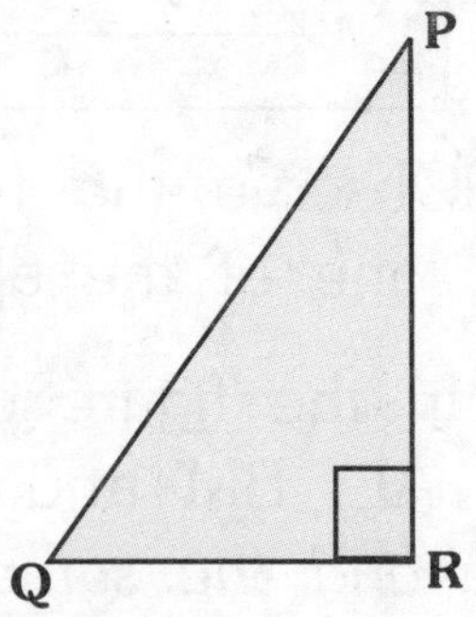

7. Daw any triangle on a tracing paper and fold it to find its orthocentre.

8. Draw an equilateral triangle on a tracing paper. Draw its altitudes that meet at H. Check up by folding the triangle whether the altitudes can serve as axes of symmetry or not.

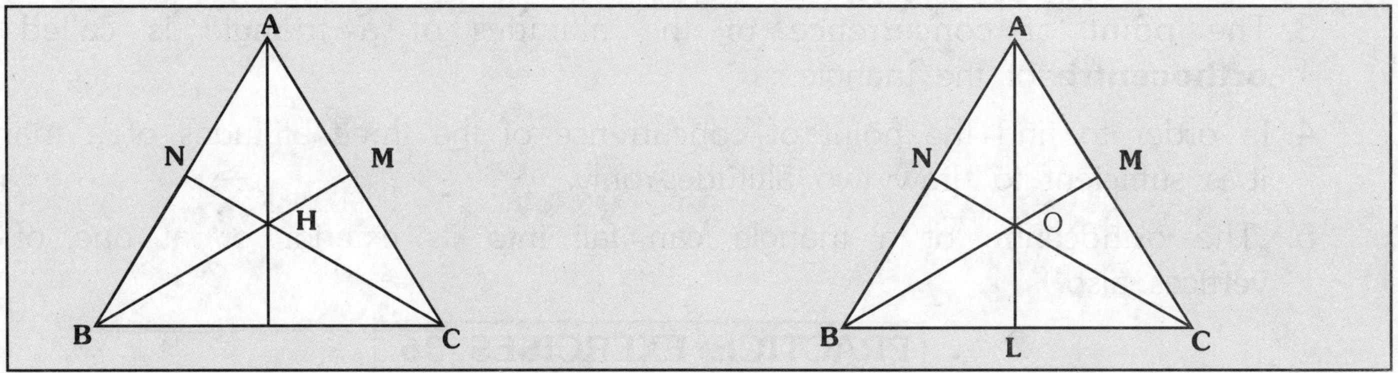

9. In the equilateral triangle ABC, the three altitudes AL, BM, CN have been drawn that intersect at O. Say *yes* or *no* for each statement :

   (a) OM = ON *(b)* BO = CO *(c)* BM = CN = AL

C. RIGHT-BISECTORS OF SIDES OF A TRIANGLE

A right-bisector of the side of a triangle does two jobs :

(a) It *stands perpendicular* to the side.

(b) It *bisects the side* as well.

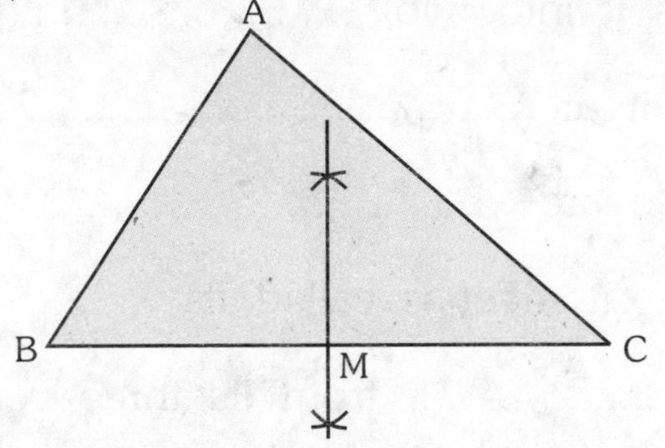

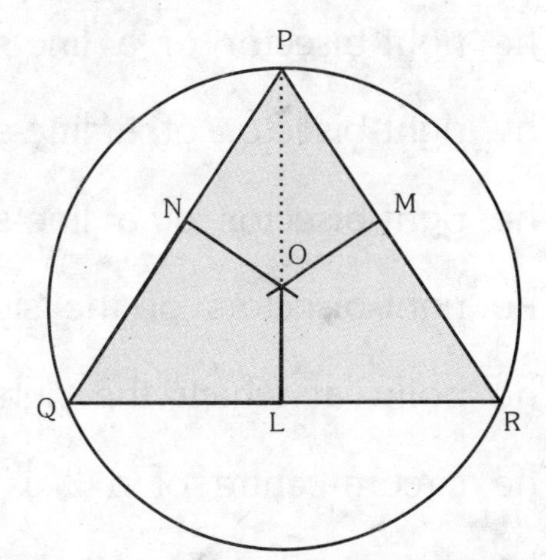

Observe the figure given above on the left. It shows a triangle ABC in which the right-bisector of the side BC has been drawn. This right-bisector cuts BC at M at right angles. Also, it divides BC into two equal parts BM and CM.

The figure on the right above is a triangle PQR which has the right-bisectors of its all the three sides drawn. These bisectors are LO, MO, NO. They intersect at a common point O. In other words, they are **concurrent** at O.

So, the right-bisectors of the sides of a triangle are concurrent. The point where the right-bisectors of the sides of a Δ intersect is called the **circum-centre** of the triangle.

The distance of the circum-centre of a triangle from any of its vertices is equal. It is called the **circum-radius** of the triangle.

SOME FACTS ABOUT THESE RIGHT-BISECTORS

1. The right-bisector of a side of a triangle is **perpendicular** to it.
2. It also **bisects** that side.
3. The right-bisectors of the sides of a triangle are **concurrent**.
4. The point at which the right-bisectors of the sides of a triangle intersect is called its **circum-centre.**
5. The circum-centre is **equidistant** from all the three vertices of the triangle.
6. The line-segment joining the circum-centre with any vertex is the **circum-radius** of the triangle.
7. If a circle is drawn with circum-centre as the *centre* and the circum-radius as *radius*. The circle will pass through all the three vertices.

PRACTICE EXERCISES 36

A. Complete each statement :

1. The right-bisector of a line-segment is called its .... bisector also.

2. The right-bisector of a line-segment divides it into two .... parts.

3. The right-bisector of a line-segment meets it at .... ∠s.

4. The right-bisectors of the sides of a triangle are ....

5. The point at which the right-bisectors of a Δ meet is called its ....

6. The circum-centre of a Δ is .... from its three vertices.

7. The distance between the circum-centre and any of the vertices of a triangle is called its ....

B. 8. Draw a line-segment PQ and draw its perpendicular bisector that meets PQ at M. How are PM and QM related ?

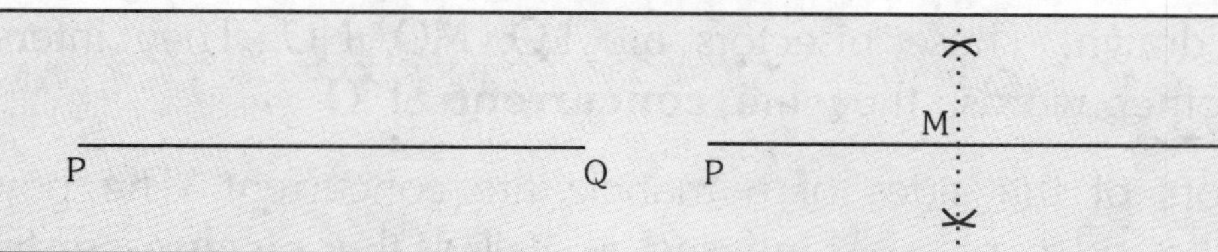

9. Draw a circle on a sheet of paper. How will you find its centre geometrically ?

(*Hint*—Draw any two chords of the circle, and draw their right-bisectors. The point where they meet is the centre of the circle.)

10. Draw a triangle ABC and find its circum-centre O. With O as centre and OA as radius draw a circle. Does it pass through B and C also ?

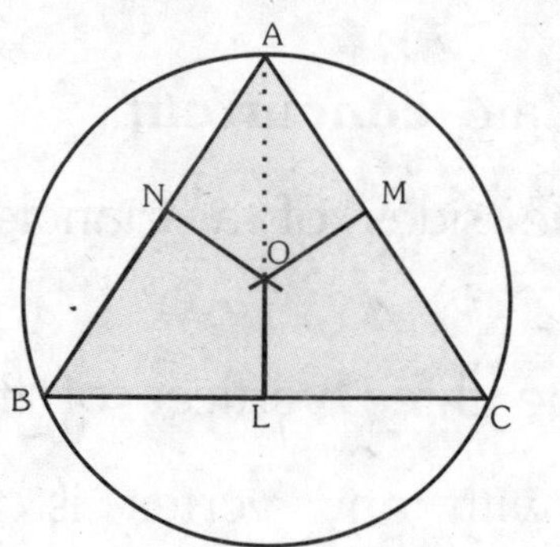

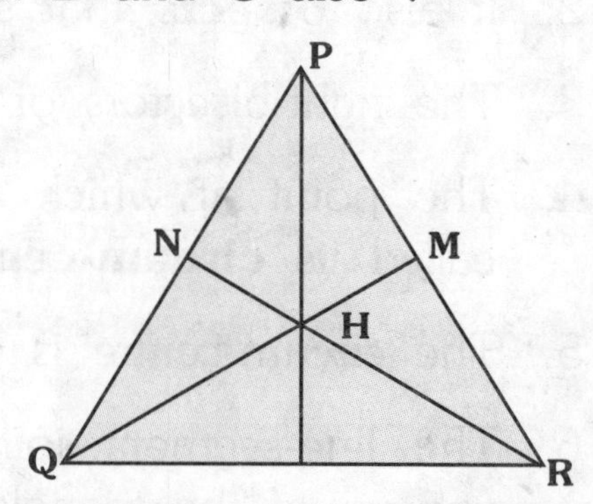

11. Δ PQR is an equilateral triangle PL, QM and RN are its medians that concur at O, *i.e.* O is the centroid of the triangle PQR. With O as centre, and radius OA draw a circle. Does it pass through the three vertices ?.

D. BISECTORS OF ANGLES OF A TRIANGLE

The *bisector of an angle* **of a triangle is a line-segment that divides the angle into two equal parts (angles) and meets the side opposite to the bisected angle.**

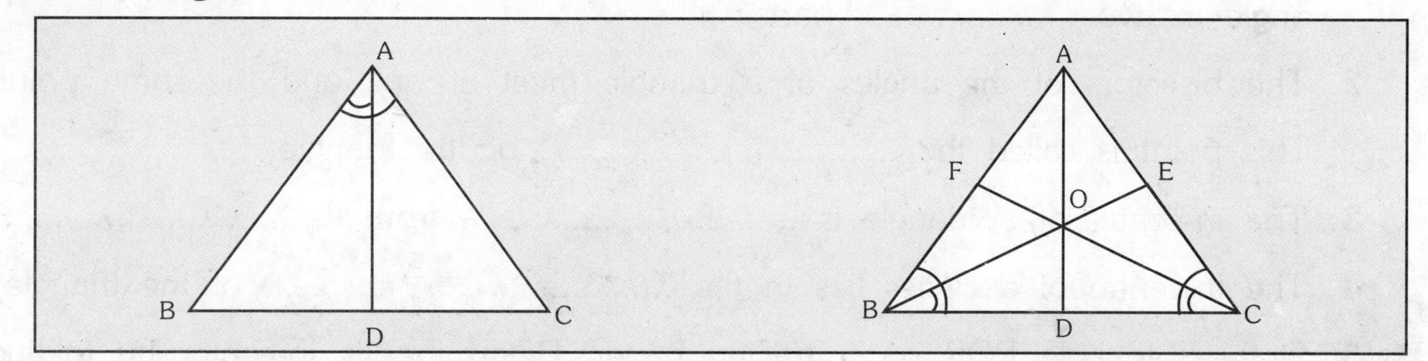

As a triangle has three angles and three sides opposite to them each to each, there can be three bisectors of its angles. The figure given above on the left shows AD, the bisector of ∠A of Δ ABC. It meets the opposite side BC at D. The figure on the right above shows bisectors of all the three angles of the triangle ABC. These bisectors are AD, BE and CF. They intersect at one and the same point O. This point is called the **in-centre** of Δ ABC.

If perpendiculars are drawn from O to sides AB, BC, CA. They will all be equal. In other words, the **in-centre** of a triangle is equidistant from its sides.

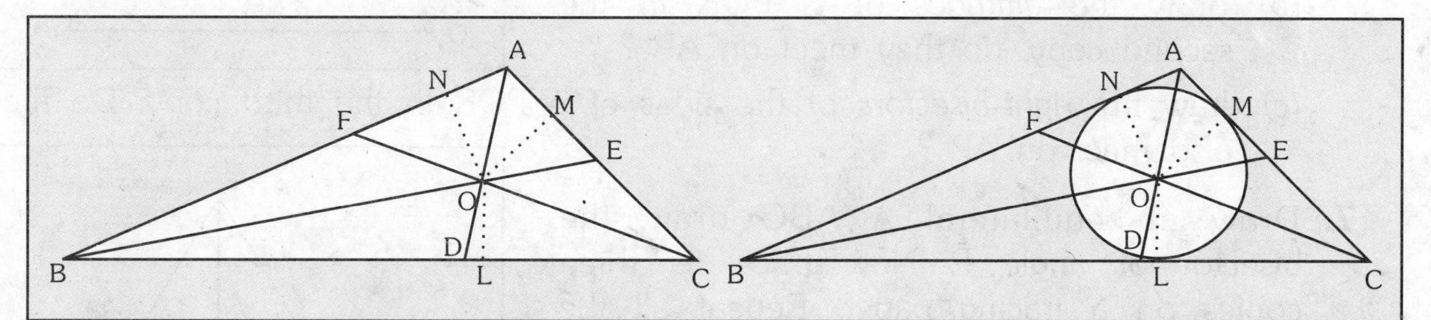

Clearly, if a circle is drawn with centre O and radius OL, OM or ON, it will touch the sides of the triangle. This circle is called the **in-circle** of Δ ABC and each of OL, OM, ON is called the **in-radius**.

SOME FACTS ABOUT BISECTORS OF ANGLES OF A Δ

1. The bisectors of the angles of a triangle are **concurrent**.
2. The point at which the bisectors of the angles of a Δ concur is called the **in-centre** of the triangle.
3. The in-centre of a triangle is **equidistant** from its sides.
4. The in-centre of a triangle **lies in its interior.**
5. The circle drawn using the in-centre as centre and touching the sides of the Δ is called the in-circle of the Δ.

PRACTICE EXERCISES 38

A. Complete each statement :

1. The bisector of an angle of a triangle is a .... that divides that angle in two .... parts.

2. The bisectors of the angles of a triangle meet at one and the same point. This point is called the .... of the triangle.

3. The in-center of a triangle is .... from its ....

4. The in-centre of a circles lies in the .... of the triangle.

B. 5. Draw a triangle PQR on a tracing paper. Determine its in-center by folding the tracing paper.

6. Given in front is an isosceles triangle with its sides PQ and PR equal. PA is the bisector of ∠P. Trace three copies of the triangle on a tracing-paper. Now—

(a) draw the *medians* of triangle PQR in one copy. Do they meet on AP ?

(b) draw the *altitudes* of Δ PQR in the second copy. do they meet on AP ?

(c) draw the *right-bisectors* of the sides of Δ PQR in the third copy. Do they also meet on AP ?

7. Draw an equilateral Δ ABC draw the bisector of angle P. Now trace its three copies on a tracing paper. Repeat all the three steps taken in question 6. What do you find ?

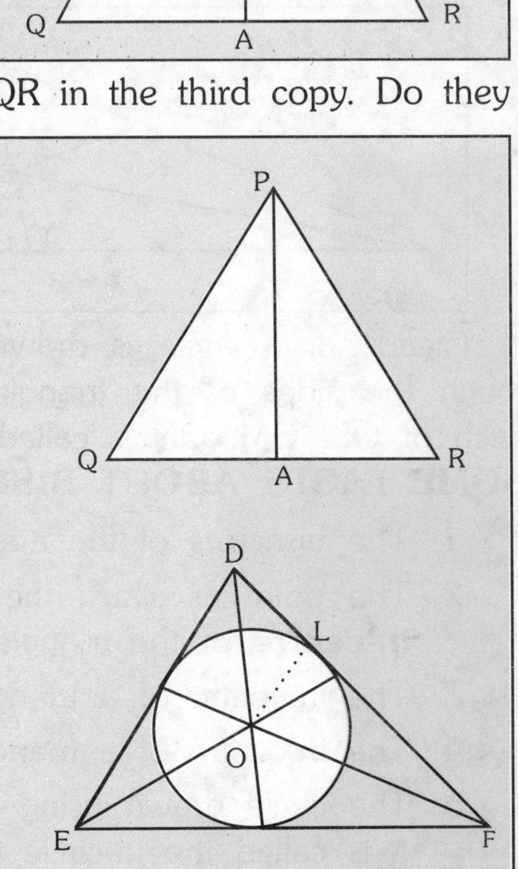

8. Draw a triangle DEF and find its in-centre O. Then taking O as the centre draw a circle that should touch the sides of Δ DEF.

(*Hint* : From the in-centre O, draw OL perpendicular to any side of the Δ. Use OL as the radius of the required circle)

20 CONGRUENT FIGURES

KNOW THESE TERMS :

1. **congruent**—two geometrical figures coinciding with each other element to element
2. **position**—way in which a figure (thing) or its parts are arranged
3. **shape**—total effect produced by an object's (figure's) outline
4. **size**—dimensions of an object or figure

WHAT IS CONGRUENCE ?

We know that every geometrical figure has a **shape, size** and **position.** We can compare the *shape* and *size* of two different figures through observation itself. But it is rarely possible for two figures to have the same **position**.

When two geometrical figures happen to have the same **shape** and **size,** they are called **congruent**. Their **position** may or *may not* be same.

In order to determine whether two figures are congruent or not, we can cut one of them and place (super-impose) it on the other. If the super-imposed figure fits on the other figure *element* to *element*. The figures have the same size, shape as well as position. In other words, they are said to be *congruent.* Given below are pairs of some congruent figures.

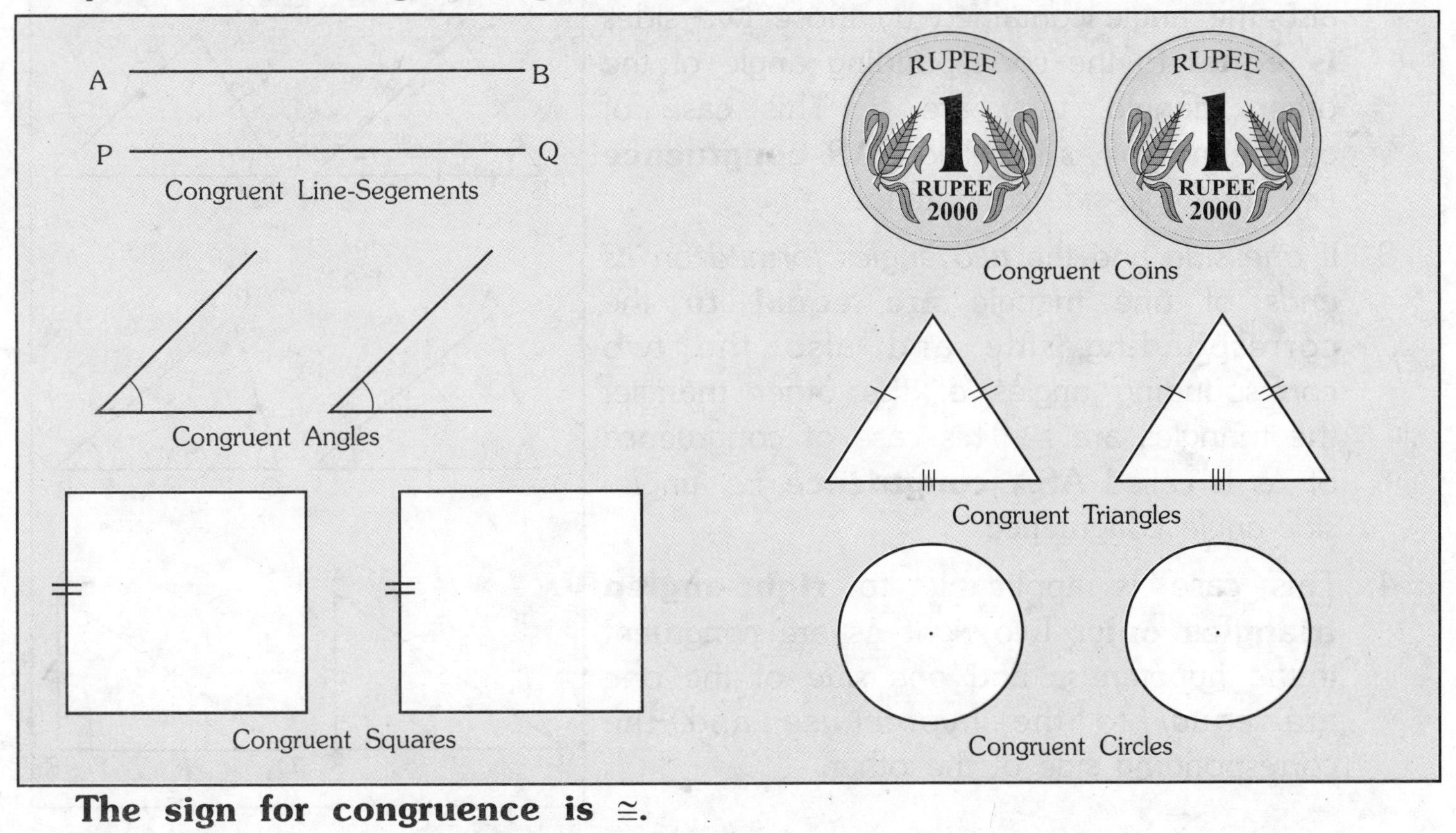

The sign for congruence is ≅.

CONGRUENT FIGURES

Here are given some points to know when different types of figures are congruent.

1. Two *line-segments* are congruent, if they have the **same length.**
2. Two *angles* are congruent if they have the **same measure**.
3. Two *squares* are congruent if they have the **same side-length**.
4. Two *rectangles* are congruent if they have the **same length** and **same breadth.**
5. Two *circles* are congruent if they have the **same radius**.

CONGRUENT TRIANGLES

A triangle has six elements, we know. These elements are **three sides** and **three angles**. If we think deeply over these elements, we can easily decide in which cases two triangle can be congruent to each other.

There are four case in which two triangles can be ≅ :

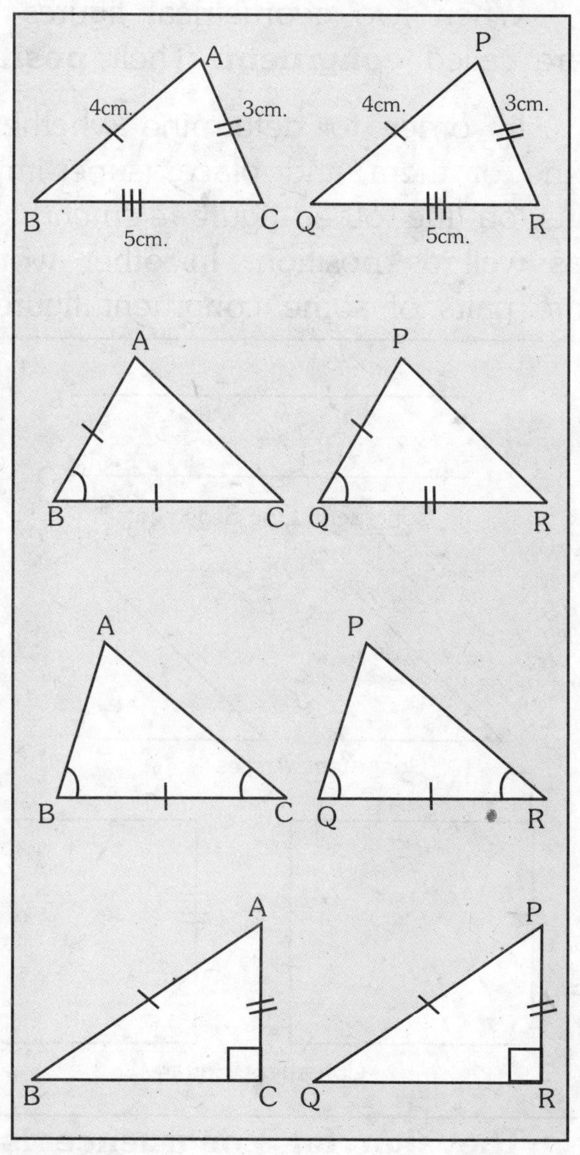

1. If *each side* of a triangle **is equal** to the *corresponding* side of the other.

   This case of congruence of Δs is called **SSS congruence**, *i.e. side-side-side* congruence.
2. If *two sides* of one triangle are respectively equal to two sides of another triangle and if also the angle contained by those two sides **is equal** to the corresponding angle of the other triangle, they are ≅. This case of congruence of Δs is called **SAS congruence** *i.e. side-angle-side* congruence.
3. If *one side* and the *two angles formed on its ends* of one triangle **are equal to** the corresponding side and also the two corresponding angles of the other triangle, the triangles are ≅. This case of congruence of Δs is called **ASA congruence** *i.e. angle-side-angle* congruence.
4. This case is applicable to **right-angled triangles only**. Two right Δs are congruent if *the hypotenuse* and *one side* of the one are *equal* to the *hypotenuse* and the corresponding side of the other.

Let us now solve some examples :

Example 1. **Two triangle ABC and DEF are congruent. Draw them and prove them congruent using SSS congruence.**

Solution : In Δs ABC and DEF

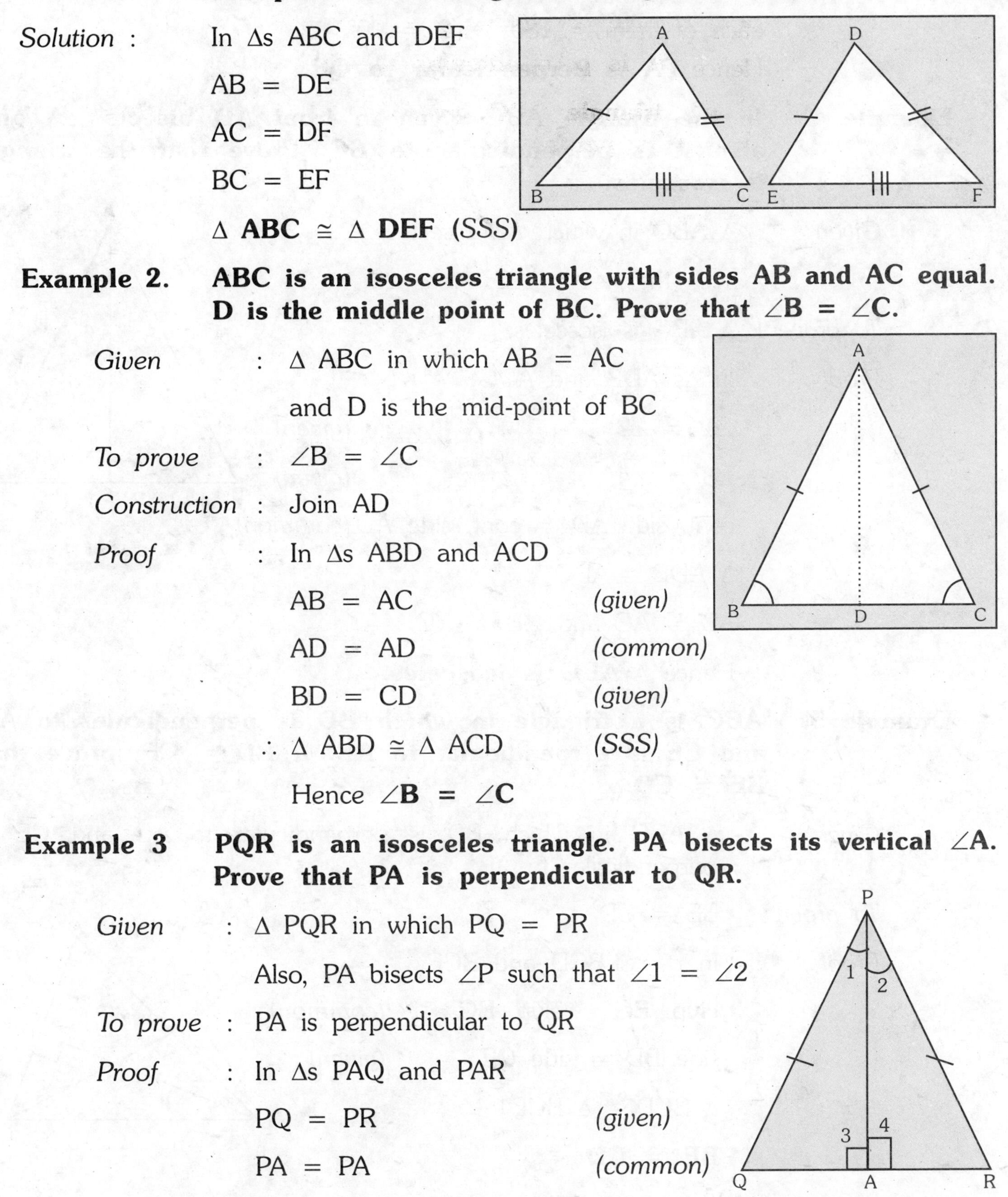

AB = DE

AC = DF

BC = EF

Δ **ABC** $\cong$ Δ **DEF** (*SSS*)

Example 2. **ABC is an isosceles triangle with sides AB and AC equal. D is the middle point of BC. Prove that $\angle$B = $\angle$C.**

Given : Δ ABC in which AB = AC and D is the mid-point of BC

To prove : $\angle$B = $\angle$C

Construction : Join AD

Proof : In Δs ABD and ACD

AB = AC (*given*)

AD = AD (*common*)

BD = CD (*given*)

$\therefore$ Δ ABD $\cong$ Δ ACD (*SSS*)

Hence $\angle$**B** = $\angle$**C**

Example 3 **PQR is an isosceles triangle. PA bisects its vertical $\angle$A. Prove that PA is perpendicular to QR.**

Given : Δ PQR in which PQ = PR

Also, PA bisects $\angle$P such that $\angle$1 = $\angle$2

To prove : PA is perpendicular to QR

Proof : In Δs PAQ and PAR

PQ = PR (*given*)

PA = PA (*common*)

cont. $\angle 1$ = cont. $\angle 2$ (*given*)

$\therefore$ Δ PAQ $\cong$ Δ PAR

$\therefore$ $\angle 3 = \angle 4$; But $\angle 3 + \angle 4 = 180°$ (*They make a straight* $\angle$)

$\therefore$ each of them $= 180° \div 2 = 90°$

Hence **PA is perpendicular to QR.**

Example 4. In the triangle ABC given in front AD bisects $\angle$A and also it is perpendicular to BC. Prove that the triangle is isosceles.

Given : Δ ABC in which AD bisects $\angle$A

such that $\angle 1 = \angle 2$. Also, $\angle 3 = \angle 4 = 90°$

To prove : Δ ABC is isosceles

Proof : In Δs ADB and ADC

$\angle 1 = \angle 2$ (*given*)

$\angle 3 = \angle 4$ (*given*)

cont. side AD = cont. side AD (*common*)

$\therefore$ Δ ADB $\cong$ ADC

$\therefore$ AB = AC and $\angle B = \angle C$

Hence Δ **ABC is isosceles.**

Example 5. ABC is a triangle in which BD is perpendicular to AC and CE is perpendicular to AB. If BD = CE, prove that BE = CD.

Given : Δ ABC in which BD is perpendicular to AC and CE is perpendicular to AB

To prove : BE = CD

Proof : In rt. Δs BCD and BCE

Hyp. BC = Hyp. BC (*common*)

side BD = side CE (*given*)

$\therefore$ Δ BCD $\cong$ Δ BCE

$\therefore$ **BE = CD**

PRACTICE EXERCISES 39

A. Answer :

1. How many cases of the congruence of Δs are there ? ....

2. How do we indicate the congruence of two Δs with *corresponding sides* equal each to each ? ....

3. How do we indicate the congruence of two Δs with *two sides* and the *contained angle* of the one equal to two corresponding sides and the corresponding contained angle of the other ? ....

4. How do we indicate the congruence of two Δs with *two angles* and the *contained side* of the one equal to two corresponding angles and the corresponding contained side of the other ? ....

5. How do we indicate the congruence of two right Δs ? ....

B. Given below are pairs of congruent triangles with proper markings of equality between corresponding elements. Which case of congruency is applicable to each pair ?

6.

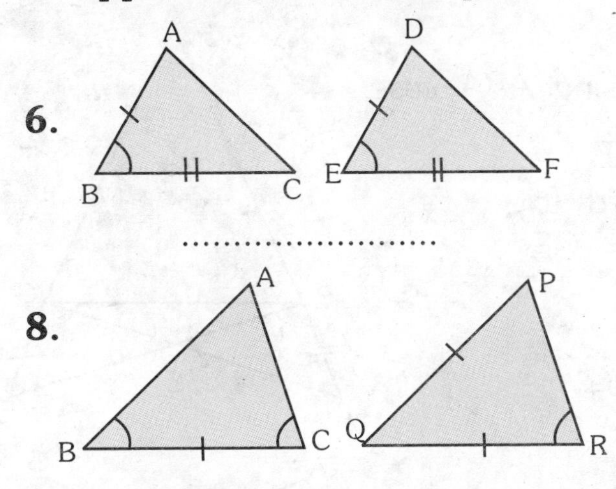

....

7.

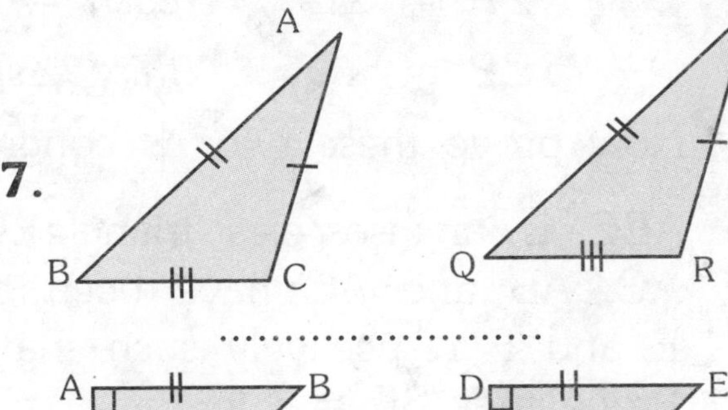

....

8. ....

9. A, B, C — D, E, F ....

10. Prove that in an isosceles triangle the angles opposite to the equal sides are also equal.

11. Show that the bisector of the vertical angle of an isosceles triangle meets the opposite side (base) at right angles.

12. In the figure given in front—

AB = AP and BC = PC

Prove that $\angle P = \angle B$

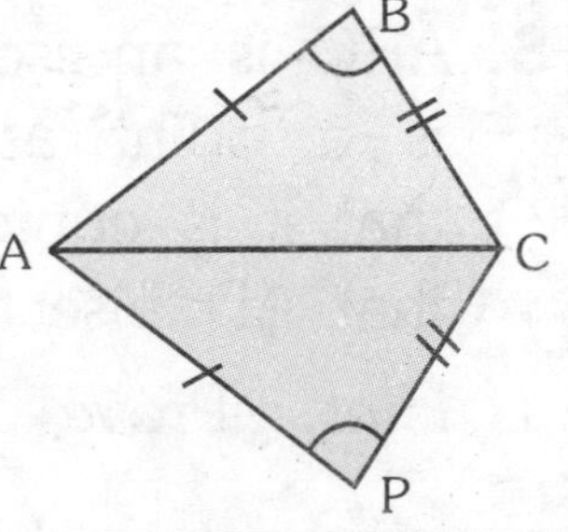

13. In the figure given in front, AB is perpendicular to PQ and AC is perpendicular to QR. Also AB = AC. Prove that—

(a) Δ ABQ $\cong$ Δ ACQ

(b) BQ = CQ

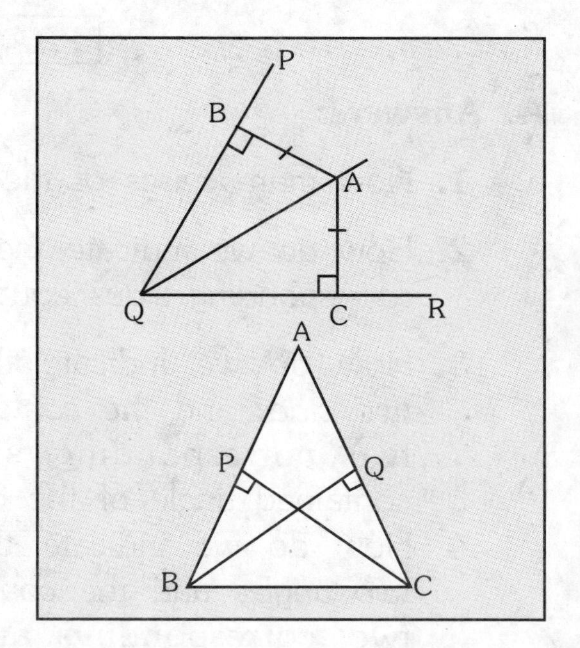

14. The adjoining figure shows an isosceles triangle with sides AB and AC equal. Points P, Q lie on sides AB, AC respectively such that BP = CQ. Prove that BQ = CP

Hint : Prove Δs BCP $\cong$ BCQ

15. In the figure given in front PA and QB are both perpendicular to AB and also they are equal. Prove that PQ bisects AB

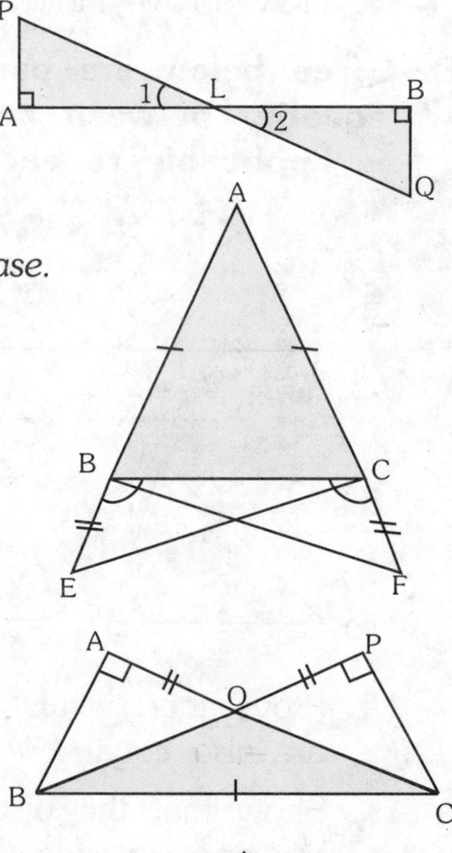

Hint : In Δs APL and BQL

$\angle 1 = \angle 2$ *(vert. opp. $\angle$s)*

$\angle A = \angle B$ *(each = 90°)*

$\angle P = \angle Q$ *(third $\angle$s)*

Now prove these two Δs congruent using *ASA case.*

16. ABC is an isosceles triangle with AB = AC. AB and AC have been produced to E and F respectively such that BE = CF. Prove that BF = CE

Hint : Prove Δs BCE $\cong$ BCF using SAS case. Before it, prove that $\angle$EBC = $\angle$FCB

17. Two right triangles ABC, PBC have been drawn on a common base BC such that $\angle$A and $\angle$P are rt. angles. Also, AC = PB. Prove that AB = PC

18. ABC is an isosceles Δ with AB = AC. D is a point as shown in the figure such that it is equidistant from B and C. Prove that AD bisects $\angle$A and $\angle$D.

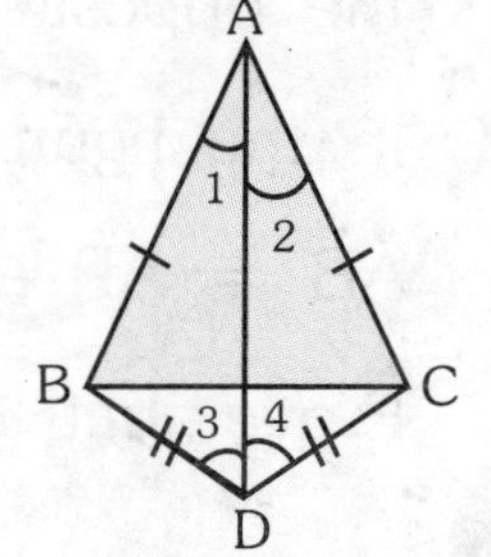

Hint : Prove Δs ABD $\cong$ ACD using SSS case.

21 QUADRILATERALS

KNOW THESE TERMS :

1. **quadrilateral**—polygon having four sides and four angles
2. **convex quadrilateral**—quadrilateral with each of its angles less than 180°
3. **concave quadrilateral**—quadrilateral with at least one angle larger than 180°
4. **quadrilateral region**—interior of a quadrilateral and the quadrilateral itself

QUADRILATERALS

A *quadrilateral* **is a plane figure with four straight sides, *i.e.* a four-sided polygon**.

There are two features to be remembered regarding quadrilaterals :

(a) No three vertices of a quadrilateral are collinear.

(b) Adjacent sides of a quadrilateral do not intersect except at its angular points.

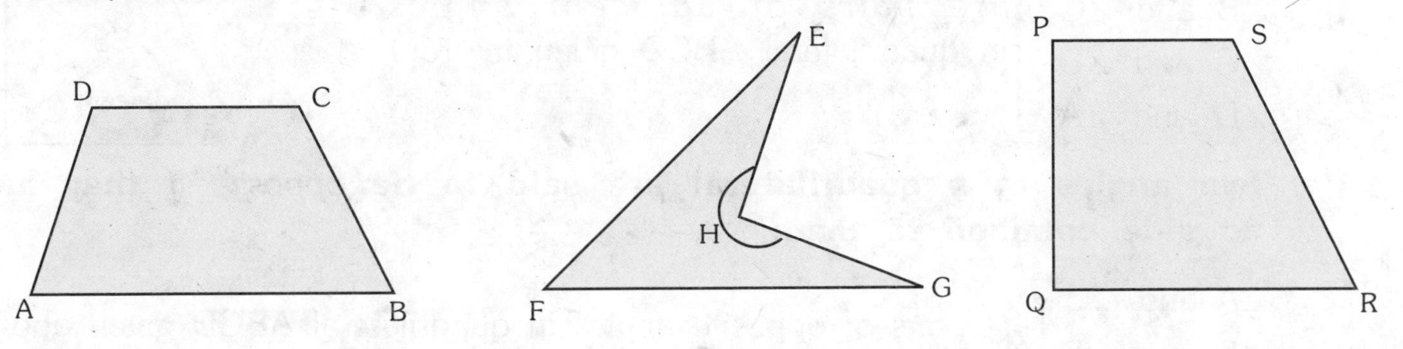

The figures given above are quadrilaterals ABCD, EFGH and PQRS respectively. A quadrilateral has four angular points and so it has four angles that is why it is called a **quadrangle** also.

Remember that the *sides of a quadrilateral* mark its **boundary**.

B. TWO TYPES OF QUADRILATERALS

Observe the three quadrilaterals given above. Quadrilaterals ABCD and PQRS are such quadrilaterals as have each of their angles measuring less than 180°. Such quadrilaterals are called *convex quadrilaterals*.

A convex quadrilateral has each of its angles measuring less than 180°.

But quadrilateral EFGH has one of its angles (∠EHG) larger than 180°, *i.e.* a *reflex angle*. Such a quadrilateral is called a *concave quadrilateral*.

A *concave quadrilateral* **is a quadrilateral that has at least one of its angles larger than 180°.**

ADJACENT SIDES, OPPOSITE SIDES

(a) **Two sides of a quadrilateral are called** *adjacent sides* **if they meet at a common vertex** ; as—

Sides AB and AD in quadrilateral ABCD given in front. Similarly, sides AB and BC ; BC and CD ; CD and AD are pairs of adjacent sides.

(b) **Two sides of a quadrilateral are called opposite sides if they do not have any common vertex, i.e. they are not adjacent** ; as—

Sides AB and CD and sides BC and AD are pairs of opposite sides in the quadrilateral ABCD.

C. ADJACENT ANGLES, OPPOSITE ANGLES

(a) **Two angles of a quadrilateral are said to be** *adjacent* **if they are formed at the end-points of a common side** ; as—

$\angle A$ and $\angle B$, $\angle B$ and $\angle C$, $\angle C$ and $\angle D$, $\angle D$ and $\angle A$ are *pairs of adjacent angles* in quadrilateral ABCD given in front

(b) **Two angles of a quadrilateral are said to be** *opposite* **if they have no side common to them** ; as—

$\angle A$ and $\angle C$, $\angle B$ and $\angle D$ are pairs of opposite angles in quadrilateral ABCD given above.

D. INTERIOR, EXTERIOR, QUADRILATERAL REGION

We know that three non-collinear points can determine a *plane*. A quadrilateral has four vertices, three of which must be non-collinear. The plane of a quadrilateral has numerous points which fall into three classes as under :

(a) **The points that lie enclosed by the quadrilateral** ; *as* points L, M in the quadrilateral PQRS given in front. They lie in the interior of quadrilateral PQRS. Any point lying enclosed by the quadrilateral just like L or M is called an **interior point**.

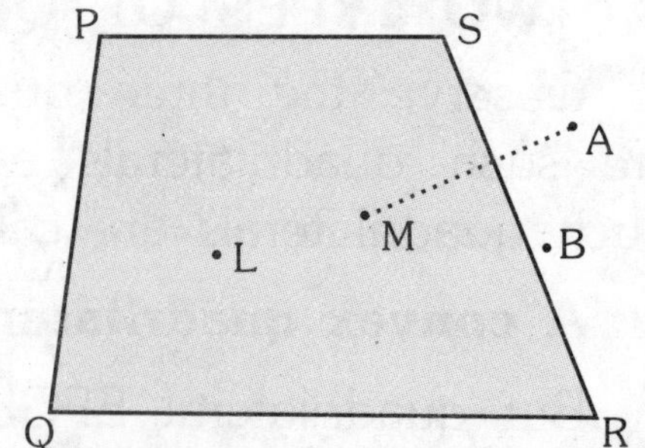

(b) **The points that are not enclosed by the quadrilateral** ; *as* Points A, B outside quadrilateral PQRS shown above. These points lie in the exterior of quadrilateral ABCD. Any point lying not enclosed by a quadrilateral just like A, B is called its **exterior point**.

(*c*) **The interior of a quadrilateral together with the quadrilateral itself is called its quadrilateral region.**

We can well see that if we want to go from the point M to the point A or B, we shall have to cross the side RS of the quadrilateral PQRS given on page 182. In other words, we cannot go from the interior of a quadrilateral to its exterior without crossing one of its sides. Clearly, the sides of a quadrilateral mark the **boundary** of the quadrilateral.

PRACTICE EXERCISES 40

A. Complete each statement :

1. A quadrilateral has .... sides and .... angles.

2. A quadrilateral has .... diagonals that .... each other.

3. A quadrilateral has .... vertices, any three of which are ....

4. Two adjacent sides of a quadrilateral have a common ....

5. Two adjacent angles of a quadrilateral have an .... common.

6. Two opposite sides of a quadrilateral have no .... vertex.

7. Two opposite angles of a quadrilateral have no common ....

B. Given in front is a quadrilateral PQRS. Write the correct answer to each question :

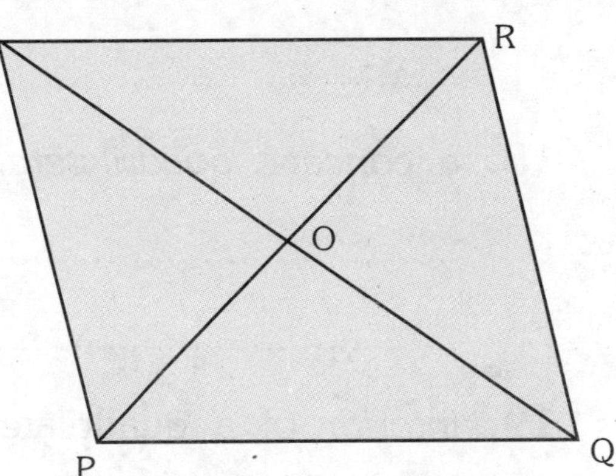

8. How many vertices has it ? Name them.

....

9. How many sides has it ? Name them.

....

10. How many angles has it ? Name them.

....

11. How many diagonals has it ? Name them.

....

12. How many pairs of *adjacent angles* has it ? Name them.

....

....

13. How many pairs of *adjacent sides* has it ? Name them.

....

....

14. How many pairs of *opposite sides* has it ? Name them.

....

....

15. How many pairs of *opposite angles* has it ? Name them.

....

....

C. Define—

16. a *quadrilateral* :

....

....

17. a *convex quadrilateral* :

....

....

18. a *concave quadrilateral* :

....

....

19. *interior* of a quadrilateral :

....

....

20. *exterior* a quadrilateral :

....

....

21. a *quadrilateral region* :

....

....

22. *boundary* of a quadrilateral :

....

....

23. *diagonal* of quadrilateral :

....

....

24. Draw a quadrilateral ABCD along with its *diagonals*. Where do they intersect ? In what type of figures is the quadrilateral divided now ?

25. What is the sum of the angles of a quadrilateral ? Can you prove it ?

....

COMMON TYPES OF QUADRILATERALS

Some common types of quadrilaterals are as under :

1. TRAPEZIUM

A *trapezium* is a quadrilateral with two of its sides parallel and the other two non-parallel.

Given in front is a trapezium ABCD. It has its sides AB and CD parallel and unequal while its sides BC and AD are non-parallel. DL is drawn perpendicular to AB. It is the **height** of the trapezium.

2. PARALLELOGRAM

A *parallelogram* is a quadrilateral that has both its pairs of opposite sides parallel.

Given in front is a parallelogram PQRS. In it, PQ is parallel to RS while QR is parallel to PS. SL is drawn perpendicular to PQ. It is the **height** of the parallelogram.

3. RHOMBUS

A *rhombus* is a parallelogram whose all sides are equal but no angle is a right angle.

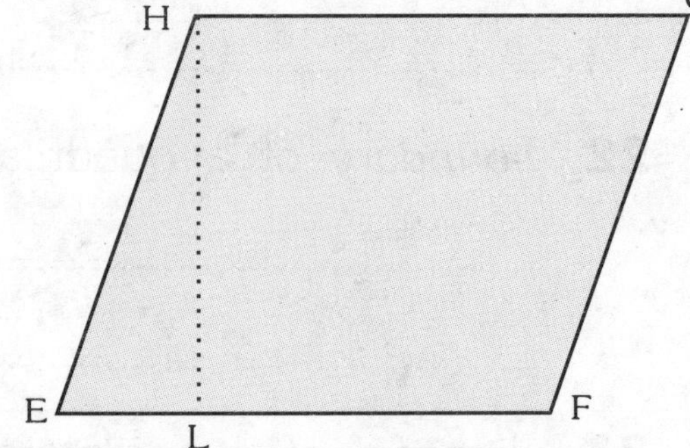

The adjoining figure EFGH is a rhombus. In it EF = FG = GH = HE and also EF is parallel to GH and FG is parallel to HE. HL is drawn perpendicular to EF. It is the height of the rhombus.

4. RECTANGLE

A *rectangle* is a parallelogram with each of its angles a right angle.

The figure in front is a rectangle ABCD. Each of its angles A, B, C, D is a right angle and its opposite sides are parallel and equal just like those of a parallelogram.

5. SQUARE

A *square* is a rhombus each of whose angles is a right angle. *Or* **a *square* is a rectangle with all the four sides equal.**

Given in front is a square ABCD in which AB = BC = CD = DA. Also, each of its angles is a right angle.

ANGLE-SUM PROPERTY OF QUADRILATERALS

Draw any two or three quadrilaterals at random as shown below. Measure the angles of each of them using a protractor and find their sum. You will see that it is equal to **360°** or **4 rt ∠s** in each case.

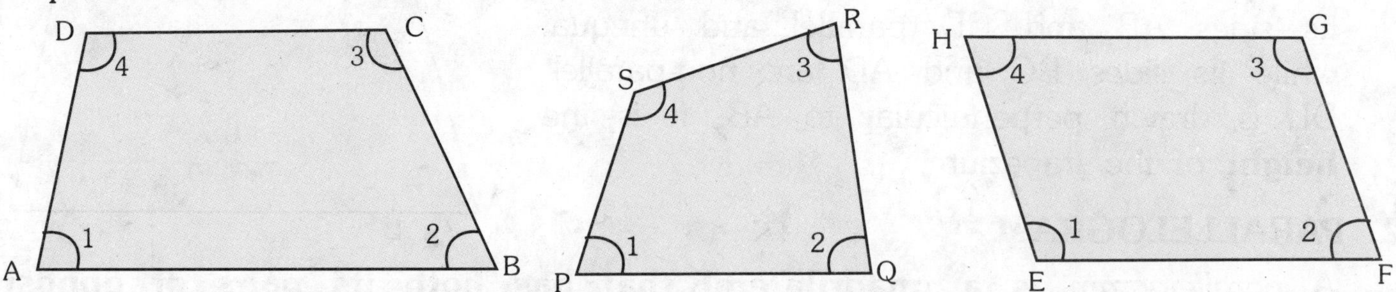

Measure the angles of these quadrilaterals and fill in the following table.

Quadrilateral	*∠1*	*∠2*	*∠3*	*∠4*	*sum of the angles*
ABCD					
PQRS					
EFGH					

So, it is clear :

The sum of the angles of a quadrilateral is equal to 360° or 4rt. ∠s.

We can prove this fact as follows :

Given : A quadrilateral ABCD

To prove : $\angle A + \angle B + \angle C + \angle D = 4$rt. ∠s.

Construction : join AC

Proof : The quadrilateral ABCD has got divided into two Δs ABC and ADC.

$\angle 1 + \angle B + \angle 3 = 2$ rt ∠s. (*∠sum of a Δ*)

Also, $\angle 2 + \angle D + \angle 4 = 2$ rt ∠s (*∠sum of a Δ*)

$\therefore (\angle 1 + \angle 2) + \angle B + (\angle 3 + \angle 4) + \angle D = (2 + 2)$ rt. ∠s

or $\angle A + \angle B + \angle C + \angle D = 4$ rt. ∠s.

Example 1. Two of the angles of a quadrilateral are 65° and 75° respectively. If the other two angles are equal, find their measures.

Solution : Let the quadrilateral be ABCD as shown in front. Suppose the given angles of 65° and 75° are ∠D and ∠C.

$\angle C + \angle D = 75° + 65° = 140°$

Now $\angle A + \angle B + \angle C + \angle D = 360°$

$\angle A + \angle B + 140° = 360°$

or $\angle A + \angle B = 360° - 140° = 220°$

But $\angle A = \angle B$

$\therefore \angle A = \angle B = 220° \div 2 =$ **110° each** *Ans.*

Example 2. The angles P, Q, R and S of a quadrilateral are in the ratio 1 : 2 : 3 : 4. Find their measures.

Solution. *First method* :

Let the quad. PQRS be as shown on page 188.

Ratio among its angles P, Q, R, S

= 1 : 2 : 3 : 4

Sum of the ratios = 1 + 2 + 3 + 4 = 10

$\angle P + \angle Q + \angle R + \angle S = 360^\circ$

$\therefore \angle P = \frac{360^\circ}{10} \times 1 = \mathbf{36^\circ}$

$\angle Q = \frac{360^\circ}{10} \times 2 = \mathbf{72^\circ}$

$\angle R = \frac{360^\circ}{10} \times 3 = \mathbf{108^\circ}$

and $\angle S = \frac{360^\circ}{10} \times 4 = \mathbf{144^\circ}$ *Ans.*

S R P Q

Alternative Method :

Let the angles of the quadrilateral $= x^\circ, 2x^\circ, 3x^\circ, 4x^\circ$

$\therefore x^\circ + 2x^\circ + 3x^\circ + 4x^\circ = 360^\circ$ ($\angle$ *sum of a quad)*

or $x + 2x + 3x + 4x = 360$

or $10x = 360$

or $x = 360 \div 10 = 36$

$\therefore$ angles of the quadrilateral are

$36^\circ, (36 \times 2)^\circ, (36 \times 3)^\circ, (36 \times 4)^\circ$

$=$ **36°, 72°, 108°, 144°** *Ans.*

PRACTICE EXERCISES 40

A. Write *T* for the true statements and *F* for the false ones :

1. A rhombus is an *equilateral* parallelogram. ....

2. A rectangle is an *equiangular* parallelogram. ....

3. A square is an *equilateral* and *equiangular* quadrilateral. ....

4. A square is a rt. $\angle$d rhombus. ....

5. Opposite sides of a parallelogram are not parallel. ....

6. The angle sum of a quadrilateral is 180°. ....

7. A square has all its sides equal. ....

B. Name—

8. two types of quadrilaterals with all the sides equal.

....

9. two types of quadrilaterals with each of the angles = 90°.

....

10. four types of quadrilaterals with each pair of opposite sides parallel.

....

11. a quadrilateral with only one pair of opposite sides parallel.

....

C. 12. Given in front is a triangle PQR. DE is drawn parallel to QR as shown in the figure given in front. What name will you give to the quadrilateral DERQ ?

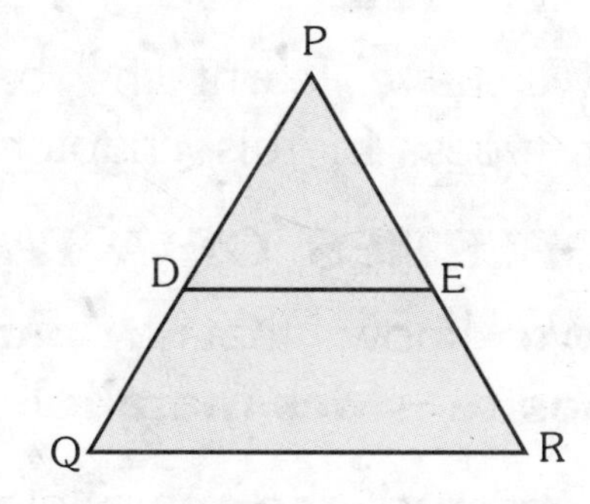

13. The measures of two angles of a quadrilateral are 35° and 125°. If its other two angles are equal, find the measure of either of them.

14. The angles of a quadrilateral are in the ratio 3 : 5 : 7 : 9. Find their values in terms of degrees.

15. The sum of two angles of a quadrilateral is 190° and the other two angles are equal. Find the value of either of them.

16. A quadrilateral has all its angles of the same measure. What is that same measure ?

17. Three angles of a quadrilateral are equal while the fourth angle measures 150°. Find the measure of the equal angles.

18. ABCD is a trapezium with its sides AB and CD parallel to each other. If $\angle A = 60°$ and $\angle B = 40°$, find the measures of $\angle C$ and $\angle D$.

19. *(a)* What is meant by an isosceles trapezium ? How is it different from an ordinary trapezium ?

(b) Are the parallel sides of a trapezium equal or not.

20. The sides of a quadrilateral PQRS have been produced in order as shown in front as shown infront. What is the sum of the four exterior angles a, b, c, d ?

22 MORE ABOUT QUADRILATERALS

KNOW THESE TERMS :
1. **parallelogram**—four-sided rectilinear figure with opposite sides parallel
2. **rhombus**—an oblique equilateral parallelogram
3. **diagonal**—line-segment that joins two opposite vertices of a quadrilateral
4. **equilateral quadrilateral**—a quadrilateral with all the four sides equal

We have learnt the basic facts about quadrilaterals. Also, we have read about their types. In this chapter we shall study their properties.

PROPERTIES OF A PARALLELOGRAM

We know that a **parallelogram is a quadrilateral with each pair of opposite sides parallel.**

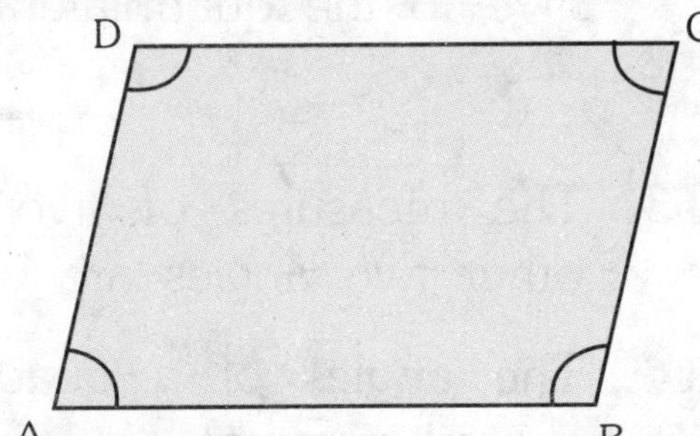

Observe the parallelogram ABCD given in front. In it, AB and CD make one pair of opposite sides while BC and AD make the other pair of opposite sides. We also know that AB is parallel to CD and BC is parallel to AD.

Let us try to know other facts about the **sides** and **angles** of a parallelogram.

Draw two or three parallelograms at random. Measure their sides and angles and fill up the table given below.

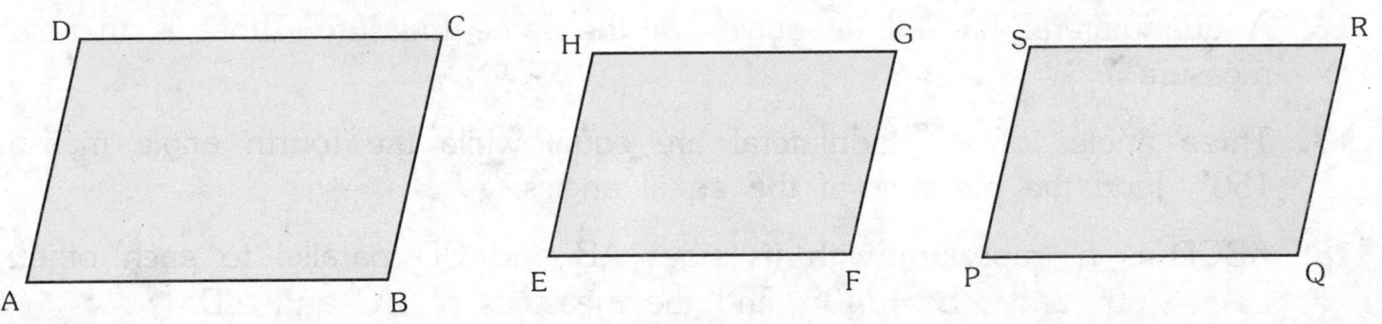

Parallelogram	*Lengths of the sides*	*Measures of angles*	*Result*
ABCD	AB = ... BC = ... CD = ... AD = ...	∠A = ... ∠B = ... ∠C = ... ∠D = ...	**AB = CD, ∠A = ∠C** **BC = AD, ∠B = ∠D**
EFGH	EF = ... FG = ... GH = ... HE = ...	∠E = ... ∠F = ... ∠G = ... ∠H = ...	**EF = GH, ∠E = ∠G** **FG = HE, ∠F = ∠H**
PQRS	PQ = ... QR = ... RS = ... PS = ...	∠P = ... ∠Q = ... ∠R = ... ∠S = ...	**PQ = RS, ∠P = ∠R** **QR = PS, ∠Q = ∠S**

So, we can say that—

1. The opposite sides of a parallelogram are equal.

2. The opposite angles of a parallelogram are equal.

DIAGONALS OF A PARALLELOGRAM

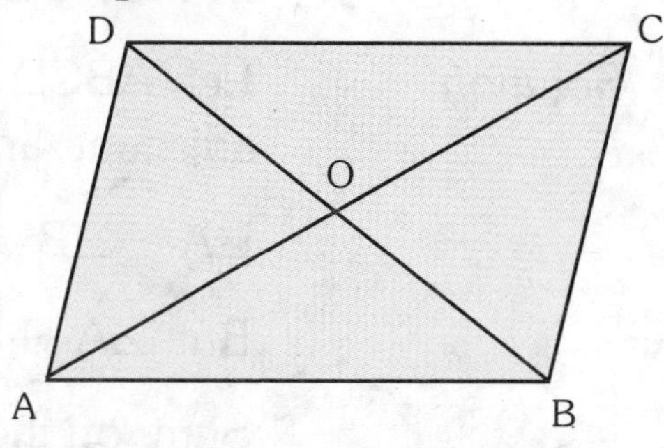

Observe the parallelogram ABCD given in front. Its diagonals AC and BD have been drawn. They intersect at O which lies in the interior of the parallelogram. Let us try to know some facts about the diagonals AC, BD and their intersection.

Measure the diagonals AC and BD. Also measure AO, CO and BO, DO. Now fill in the following table :

Diagonal	*Length*	*Parts of diagonals*	*Length*
AC	....	AO	....
		CO	....
BD	....	BO	....
		DO	....

What do you observe ? Answer :

1. Are AC and BD equal ? ....
2. Is AO = CO ....
3. Is BO = DO ....
4. Is AD parallel to BC ....
5. Is AB a transversal to AD, BC ? ....
6. Are ∠A, ∠B interior ∠s ? ....
7. Are they together = 180° ....

So, the diagonals of a parallelogram bisect each other.

We can sum up the properties of a parallelogram as under :

1. **The** *opposite sides* **of a parallelogram are** *equal* **and** *parallel.*
2. **The** *opposite angles of* **a parallelogram are** *equal.*
3. **The** *diagonals of a parallelogram are normally* **not equal.**
4. **The** *diagonals* **of a parallelogram** *bisect each other.*
5. **The** *adjacent interior ∠s* **of a parallelogram are** *together equal to 180°.*

Let us now solve some example :

Example 1. The adjacent angles of a parallelogram are in the ratio 2 : 3. Find all the angles of the parallelogram.

Solution : Let ABCD be the parallelogram as shown in front and its two adjacent angles be $\angle A$, $\angle B$

$\angle A : \angle B = 2 : 3$

But $\angle A + \angle B = 180^\circ$ because they are interior adjacent $\angle$s

Sum of the ratios $= 2 + 3 = 5$

$\therefore \quad \angle A = \frac{180^\circ}{5} \times 2 = \mathbf{72^\circ}$

and $\angle B = \frac{180^\circ}{5} \times 3 = \mathbf{108^\circ}$

Now we know that—

The opposite $\angle$s of a parallelogram are equal

$\therefore \quad \angle C = \angle A = \mathbf{72^\circ}$ and $\angle D = \angle B = \mathbf{108^\circ}$

Hence $\angle$s of the parallelogram are **72°, 108°, 72°, 108°** *Ans.*

Example 2. The longer side of a parallelogram is 7·2 cm. and it is half as much again as the shorter side. Find the perimeter of the parallelogram.

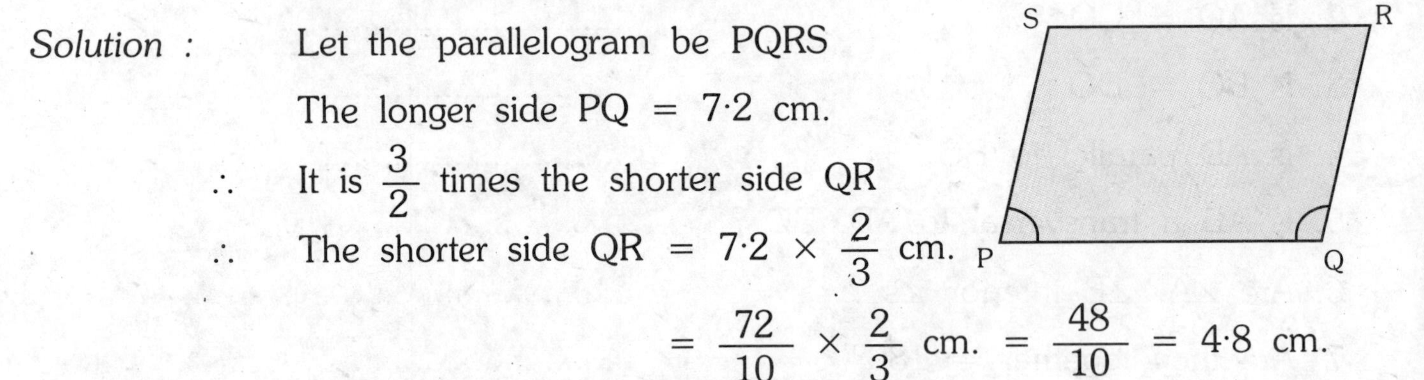

Solution : Let the parallelogram be PQRS

The longer side PQ = 7·2 cm.

$\therefore$ It is $\frac{3}{2}$ times the shorter side QR

$\therefore$ The shorter side $QR = 7{\cdot}2 \times \frac{2}{3}$ cm.

$= \frac{72}{10} \times \frac{2}{3}$ cm. $= \frac{48}{10} = 4{\cdot}8$ cm.

Now, we know that—

PQ = RS and QR = PS

$\therefore$ Perimeter of the parallelogram $= PQ + QR + RS + PS$

$= (7{\cdot}2 + 4{\cdot}8 + 7{\cdot}2 + 4{\cdot}8)$ cm.

$= 2\,(7{\cdot}2 + 4{\cdot}8)$ cm.

$= 2 \times 12$ cm. $=$ **24 cm.** *Ans.*

PROPERTIES OF A RHOMBUS

A rhombus is a parallelogram with all its sides equal and with no angle equal to 90°.

A rhombus has all the properties of a parallelogram but it possesses one additional property. This property is there **because its sides are equal**.

Observe the rhombus ABCD given in front.

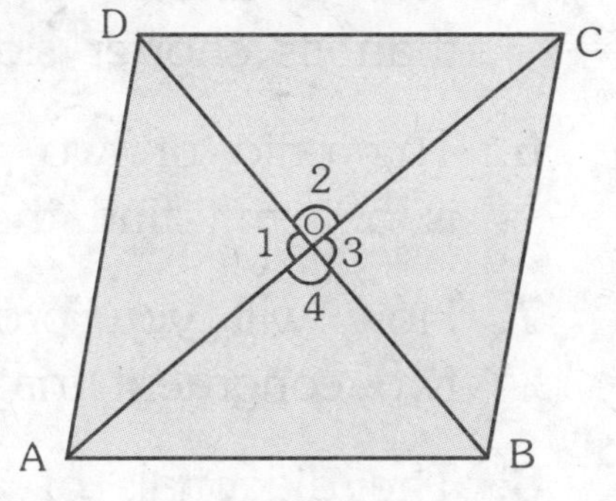

$\because$ It is a parallelogram

$\therefore$ AB = CD and BC = AD

$\angle A = \angle C$ and $\angle B = \angle D$

AO = CO and BO = DO

Now measure the angles 1, 2, 3, 4 formed at O where the diagonals of the rhombus intersect. Then fill in the table given below :

Name of the angle	*Measure*
$\angle 1$	
$\angle 2$	
$\angle 3$	
$\angle 4$	

*You will see that each of these angles is a **right angle.***

So, we can say :

The diagonals of a rhombus bisect each other at rt. $\angle$s.

This quality of a rhombus is in addition to all other properties of parallelograms. So, a rhombus has the following properties :

1. *All the sides of a rhombus are equal in length.*
2. *No angle of a rhombus is a right angle.*
3. *The diagonals of a rhombus are not equal in length.*
4. *The diagonals of a rhombus bisect each other at right $\angle$s.*

PRACTICE EXERCISES 42

A. **1** One of the angles of a parallelogram is 80°. Find its other three angles.

2. Two adjacent angles of a parallelogram are equal to each other. Find all its angles. Can you given it another name ?

3. Two adjacent angles of a parallelogram are in the ratio 1 : 2. Find the measures of all its angles.

4. Two adjacent sides of a parallelogram are 4 cm. and 5 cm. respectively. Find its perimeter.

5. The perimeter of a parallelogram is 28 cm. and its longer side is larger than its shorter side by 2 cm. Find the lengths of its sides.

6. The ratio of two adjacent sides of a parallelogram is 2 : 3. If its perimeter is 50 cm., find the lengths of its sides.

7. How will you prove that each diagonal of a parallelogram divides it into two congruent triangles.

8. The diagonals of a quadrilateral intersect at O. This point O divides one of the diagonals in the ratio 3 : 4. Can the quadrilateral be a parallelogram ? If yes, why and if not, why ?

9. ABCD is a parallelogram in which CE is the bisector of $\angle C$ and AF is the bisector of $\angle A$. Answer and explain :

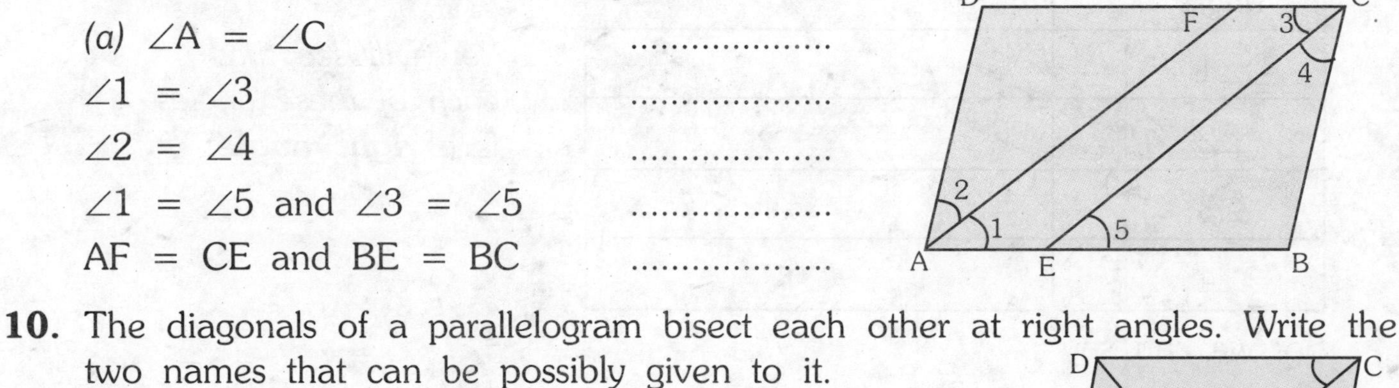

(a) $\angle A = \angle C$ ....

$\angle 1 = \angle 3$ ....

$\angle 2 = \angle 4$ ....

$\angle 1 = \angle 5$ and $\angle 3 = \angle 5$ ....

AF = CE and BE = BC ....

10. The diagonals of a parallelogram bisect each other at right angles. Write the two names that can be possibly given to it.

11. ABCD is a rhombus and its diagonals intersect at O.

(a) Is Δ BOC $\cong$ Δ DOC ?

If yes, which case of congruence is applicable ?

(b) Is $\angle BCO \cong \angle DCO$?

(c) Do the diagonals of the rhombus bisect the angles that they pass through ?

12. A quadrilateral has its diagonals intersecting at right angles. Say whether it can be—

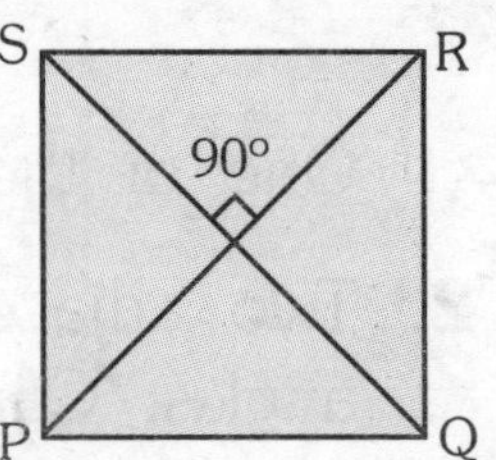

(a) a rectangle *(b)* a square

(c) a rhombus *(d)* a trapezium

PROPERTIES OF A RECTANGLE

We know that a rectangle is also a *parallelogram* with each of its angles equal to 90°.

Observe the rectangle ABCD given in front.

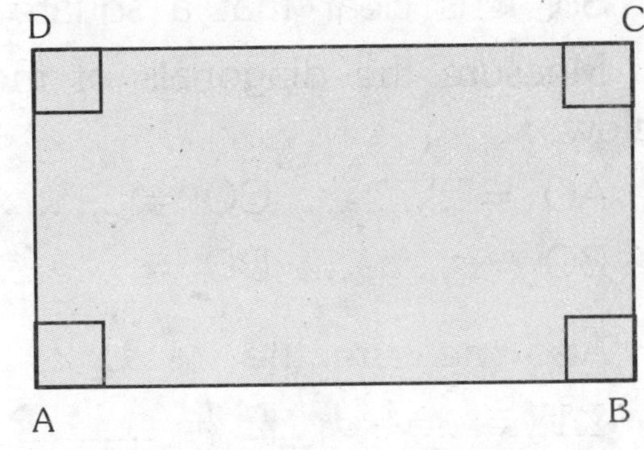

$\because$ Rectangle ABCD is a parallelogram

$\therefore$ AB = CD and BC = AD

AB is parallel to CD and BC is parallel to AD

$\angle A = \angle C$ and $\angle B = \angle D$

$\angle A = \angle B = \angle C = \angle D = 90°$.

Diagonals of a rectangle

Draw three rectangles at random and draw their diagonals as shown in the figures given below :

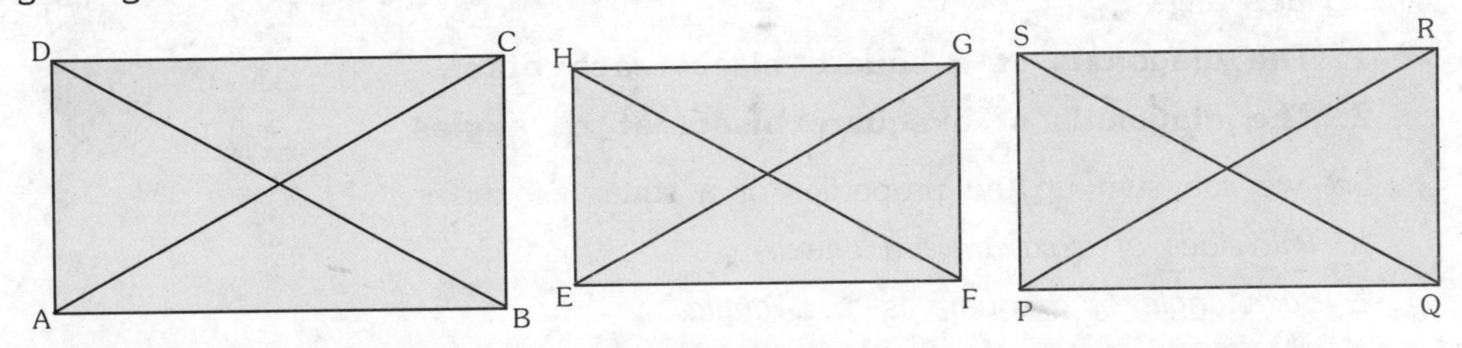

Measure the diagonals of each rectangle and fill in the following table.

Rectangle	*Diagonals*		*Result*
ABCD	AC = ...	BD = ...	AC, BD are ....
ABCD	EG = ...	HF = ...	EG, HF are ....
PQRS	PR = ...	SQ = ...	PR, SQ are ....

So, we can sum up the properties of a rectangle as under :

1. *Opposite sides of a rectangle are equal.*
2. *Opposite sides of a rectangle are parallel.*
3. *Each angle of a rectangle is equal to 90°.*
4. *Diagonals of a rectangle are equal.*
5. *Diagonals of a rectangle bisect each other.*

PROPERTIES OF A SQUARE

A *square* is a parallelogram with all its sides equal and each of its angles equal to 90°.

In other words—

A square is an equilateral rectangle.

So, it is clear that a square has all the properties of a rectangle.

Measure the diagonals of the adjoining square and their parts. Write their length below :

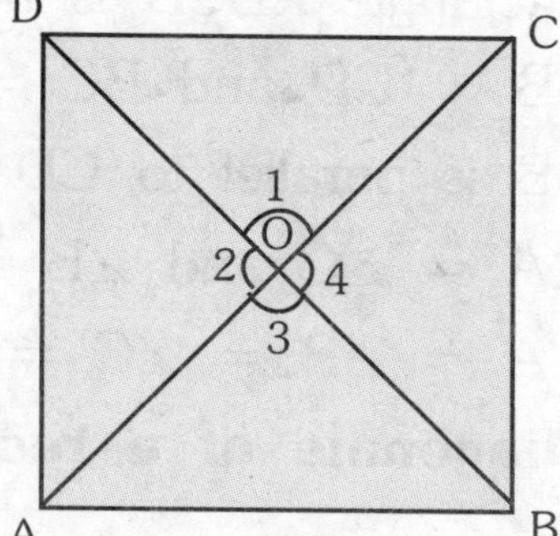

AO = ... CO = ...

BO = ... DO = ...

Also measure the ∠s 1, 2, 3, 4

∠1 = ... ∠2 = ...

∠3 = ... ∠4 = ...

What do we observe ? We observe two facts about the diagonals of a square. These facts are—

1. The diagonals of a square bisect each other.

2. The diagonals of a square bisect at rt. angles.

So, we can sum up the properties of a squar as under :

1. *The sides of a square are equal.*
2. *Each angle of a square is a rt. angle.*
3. *The diagonals of a square are equal in length.*
4. *The diagonals of a square bisect each other at rt. ∠s.*

ABOUT A TRAPEZIUM

A *trapezium is a quadrilateral that has two of its sides parallel and unequal while the other two sides non-parallel.*

The non-parallel sides of a trapezium may be equal or not. *If these non-parallel sides are equal, the trapezium is called an* **isosceles trapezium**.

PRACTICE EXERCISES 43

A. Write *T* for each true statement and *F* for each false statement :

1. A rectangle is a right parallelogram. ....

2. A square is an equilateral rectangle. ....

3. The sides of a rectangle are equal. ....

4. The diagonals of a rectangle bisect at rt. ∠s. ....

5. The diagonals of a square bisect at rt. ∠s. ....

6. The diagonals of a rectangle are equal. ....

7. A square is a right rhombus. ....

B. 8. A carpenter made a window-frame. When its diagonals were measured, they were found to be equal. What shape is the window ?

9. PQRS is a rectangle. SA and BQ are perpendiculars drawn from S and Q on the diagonal PR. Prove that SA = BQ

(*Hint.* Prove ∠s BQR and SAP ≅)

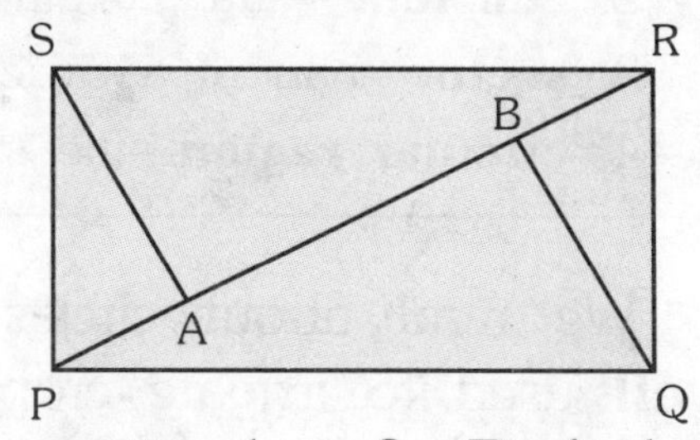

10. The adjacent angles of a parallelogram are in the ratio 1 : 2. Find the measures of all its angles.

11. The diagonals of a parallelogram ABCD intersect at O. A line-segment passing through O meets AD and BC at X and Y respectively. Explain the following :

(a) OB = OD

(b) ∠1 = ∠2

(c) ∠3 = ∠4

(d) Δ BOY ≅ Δ DOX

Also, say whether O bisects XY or not ?

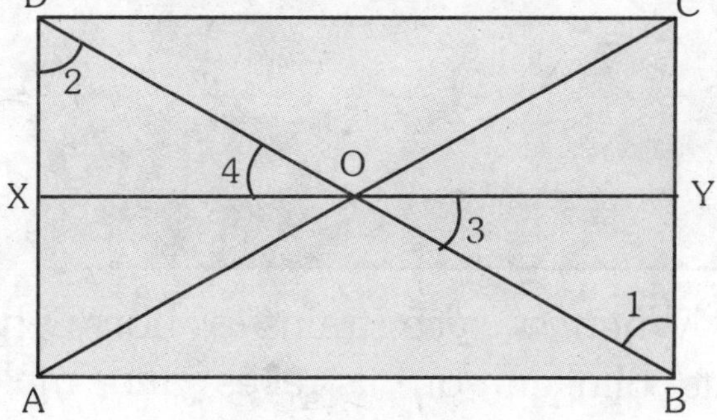

12. Draw a parallelogram PQRS in which PQ = 4 cm., PS = 3 cm. and ∠P = 60°. Draw its diagonals and measure their lengths.

13. Draw a parallelogram ABCD with AB = 5 cm., AD = 3 cm. and BD = 4·5 cm. Measure AC.

14. One of the diagonals of a rhombus is equal to its side. Find the angles of the rhombus.

15. One diagonal of a rectangle is 6 cm. in length while one of its sides is 4 cm. long construct the rectangle.

16. The sides of a rectangle are in the ratio 2 : 3. Draw the rectangle if its perimeter is 20 cm.

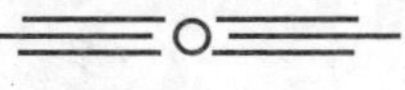

23 CIRCLES

KNOW THESE TERMS :

1. **syce**—person who grooms and trains horses
2. **constant**—quantity that does not change (vary)
3. **sector**—part of a circle's interior cut off by two radii
4. **circular region**—the interior of a circle plus the circle itself

We read about circles in the previous class. Have you ever seen a **Persian well** used to irrigate crops. A camel goes round and round to draw water out of the well. The *passage* it moves along is a **circle**.

When a syce trains a horse, he ties a rope round the neck of the horse. He puts blinkers on its eyes and makes it run round himself at a distance equal to the length of the rope. The *running course* of the horse is a **circle**.

Coming to the point, we have a geometrical instrument in the geometry-box. This instrument is called the **compasses** and it is used to *describe circles* as shown below.

Let us try to know important facts about circles.

1. CENTRE, RADIUS

We have seen that a circle is there when any point (*say A*) A moves in a plane such that its distance from another fixed point (*say O*) remains *constant* (always the same). See the figure on page 199.

The point A moves along a path *point by point*. When it is back at its *starting point,* it has described a **circle** as shown in front.

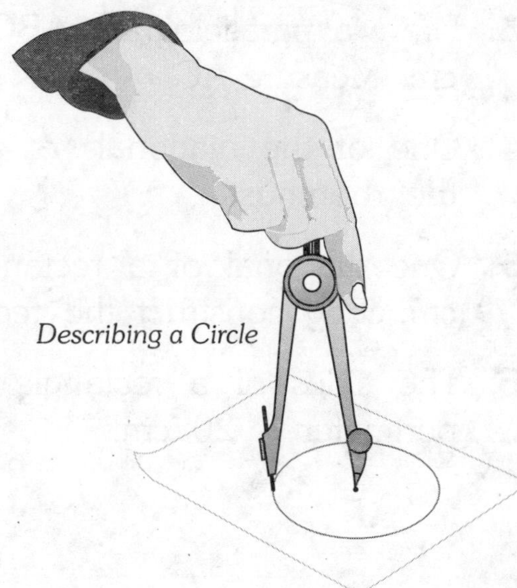

Describing a Circle

So, we get the following definitions :

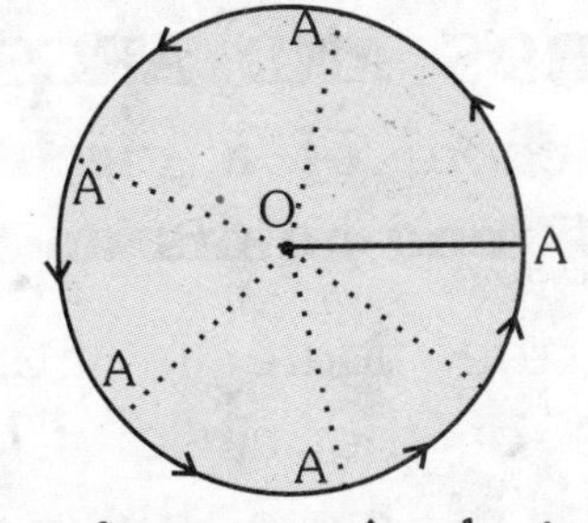

1. The *fixed point* O is the **centre** of the circle that is described by A.
2. The *constant distance* between O and A is called the **radius** of the circle.

Clearly, all the dotted lines show the various positions of point A during its course of movement to describe the circle. Thus, all the *radii of a circle are equal.*

DIAMETER, CIRCUMFERENCE

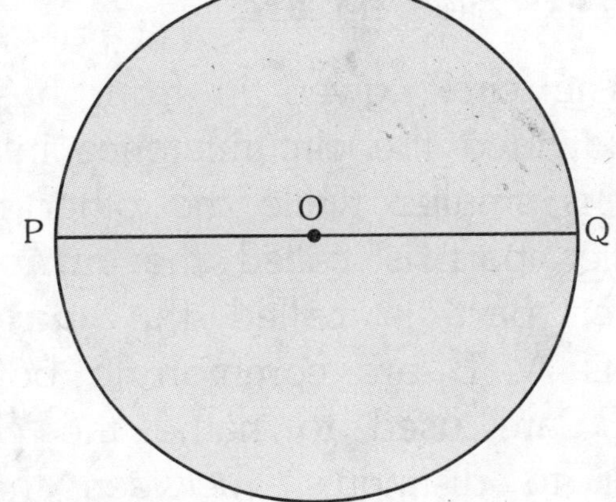

Observe the figure given in front. It shows a circle with centre O. Also, a line-segment POQ has been drawn that passes through O and has its end-points on the circle.

Clearly—

OP = radius of the circle

OQ = radius of the circle

OP + OQ or POQ = 2 × radius of the circle.

The line-segemnt POQ is called the **diameter** of the circle. The *round boundary that marks the circle* is called its **circumference**.

Thus we see that—

(a) **Diameter = 2 × radius**

(b) **All diameters are of equal length.**

Also remember that the symbol used for **radius** is r and the symbol used for the **circumference** is $\bigcirc^{ce}$.

INTERIOR, EXTERIOR, CIRCULAR REGION

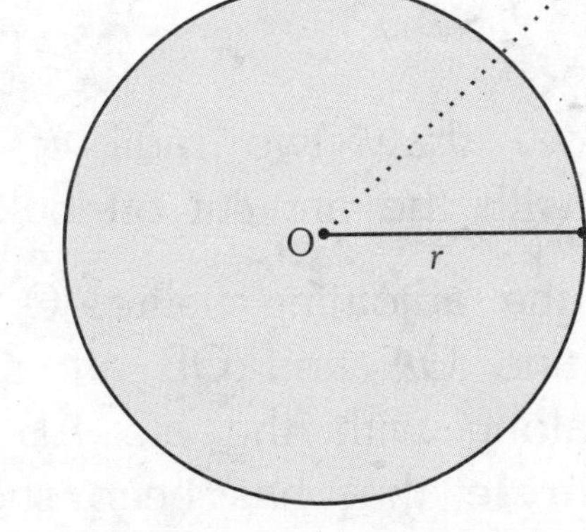

Given in front is a circle with centre O and radius r (OP). P is a point on the circle and Q is a point outside the circle.

The circumference of the circle marks its boundary. The plane of the circle enclosed inside this boundary is called the **interior** of the circle.

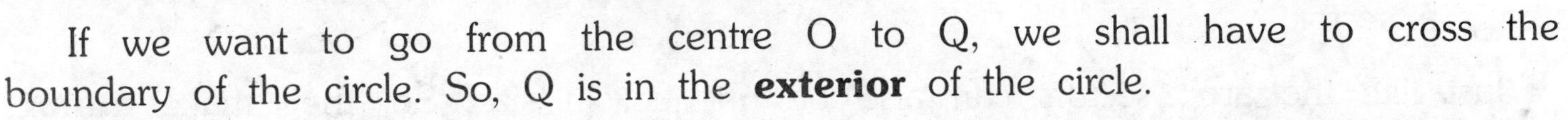

If we want to go from the centre O to Q, we shall have to cross the boundary of the circle. So, Q is in the **exterior** of the circle.

The *interior* of the circle and the *circle itself* together form the **circular region** of the circle.

CHORDS AND ARCS

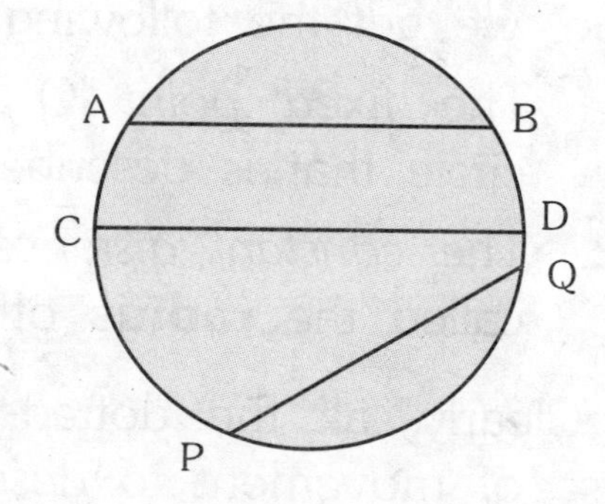

A *chord* of a circle is a line-segment that has its end-points on the circle.

In the figure in front, AB, CD and PQ are chords of the circle. Clearly, diameter CD is the longest of these three chords. So, **diameter is the longest chord in a circle.**

A chord divides the circumference of the circle into two parts. Each of these parts is called an **arc**.

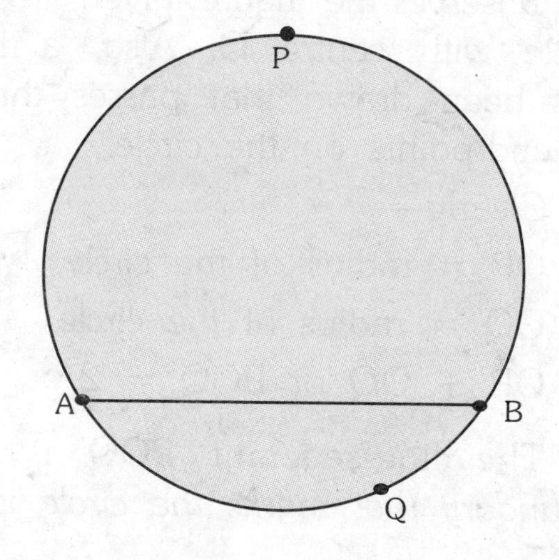

The circle given in front has a chord AB. It has divided the circumference into two parts. One part is smaller while the other is the larger. The smaller part is called the **minor arc** while the longer part is called the **major arc.** Clearly, points A, B are common to both the arcs. Also, A, B are used to name the chord AB. So, in order to distinguish between them. We use the symbol ($\frown$) for the arc. Thus—

We write the chord AB as **chord AB**

We write the arc AB as $\mathbf{\overset{\frown}{AB}}$

Moreover to distinguish between the minor and major arcs, we often take a point on either of the arcs and name them along with the points ; as—

In the above circle, *major arc AB* is written as $\overset{\frown}{APB}$ and the *minor arc AB* is written as $\overset{\frown}{AQB}$.

SECTOR

If we draw two radii of a circle, they enclose a part of the circle's interior along with the arc cut off by them. This part is called a **sector** of the circle.

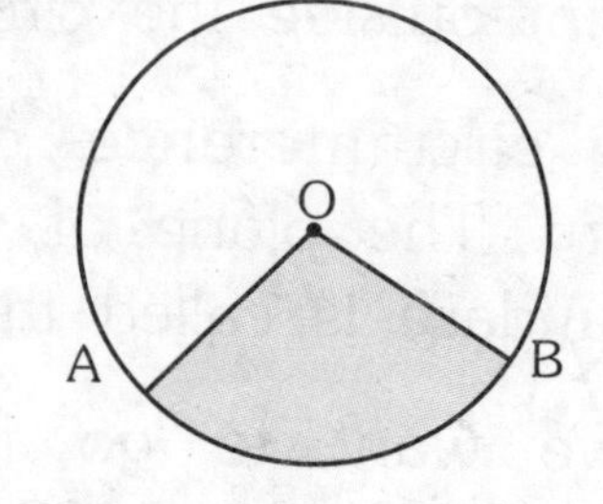

In the adjoining figure. O is the centre of the circle and OA and OB arc two radii. These two radii along with the arc AB enclose a **part of the circle** that has been shown in colour. This part is a *sector*.

Just like the arcs, sectors can also be unequal in size. So, they make **minor** and **major** *sectors.* In the adjoining figure, the coloured part is a *minor sector* while the uncoloured part is the *major sector* of the circle.

PRACTICE EXERCISES 44

A. Fill up each blank :

1. A circle is a perfectly round plane figure with its .... equidistant from a central point.
2. The centre of a circle is a point equidistant from all points on its ....
3. The radius of a circle is the .... joining its centre to any point on its circumference.
4. The diameter of a circle is the line-segment passing through its .... to join two points on its circumference.
5. A chord of a circle is a line-segment joining the ends of an .... of the same circle.
6. An arc of a circle is a part of the circumference cut off by the end-points of a .... of the same circle.
7. The circumference of a circle is the endless round curve that marks its .... *i.e.* separates its *interior* from its *exterior*.
8. A sector of a circle is a part of its .... cut off by any two radii of the same circle.

B. 9. The radious of a circle is 2·5 cm. Find its diameter.

10. The diameter of a circle is 7 cm. Find its radius.
11. Draw a circle on a sheet of paper. How will you find its centre by folding the sheet of paper.
12. Draw a circle with centre O. Take two points A and B inside the boundary of the circle join A and B. Does the line-segment AB lie in the *interior* of the circle ?
13. You have a one-rupee coin and a pencil with you. How will you draw a circle using them ?
14. Draw a circle and take two points P, Q outside its boundary. Join P and Q. Does the line-segment PQ lie in the *interior* or *exterior* of the circle ?
15. Draw a circle with radius = 2 cm. having its centre at O. With the same centre O, draw another circle with radius = 3 cm. What are the two circles called ?

16. What is meant by the *circular region* of a circle ?

17. With O as centre and radius equal to 2·5 cm. draw a semi-circle.

18. Draw a circle with radius 4 cm. Draw a chord AB dividing the circle into two unequal parts. Take two points on the circumference and name the *minor arc* as well as the *major arc.*

19. Draw a circle with radius 3·5 cm. Draw a diameter of the circle and measure it. What is its ratio to the radius of the circle.

20. Draw a circle with centre O and any radius. Draw a diameter POQ. Take two points A and B on one side of the diameter. Join both the points with P and Q. Measure ∠A and ∠B. What is their relation ?

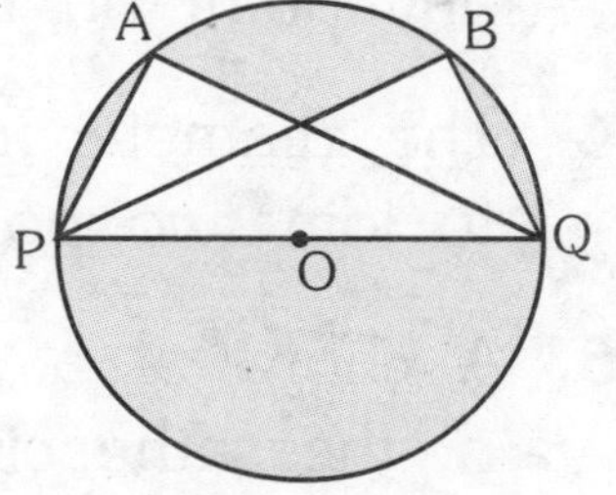

21. Draw a circle with centre O and any radius. Draw a diameter AOB and mark a point P on one side of it. Join it with the ends of the *diameter, i.e.* with A and B. Measure ∠P. Is it *acute, obtuse* or *right* ?

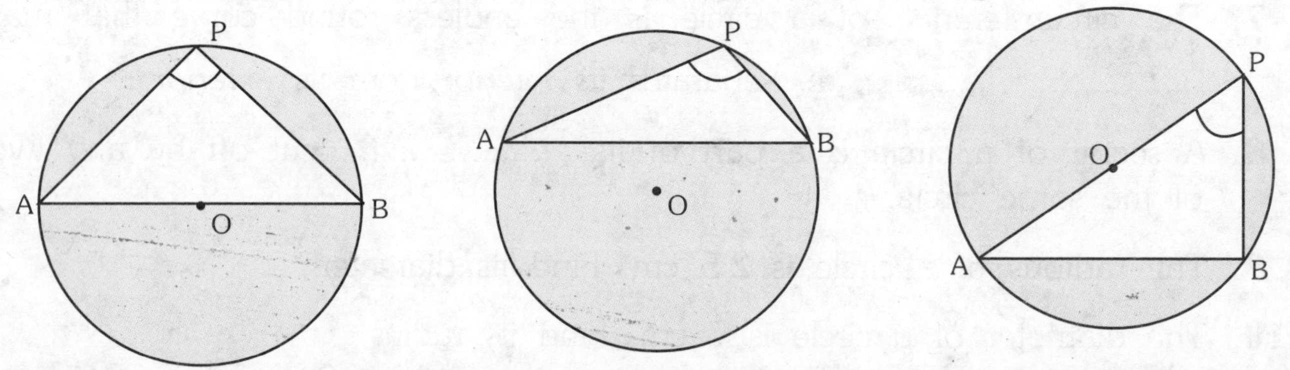

NOTE : The angle on a *semi-circle* is always a **right angle**. But and angle on a *minor arc* is an **obtuse angle** while an angle on a *major arc* is an **acute angle.**

22. Draw a circle with centre O and any radius. Draw a chord AB dividing the circumference into two unequal parts. Take a point P on the *minor arc* and join it with A and B. Is ∠P *acute, obtuse* or *right ?*

23. Draw a circle with centre O and any radius. Draw a chord AB dividing the circumference into two unequal parts. Take a point P on the *major arc* and join it with A an B. Is ∠P *acute, obtuse* or *right* ?

24. Draw any circle with any radius. Draw a diameter of this circle. Measure the diameter using a scale and the circumference using a thread. Find the relation between the diameter and the circumference.

(*Hint* : The circumference will be found to be a little more than 3 times the diameter.)

24 PRACTICAL GEOMETRY

KNOW THESE TERMS :

1. **ruler**—the measuring scale having *centimetres* and *inches* marked on it
2. **compasses**—a geometrical instrument used to draw circles
3. **hypotenuse**—the side of a rt. triangle opposite to the rt. angle
4. **altitude**—the side of a rt. triangle that is perpendicular to the other side

Teaching of practical geometry aims at teaching the methods of drawing accurate plane figures using the *given data*. This practice proves useful in various situations in life. In science and engineering, this knowledge proves very useful.

We use only **a ruler** and **compasses** in place of the protractor and the set squares to construct various figures. We can, however, use the protractor to verify the accuracy of the figures drawn using the ruler and the compasses.

A. BASIC CONSTRUCTIONS

We learnt some basic constructions in the previous classes. Let us review them.

CONSTRUCTION 1 : **To draw an angle of 60°.**

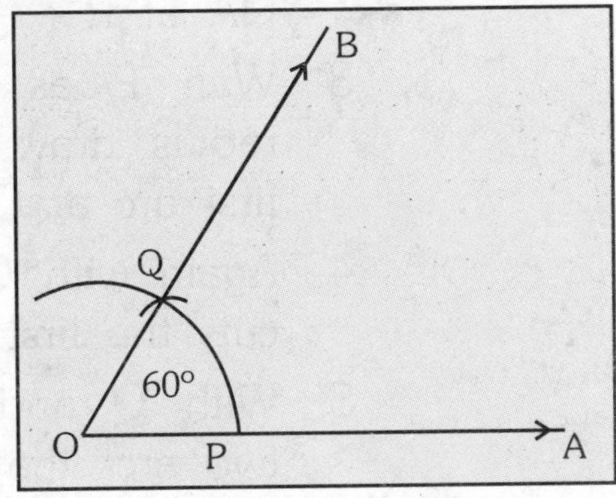

Steps :
1. Draw a ray OA.
2. With O as centre and a proper radius, draw an arc meeting OA at P.
3. With P as centre and the same radius, draw another arc that cuts the previous arc at Q.
4. Join OQ and produce it to make a ray OB

∠AOB is the required angle of 60°.

CONSTRUCTION 2 : **To draw an angle of 30°.**

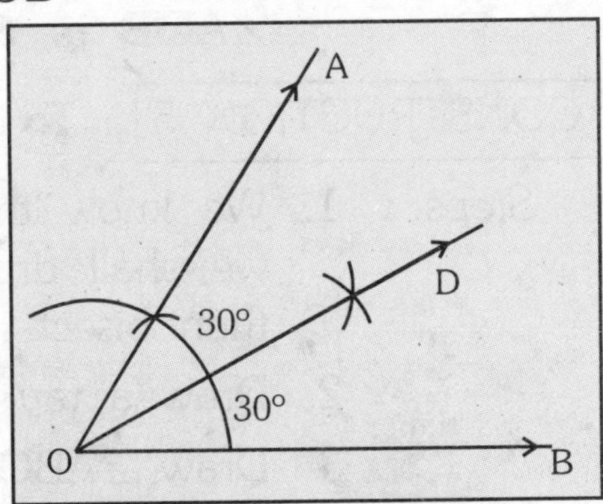

Steps :
1. We know that 30° = 60° ÷ 2. So, we shall draw an angle of 60° and then bisect it.
2. Draw ray OB.
3. Draw ∠AOB = 60° (*as in Const. 1*)
4. Draw its bisector OD.

∠DOB = 30° and also **∠AOD = 30°.**

CONSTRUCTION 3 : To draw an angle of 120°.

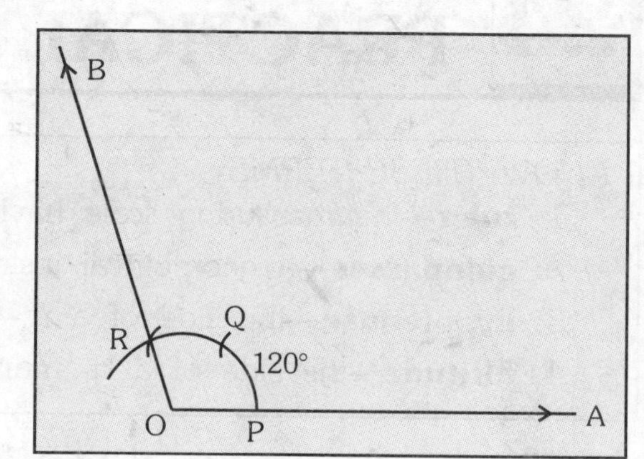

Steps :
1. Draw a ray OA as in the above example.
2. With O as centre and a proper radius, draw a big arc that meets OA at P.
3. With P as centre and the same radius draw an arc that cuts the previous big arc at Q.
4. Again with Q as centre and the same radius, draw another arc that cuts the big arc at R again.
5. Join OR and produce it into ray OB.

∠AOB is the required angle of 120°.

CONSTRUCTION 4 : To draw an angle of 90°.

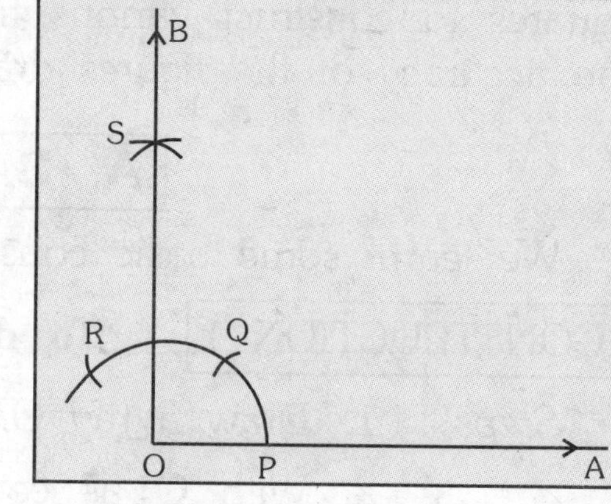

Steps :
1. Draw a ray OA.
2. With O as centre and a proper radius, draw an arc that meets OA at P.
3. With P as centre and the same radius draw an arc that cuts the first arc at Q.
4. Again with Q as centre and the same radius draw another arc that cuts the first arc at R again.
5. With Q and R as centres respectively and the same radius draw two arcs that cut each other at S.
6. Join OS and produce it to make ray OB.

∠AOB is the required angle of 90°.

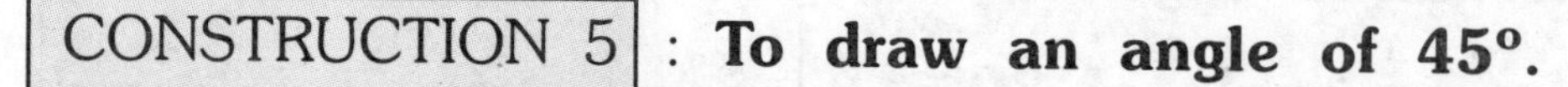

CONSTRUCTION 5 : To draw an angle of 45°.

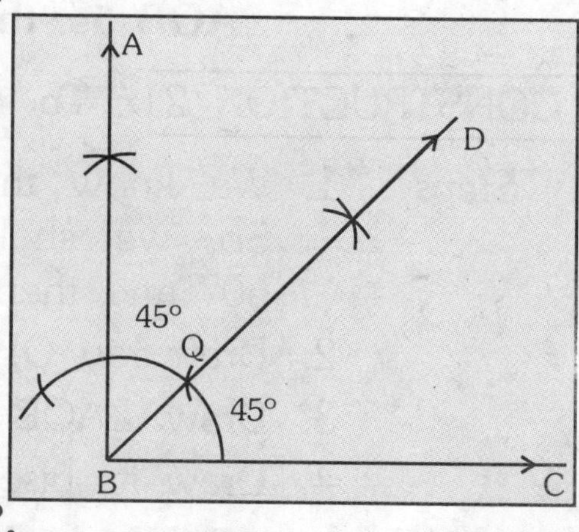

Steps :
1. We know that 45° = 90° ÷ 2. So, we shall draw an angle of 90° and then bisect it.
2. Draw a ray BC.
3. Draw ∠ABC = 90° (*as in Const. 4*)
4. Draw BD the bisector of ∠ABC

∠ABD = 45° and also **∠CBD = 45°.**

CONSTRUCTION 6 : To bisect an angle.

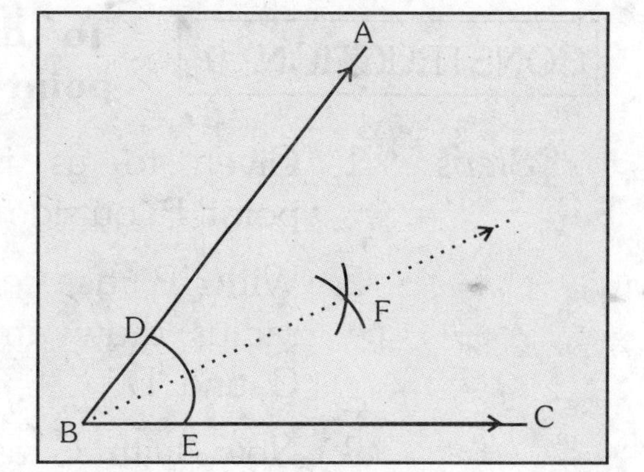

Steps :
1. Let ∠ABC be the given angle to be bisected.
2. With B as centre and a suitable radius draw an arc that meets BC at E and BA at D.
3. With D as centre and radius more than half DE draw an arc.
4. With E as centre and the same radius draw another arc that cuts the first arc at F.
5. Join BF and produce it.

The ray BF is the required bisector.

CONSTRUCTION 7 : To draw the rt. bisector of a line-segment.

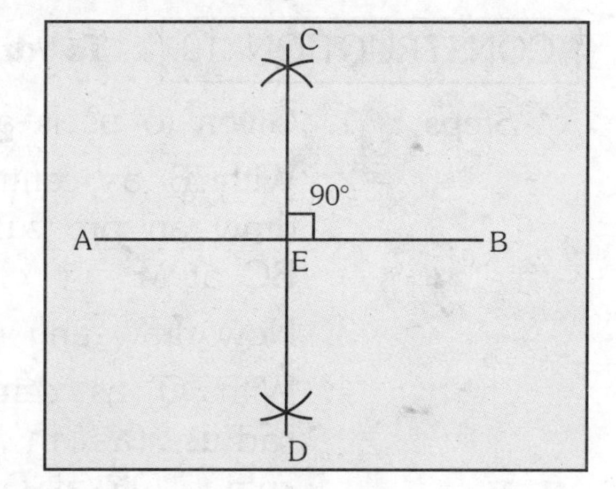

Steps :
1. Draw a line-segment AB = 5 cm.
2. With A as centre and radius more than half AB draw arcs on both sides of AB.
3. With B as centre and the same radius draw arcs on both sides of AB cutting the previous arcs in C and D respectively.
4. Join CD that will cut AB at E.

E bisects AB at rt. angles such that AE = BF

CONSTRUCTION 8 : To draw a perpendicular to a given line at a point on it.

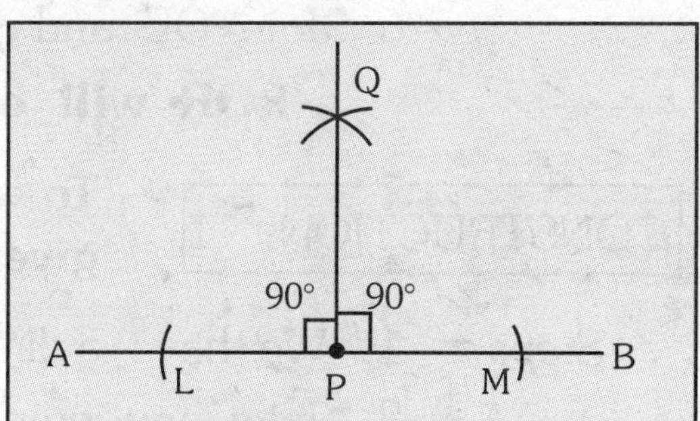

Steps :
1. Take a line AB and a point P on it.
2. With P as centre and a suitable radius, draw arcs that cut AB at L and M.
3. With L as centre and radius more than LP draw an arc.
4. With M as centre and the same radius draw another arc that cuts the previous arc at Q.
5. Join PQ and produce it. **QP is the required perpendicular**, *i.e.* QP is perpendicular to AB. Measure the angles QPA and QPB.

Each of them will be equal to 90°.

CONSTRUCTION 9 : **To draw a perpendicular to a given line from a point outside it.**

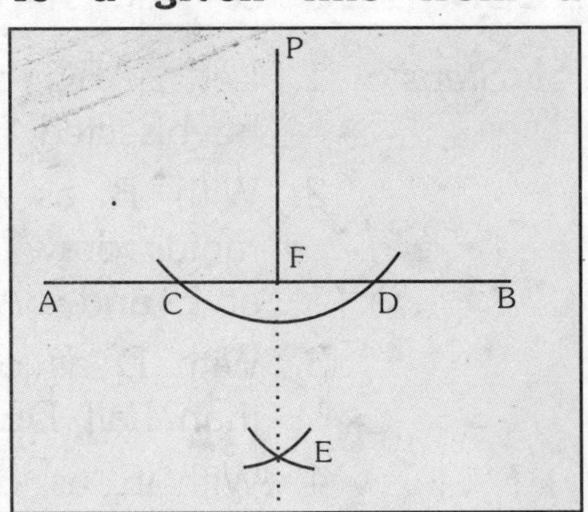

Steps :
1. Given to us is a line AB and a point P outside it.
2. With P as centre and a suitable radius draw an arc that cuts AB at C and D.
3. Now, with C as centre and a radius more than half CD draw an arc.
4. Again with D as centre and the same radius, draw another arc that cuts the previous arc at E.
5. Join PE that cuts AB at F.

Then PF is the required perpendicular.

CONSTRUCTION 10 : **To draw an angle equal to a given angle.**

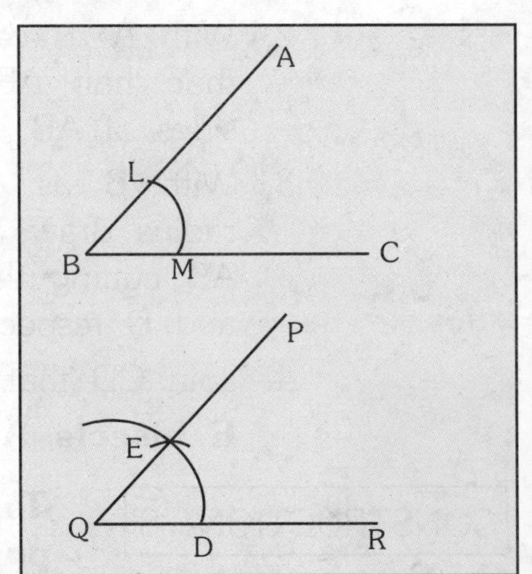

Steps :
1. Given to us is an angle ABC.
2. With B as centre and any radius, draw an arc cutting BA at L and BC at M.
3. Now draw any ray QR.
4. With Q as centre and the same radius (as in 2) draw an arc cutting QR at D.
5. With D as centre and radius equal to LM cut the above arc at E.
6. Join QE and produce it into ray QP.

∠PQR will be the required angle equal to ∠ABC.

CONSTRUCTION 11 : **To draw a line parallel to a given line through a given point.**

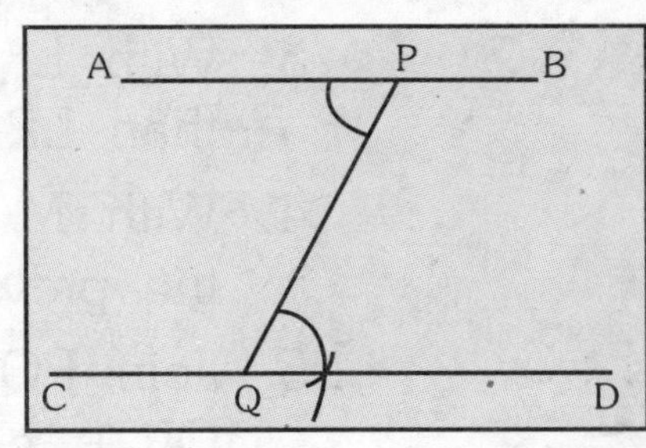

Steps :
1. We have a line AB and a point Q outside.
2. Take any point P on AB.
3. Join PQ.
4. Draw ∠PQD = alternate ∠QPA
5. Produce DQ to C to form line CD

CD is the required line parallel to AB.

B. CONSTRUCTION OF TRIANGLES

CONSTRUCTION 12 : **To draw a triangle whose three sides are given to be 4 cm., 5 cm. and 6 cm.**

Steps :
1. Draw a line-segment BC = 6 cm.
2. With B as centre and radius = 5 cm. draw an arc on one side of BC.
3. With C as centre and radius = 4 cm. draw another arc that cuts the first arc at A.
4. Join AB and AC. **Then Δ ABC is the reqd. triangle.**

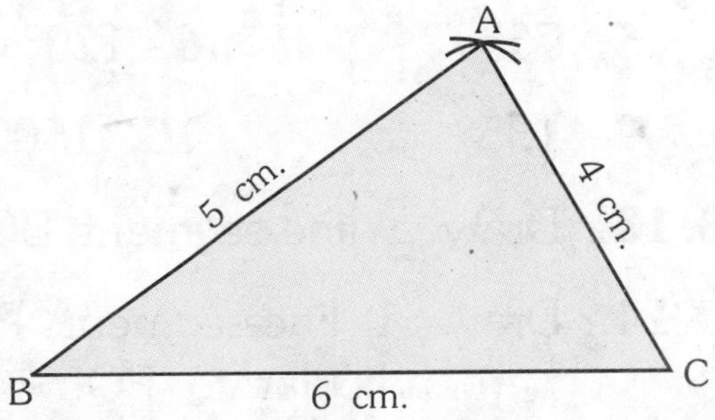

CONSTRUCTION 13 : **To construct a triangle whose two sides AB and BC arc 4 cm. and 6 cm. respectively and $\angle B = 60^\circ$.**

Steps :
1. Draw a line-segment BC = 6 cm.
2. At B draw $\angle CBX = 60^\circ$.
3. Out of BX, cut off BA = 4 cm.
4. Join AC. **Then ABC is the reqd. Δ.**

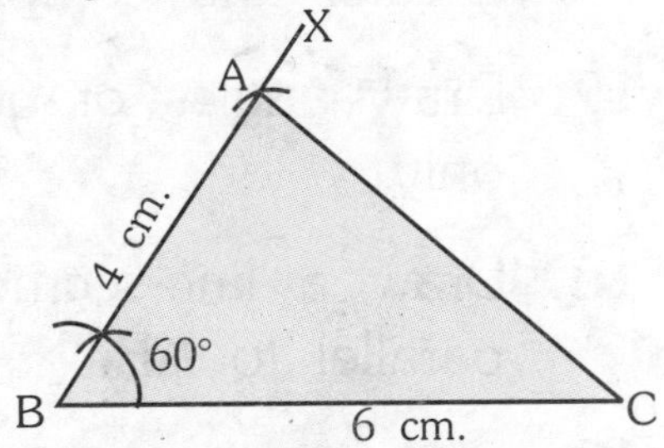

CONSTRUCTION 14 : **To construct a triangle whose base BC = 5 cm. $\angle B = 45^\circ$ and $\angle C = 60^\circ$.**

Steps :
1. Draw a line-segment BC = 5 cm.
2. At B, draw $\angle CBX = 45^\circ$.
3. At C draw $\angle BCY = 60^\circ$
4. Let BX and CY intersect at A.

Then ABC is the reqd. triangle.

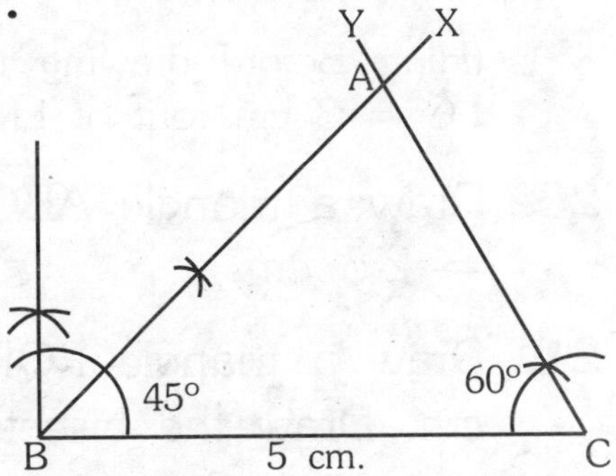

CONSTRUCTION 15 : **To construct a right triangle whose altitude BC = 3 cm. and base AB = 4 cm.**

Steps :
1. Draw a line-segement AB equal to the given base = 4 cm.
2. Draw BL perpendicular to AB at B
3. Out of BL, cut off BC equal to the given right arm= 3 cm.
4. Join AC.

ABC is the required rt. triangle.

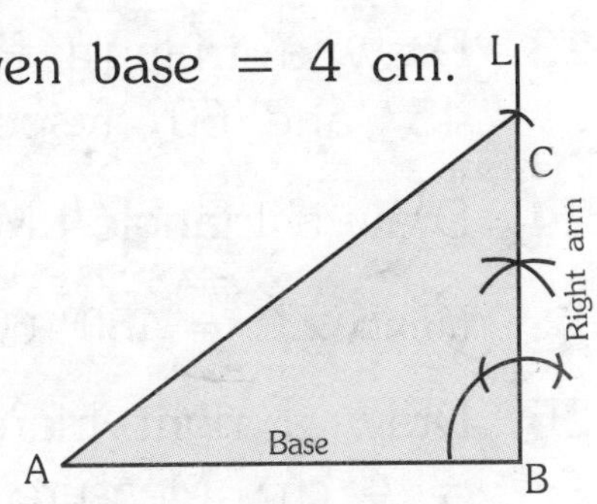

PRACTICE EXERCISES 45

A. Draw the following angles using a ruler and compasses :

1. 60°	**2.** 90°	**3.** 30°	**4.** 45°
5. 75°	**6.** 120°	**7.** $112{\cdot}5^\circ$	**8.** 120°
9. 135°	**10.** 150°	**11.** $22{\cdot}5^\circ$	**12.** $37{\cdot}5^\circ$

B. 13. Draw a line-segment BC = 5 cm. Draw its right-bisector.

14. Draw a line-segment PQ = 7 cm. Take a point L in it and draw LM perpendicular to PQ.

15. Draw a line-segment BC = 6·5 cm. take any point P outside it. Draw PQ perpendicular to BC that meets BC at Q.

16. Draw an angle of 75° using a protractor. Draw an angle equal to it using a ruler and compasses only.

17. Draw angles of 60° and 90° and bisect them using a ruler and compasses only.

18. Draw a line-segment AB = 8 cm. Using a ruler and compasses, draw PQ parallel to AB.

19. Draw a line-segment AB = 4 cm. Draw another line-segment CD parallel to it at a distance of 3 cm.

(*Hint.* Before drawing the parallel line-segment, draw LM perpendicular to AB. Cut off LC = 3 cm. out of LM. Then draw a line-segment parallel to AB through C.)

20. Draw a triangle ABC such that its side BC = 5 cm., AB = 4 cm. and AC = 2·5 cm.

21. Draw a triangle PQR such that QR = 5 cm., PQ = 4·5 cm. and PR = 6 cm. Draw the bisector of $\angle P$. Where does it meet the side QR ?

22. Draw a Δ ABC with $\angle A = 60^\circ$, AB = 5 cm. and AC 6 cm. Draw the right bisector of BC. Join its mid-point D with vertex A. How would you name AD.

23. Draw a triangle PQR whose base QR = 4 cm. and the two base angles 45° and 60° respectively.

24. Draw a triangle LMN whose base MN = 5·3 cm., $\angle M = 60^\circ$ and $\angle A = 75^\circ$

(*Hint.* $\angle C = 180^\circ - 60^\circ - 75^\circ = 45^\circ$)

25. Draw a right triangle ABC whose base BC = 3 cm. and the rt. arm CA = 4 cm. Measure the hypotenuse AB and check its length by calculation.

MISCELLANEOUS EXERCISES IV

A. Answer :

1. How many elements does a Δ have ? ....

2. Can a right triangle have two rt, ∠s ? ....

3. How many obtuse angles can a Δ have ? ....

4. What is the sum of the ∠s of a triangle ? ....

5. What is the sum of the ∠s of a quadrilateral ? ....

6. What do we call (a *triangle* + its *interior*) ? ....

7. What do we call (a *quadrilateral* + its *interior*) ? ....

8. What do we call (a *circle* + its *interior*) ? ....

B. Define—

9. a *scalene triangle* :

....

10. a *trapezium* :

....

11. a *rhombus* :

....

12. an *isosceles triangle* :

....

13. an *isosceles trapezium* :

....

14. *circumference* of a circle :

....

C. 15. Prove that an exterior angle of a triangle is equal to the sum of the two interior opposite angles.

16. Prove that the sum of the angles of a quadrilateral is equal to four right angles.

17. A triangle PQR has its side PQ = side PR. The bisectors of ∠Q and ∠R meet in O. If ∠P = 80° find the value of ∠ROQ.

18. A rt. triangle has its hypotenuse = 10 cm. and its base = 6 cm. Find its right-arm (altitude).

19. A ladder 5 metres long was set against a wall and it reached up to a vertical height of 4 metres. How far are its feet from the wall ?

20. In the figure given in front ABC and DBC are two isosceles Δs with a common base BC. If AD is joined, prove that—

(a) AD bisects $\angle A$ and $\angle D$ *(b)* $\angle ABD = \angle ACD$

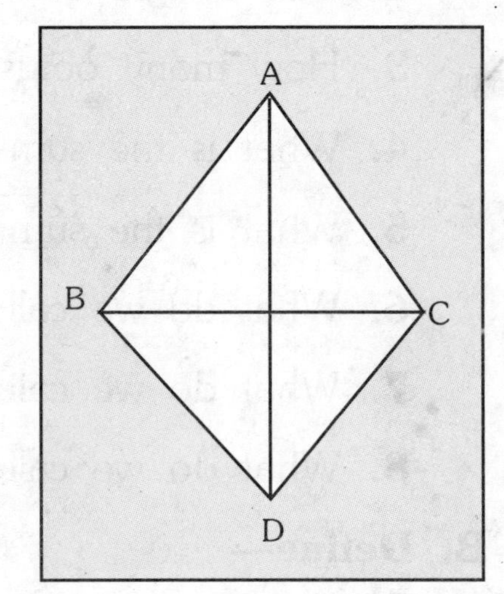

D. Explain the difference between :

21. a *concave quadrilateral* and a *convex quadrilateral.*

22. a *rhombus* and a *square.*

23. a *trapezium* and an *isosceles trapezium.*

E. Is it correct to say that—

24. a rhombus is an equilateral parallelogram ?

25. a square is an equilateral rectangle.

26. a square is a rt. $\angle$d rhombus.

27. a square is an equilateral and equiangular quadrileteral.

F. 28. Construct a triangle with sides 3 cm., 5 cm. and 7 cm. Find its *centroid.*

29. Construct a triangle ABC with its side BC = 5 cm., $\angle B = 45°$ and $\angle C = 60°$. Find its *orthocentre.*

30. Construct a triangle PQR with QR = 10 cm., PQ = 8 cm. and $\angle PQR = 60°$. Find its *incentre.*

MEMORABLE FACTS

1. The *hypotenuse* is the *longest side* in a rt. triangle.
2. The *perpendicular* is the *shortest distance* between a line and a point outside it.
3. The *square* on the hypotenuse of a rt. Δ = sum of the squares on the other two sides.
4. An acute-angled triangle has all its angles less than 90°.
5. **Any two sides** of a triangle are together *greater than* its **third side**.
6. The *medians* as well as *altitudes* of a triangle are **concurrent**.
7. **Centroid** is the point where *medians* of a triangle intersect.
8. **Orthocentre** is the point where *altitudes* of a triangle intersect.
9. **Circum-centre** is the point where *right bisectors of the sides* of a Δ intersect.
10. **In-centre** is a the point where *bisectors of the* $\angle$*s* of a Δ intersect.

UNIT V

MENSURATION AND STATISTICS

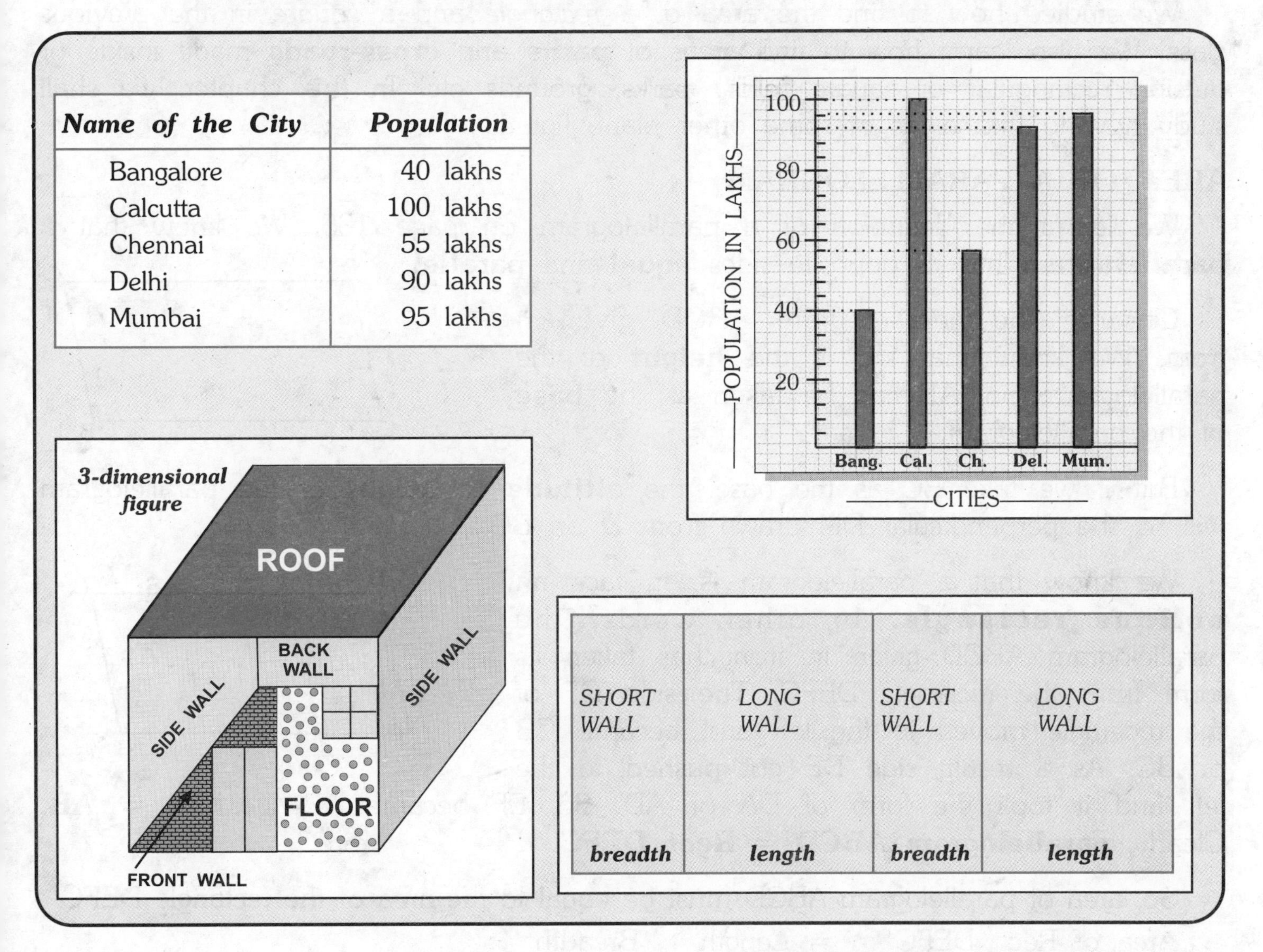

IN THIS UNIT—

25. Measurement of Area
26. Volume and Surface Area
27. Bar Graphs

25 MEASUREMENT OF AREA

KNOW THESE TERMS :

1. **oblique**—not vertical or horizontal but *slanting*
2. **corresponding**—in agreement with some *fact, part* or *position*
3. **inverse**—placed or stated in an *opposite order* or *condition*
4. **dimensions**—measurements, *i.e. length, breadth, height/depth* of a figure

We studied how to find the area of a *rectangle* and a *square* in the previous class. We also learnt how to find areas of **paths** and **cross-roads** made inside or outside rectangular or square fields, parks, grounds etc. In this chapter, we shall study how to find areas of some other plane figures.

AREA OF A PARALLELOGRAM

We learnt the definition of a parallelogram on page 185. We know that a **parallelogram** has its opposite sides **equal** and **parallel**.

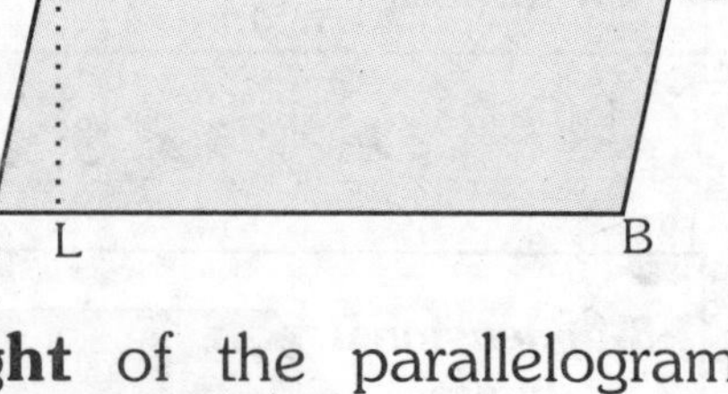

Observe the parallelogram ABCD given n front. We know that DL is the **height** of the parallelogram. So, AB can be taken as the **base** of the parallelogram.

But if we take BC as the base, the **altitude** or **height** of the parallelogram will be the perpendicular DM drawn from D on BC.

We know that a parallelogram is, in fact, an **oblique rectangle.** In other words, the parallelogram ABCD given in front has taken its form from the rectangle DEFC. The side CF of the rectangle moved to the left and became CB or BC. As a result, side DE got pushed to the left and it took the form of DA or AD. So, EF became AB, *i.e.* **EF = AB.** Clearly, **parallelogram ABCD = Rect DEFC.**

So, area of parallelogram ABCD must be equal to the area of the rectangle DEFC.

Area of Rect. DEFC = Length × Breadth

= EF × FC

= AB × FC (DE) $(\because EF = AB \text{ and } FC = DE)$

= **Base × height of the parallelogram**

∴ Area of a parallelogram = **Base × Height**

Inversely—

Base of a parallelogram = Area ÷ Height

Height of a parallelogram = Area ÷ Base

Let us now solve some examples :

Example 1 : Find the area of a parallelogram if its base = 15cm. and the corresponding altitude is 8 cm.

Solution : Base of the parallelogram = 15 cm.

Corresponding height = 8 cm.

∴ Area of the parallelogram = Base × Height

= (15 × 8) sq. cm. = **120 sq. cm.** *Ans.*

Example 2 : ABCD is a parallelogram whose longer side AB = 25cm. and the corresponding height is 16 cm. But its altitude corresponding to the shorter side is 20cm. Find the shorter side.

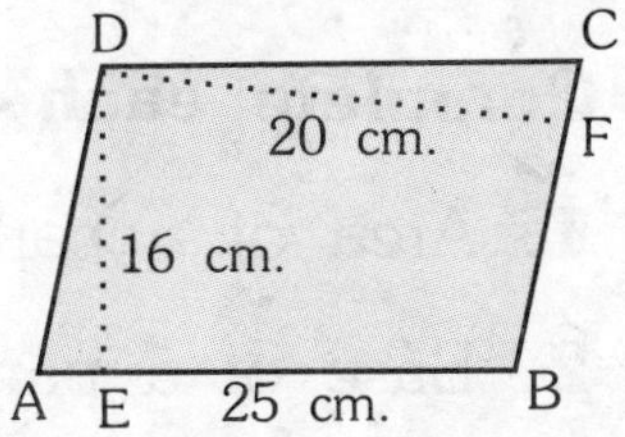

D C
20 cm. F
16 cm.
A E 25 cm. B

Solution : Longer side of the parallelogram = 25 cm.

Corresponding height = 16 cm.

∴ Its area = (25 × 16) sq. cm = 400 sq. cm

Now the altitude corresponding to the shorter side BC = 20 cm.

And Area = short side × corresponding altitude

or BC × DF = 400 sq. cm

or BC × 20cm. = 400 sq. cm (∵ BC =20 cm.)

∴ BC = (400 ÷ 20) sq. cm. = **20 cm.** *Ans.*

Example 3 : ABCD is parallelogram in which DE is drawn perpendicular to AB. Side AB = 20 cm. while side AD 13 cm. and its area = 240 sq. cm Find the length of AE.

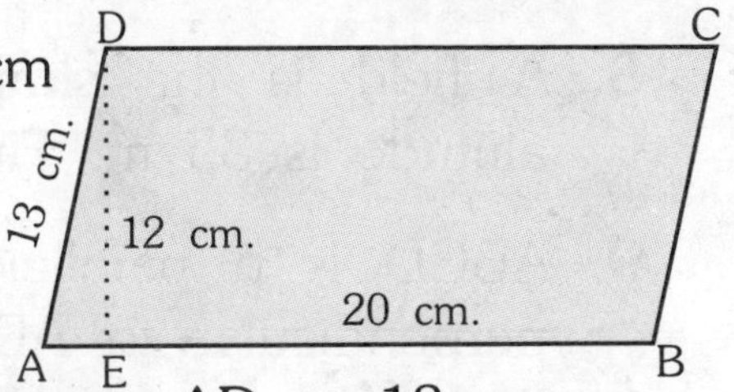

D C
13 cm.
12 cm.
20 cm.
A E B

Solution : Area of the parallelogram = 240 sq. cm

Side AB = 20 cm.

∴ Height DE = (240 ÷ 20) sq. cm.

= 12 cm.

Now Δ AED is a rt. Δ whose hypotenuse AD = 13 cm.

∴ $AE^2 = AD^2 - DE^2$ ....(*pythagorean theorem)*

$= (13)^2$ sq. cm. – $(12)^2$ sq. cm. = (169 – 144) sq. cm.

= 25 sq. cm. = $(5)^2$ sq. cm. or AE = **5 cm.** *Ans.*

Example 4 : PQRS is a parallelogram in which PL is perpendicular to QR and PM is perpendicular to RS. If QR=18 cm., RS=12 cm. and PM=9·3 cm., find PL.

Solution : PM is the height corresponding to the side RS

$\therefore$ Area = RS × PM
= 12 cm. × 9·3 cm.

Also, Area = QR × PL

or QR × PL = 12 cm. × 9·3 cm.

or 18 cm. × PL = 12 cm. × 9·3 cm. $(\because QR = 18 \text{ cm.})$

or PL $= \frac{12 \times 9 \cdot 3}{18}$ cm. = **6·2 cm.** *Ans.*

PRACTICE EXERCISE 46

A. Complete each statement :

1. Area of a parallelogram = ... × ....

2. Base of a parallelogram = ... ÷ ....

3. Height of a parallelogram = ... ÷ ....

B. 4. Find the area of a parallelogram whose base is 12 cm. and whose corresponding height is 45 cm.

5. Find the area of a parallelogram whose base = 8 cm. and altitude = 5·6 cm.

6. The area of a farm is 1 km.^{2} It is the shape of a parallelogram and it has a side equal to 5000 metres. Find its corresponding height.

7. Find the height of a parallelogram whose area is 43·5 m^2. and base is 15 dam.

8. A field is the shape of a parallelogram. It has a side 450 m and its altitude is 35 m. Find the cost of weeding it at 25 paise per square metre.

9. ABCD is a parallelogram in which CE is perpendicular to AB and BF is perpendicular to AD. If AB = 10 cm., AD = 9 cm. and CE = 8.1 cm., find BF.

10. ABCD is a parallelogram in which DL is perpendicular to AB and DM is perpendicular to BC. If AB = 18 cm. BC = 12 cm. and DL = 3·9 cm., find DM.

11. The longer side of a parallelogram and its corresponding altitude measure respectively 22·5 cm. and 16 cm. If the length of the altitude corresponding to its shorter side is 18 cm., find the length of the shorter side.

12. ABCD is a parallelogram in which DE is perpendicular to AB. If AB = 8 cm. and AD is 5 cm. and the area of the parallelogram is 24 cm^2, find AE.

13. A field is the shape of a parallelogram with its base equal to 260 m. and the corresponding height equal to 130 m. Find the cost of cultivating it at Rs 1·5 per 100 m^2.

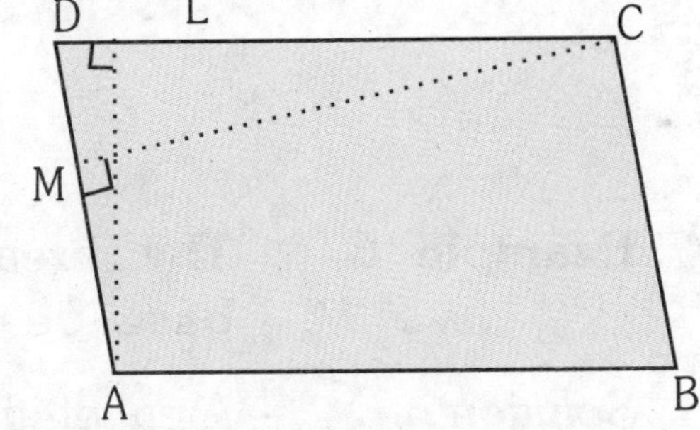

14. In the figure given in front, AL and CM are two perpendiculars drawn in the parallelogram ABCD. The area of the parallelogram is $21\frac{1}{3}$ cm^2. Find the lengths of AL and CM, if the sides of the parallelogram are 8 cm. and 5 cm.

15. The side of a rhombus is 6·5 cm. while its area is 26 cm^2. Find its altitude.

(*Hint* : A rhombus is also a parallelogram with all the four sides equal)

AREA OF A TRIANGLE

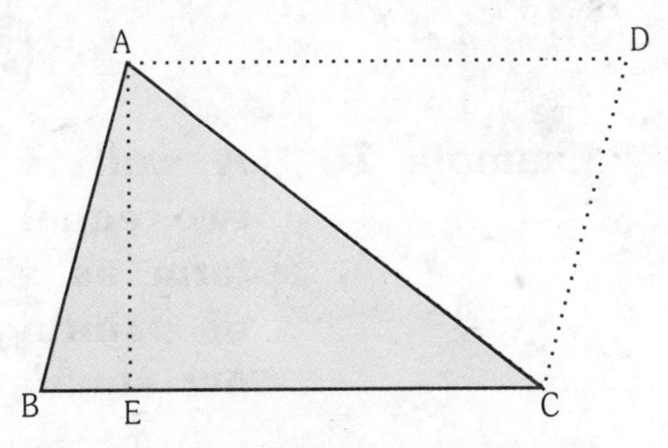

Observe the triangle ABC given in front. We see that BC is its base. If we draw a line through A parallel to BC and another line parallel to AB through C, they will intersect at a point. Let that point be D.

Clearly, ABCD is a parallelogram.

Let us draw AE perpendicular to BC. Then AE will be the height of the triangle.

$\because$ ABCD is a parallelogram

$\therefore$ AD = BC and CD = AB (*opp. sides of a* $\|^{gm}$),

In Δs ABC and ADC ; BC = AD, AB = CD and AC = AC

$\therefore$ Δ ABC $\cong$ Δ ACD (*SSS*)

$\therefore$ Δ ABC = Δ ACD or Δ ABC = $\frac{1}{2}$ $\times$ parallelogram ABCD

Now area of the parallelogram ABCD = Base $\times$ Height

Area of Δ ABC = $\frac{1}{2}$ **(Base × Height)**

Inversely, **Base of a Δ = (2 × Area) ÷ Height**

Height of a Δ = (2 × Area) ÷ Base

Example 5 : **Find the area of a triangle whose base is 16·5 cm. and height is 12·4 cm.**

Solution : Base of the Δ = 16·5 cm.

Height of the Δ = 12·4 cm.

$\therefore$ Area of the Δ $= \frac{1}{2} \times \text{Base} \times \text{Height} = \frac{1}{2} \times (16{\cdot}5 \times 12{\cdot}4)$ sq. cm

$= \frac{1}{2} \times \frac{165}{10} \times \frac{124}{10}$ sq. cm.

$= \frac{1023}{10}$ sq. cm. = **102·3 sq. cm.** *Ans.*

Example 6. **The area of a triangle is 584 sq. centrimetres. If its base be 36·5 cm. long, find its altitude.**

Solution : Area of the triangle = 584 sq. cm.

Its Base = 36·5 cm.

$\therefore$ Altitude = 2 × Area ÷ Base = (584 × 2) sq. cm. ÷ 36·5 cm.

$= \left(1168 \times \frac{10}{365}\right)$ cm. = **32 cm.** *Ans.*

Example 7. **A wall is 4·5 metres long and 3 metres high. It has two equal windows, each having its measurements and form as shown in the figure given front. Find the cost of painting the remaining wall at the rate of Rs. 15 per square metre.**

20 cm.

50 cm.

80 cm.

Solution : Length of the wall = 4·5 m

Height of the wall = 3 m

$\therefore$ Area of the wall = (4·5 × 3) sq. m

= **13·5 sq. m.**

Base of the window = 80 cm. $= \frac{4}{5}$ m

Right height of the window = 50 cm. $= \frac{1}{2}$ m

Area of its rectangular part $= \frac{4}{5} \times \frac{1}{2}$ sq. m. $= \mathbf{\frac{2}{5}}$ **sq. m.**

Area of its triangular part $= \frac{1}{2} \times \frac{20}{100} \times \frac{80}{100} = \mathbf{\frac{2}{25}}$ **sq. m.**

Total area of the window $= \left(\frac{2}{5} + \frac{2}{25}\right)$ sq. m $= \mathbf{\frac{12}{25}}$ **sq. m.**

Area of the two windows $= (\frac{12}{25} \times 2)$ sq. m $= \mathbf{\frac{24}{25}}$ **sq. m**

Area of the remaining wall $= (\frac{135}{10} - \frac{24}{25})$ sq. cm.

$= \frac{675 - 48}{50}$ sq. m $= \mathbf{\frac{627}{50}}$ **sq. cm.**

Cost of painting per sq. metre = Rs. 15

$\therefore$ Total cost of painting = Rs. $\frac{627 \times 15}{50}$ = Rs. $\frac{1881}{10}$ = **Rs 188·10** *Ans.*

AREA OF A TRAPEZIUM

Observe the trapezium ABCD given in front. Its sides AB and CD are parallel while its sides AD and BC are non-parallel.

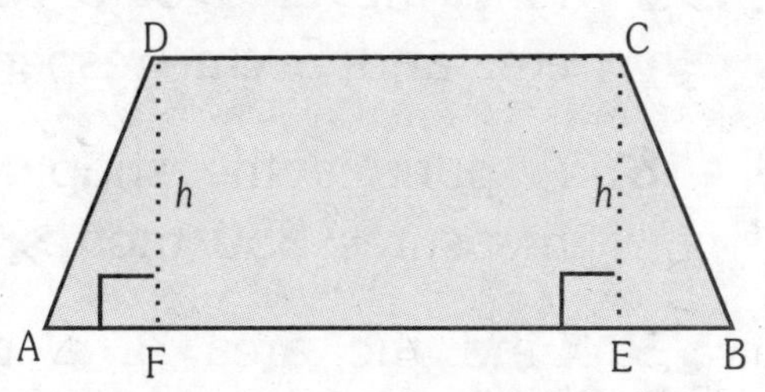

If we draw perpendiculars from C and D on AB, the trapezium will be divided into three parts as under :

Rt Δ DFA + Rect. DFEC + Rt. Δ CEB

Area of the trapezium = Areas of (Rt. Δ DFA + Rect DFEC + Rt. Δ CEB)

$= \frac{1}{2}$ (AF $\times$ DF) + (EF $\times$ DF) + $\frac{1}{2}$ (EB $\times$ CE)

$= \frac{1}{2}$ (AF $\times$ h) + (EF $\times$ h) + $\frac{1}{2}$ EB $\times$ h

$= \frac{1}{2}$ h (AF + 2EF + EB)

$= \frac{1}{2}$ h (AF + EF + EB + EF) $\quad$ ($\because$ *2EF = EF+EF)*

$= \frac{1}{2}$ h (AB + EF)

$= \frac{1}{2}$ h (AB + CD) $\quad$ ($\because$ *EF = CD)*

$= \frac{1}{2}$ h (sum of the parallel sides)

$\therefore$ **Area of a Trapezium** $=$ $\mathbf{\frac{1}{2}}$ **$\times$ height $\times$ (sum of the parallel sides)**

Inversely—

Height of a Trapezium = 2 $\times$ area $\div$ (sum of the parallel sides)

PRACTICE EXERCISES 47

A. Complete each statement :

1. Area of a triangle $= \frac{1}{2} \times$ .... $\times$ ....

2. Base of a triangle = (2 x ....) ÷ ....

3. Height of a triangle = (2 x ....) ÷ ....

4. Area of a trapezium $= \frac{1}{2} \times$ (........................ + ...)

5. Height of a trapezium = (2 × ....) ÷ ....

B. 6. Find the area of a triangle whose base is 7 cm. and height is 4 cm.

7. Find the area of a rt. triangle whose sides other than the hypotenuse are 20 cm. and 5 cm. respectively.

8. A park is the shape of a triangle. Its area is 25000 sq. metres. If its base measures 250 metres, find its altitude.

9. Find the area of a triangle whose base is 17·5 cm. and the corresponding altitude is 12·4 cm.

10. The area of a triangle is equal to that of a square having a side = 60 m. If the altitude of the triangle be 40 metres, find its base.

11. Find the area of a rt. triangle whose sides containing the right angle are 20·8 cm. and 14·7 cm. respectively.

12. Calculate the area of the coloured portion of the figure given below on the left after observing the dimensions.

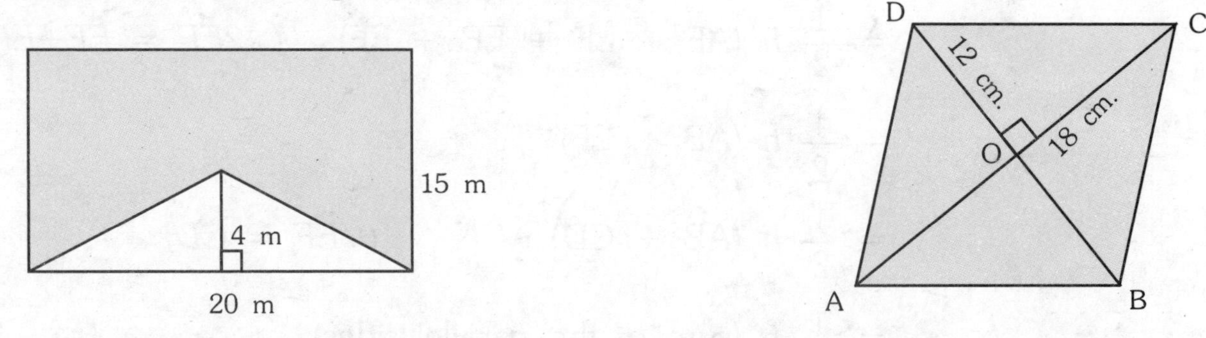

13. The diagonals of a rhombus are 12 cm and 8 cm respectively as shown in the figure given above on the right. Find its area.

(*Hint* : The diagonals have divided the rhombus into four equal rt. Δs.

Its area = 4 × area of any of these triangle (say COD)

$= 4 \times \frac{1}{2}$ CO × OD

$= 4 \times \frac{1}{2} \times \frac{1}{2} AC \times \frac{1}{2} BD$

$= 4 \times \frac{1}{2} \times \frac{1}{2} \times \frac{1}{2} \times AC \times BD = \frac{1}{2} AC = BD$

$= \frac{1}{2} \times$ **product of diagonals**

14. Find the area of a rhombus whose diagonals are 32 cm. and 48 cm. respectively.

15. Find the area of a kite of which the dimensions are as shown in front.

16. Find the area of a rhombus whose side is 5 cm. and of the longer diagonal is 8 cm.

Hint : $\because$ Diagonals of a rhombus bisect at rt. $\angle$s

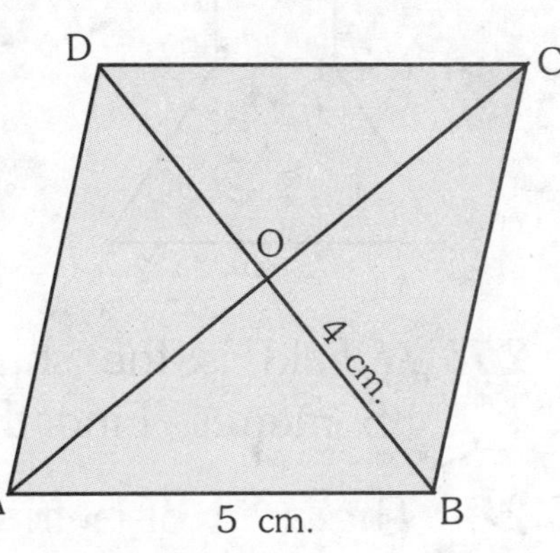

$\therefore$ In rt. Δ ABO

$AO = (\frac{1}{2} \times 8)$ cm. $= 4$ cm.

$AB = 5$ cm. ....*(hypotenuse)*

$\therefore BO^2 = 5^2 - 4^2 = 25 - 16 = 9 = 3^2$

$\therefore BO = 3$ cm. ; so $AC = 3 \times 2 = 6$ cm.

Now find the area of the rhombus.

17. Find the area of a trapezium whose parallel sides are 32 cm. and 20 cm. respectively and the distance between them is 15 cm.

18. The area of a trapezium is 475 cm^2 and the distance between its parallel sides is 19 cm. If one of the parallel sides is 27 cm. find the other.

19. An isosceles trapezium has its parallel sides equal to 25 cm. and 19 cm. respectively while each of its non-parallel sides is 5 cm. Find its area.

Hint : Clearly EF = 19 cm.

AE + FB = (25 – 19) cm. = 6 cm.

But AE = FB ......*(why ?)*

$\therefore AE = 6 \div 2 = 3$ cm.

Now $DE^2 = 5^2 - 3^2$ or $DE^2 = 16 = 4^2$ or DE = 4 cm.

Now find the area of the trapezium using its formula.

20. The area of a trapezium is 960 square centimetres. Its parallel sides are 34 cm. and 46 cm. respectively. Find its altitude.

C. Find the area of the coloured part in each figure :

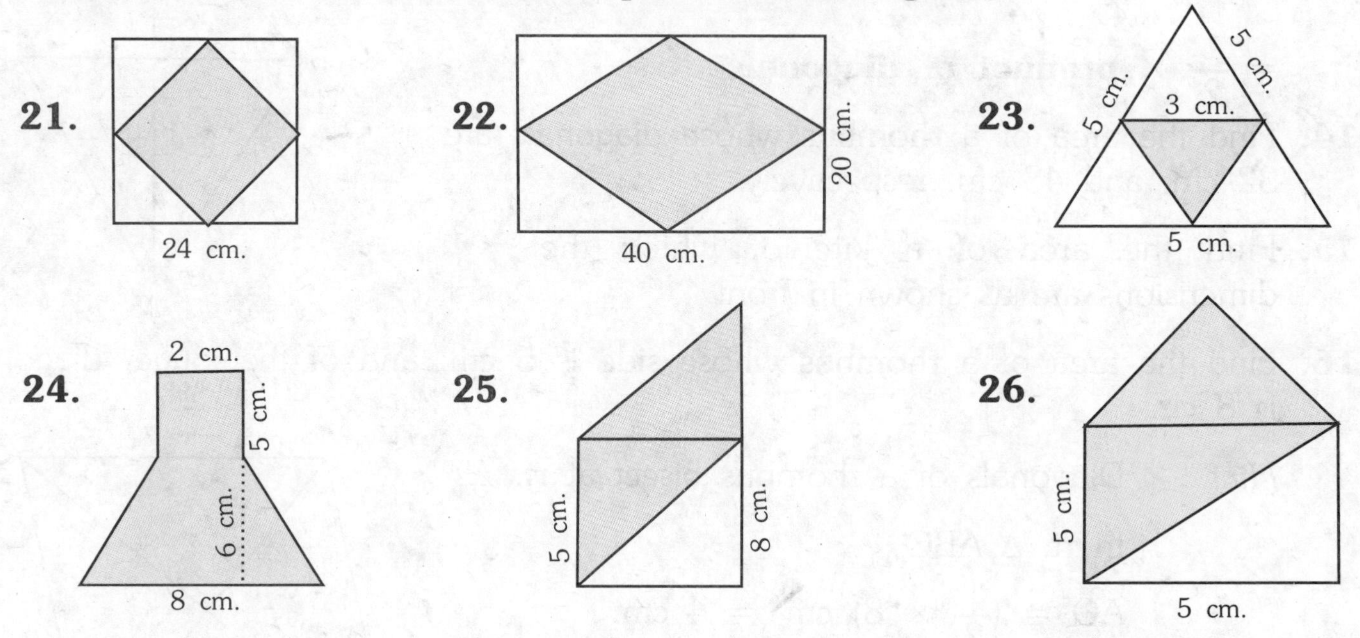

27. A field is the shape of a parallelogram. Its base is 45 metres and height is 35 metres. Find the cost of watering it at Re 1 per square metre.

28. The area of a triangle is 20·5 m^2. Find its base if its height is 5 metres.

29. Ratio between the lengths of the parallel sides of a trapezium is 2 : 3 and the distance between them is 15 cm. Its area is 600 cm^2. Find the lengths of its parallel sides.

30. The lengths of the parallel sides of an isosceles trapezium arc 36 cm. and 20 cm. respectively. Find the length of its non-parallel sides if it has an area = 168 sq. centimetres.

31. A trapezium has its sides as under :

(*a*) Parallel sides AB, CD = 10 cm., 20 cm.

(*b*) Non-parallel side AD = 15 cm.

(*c*) Non-parallel side BC = 15 cm.

Find its area.

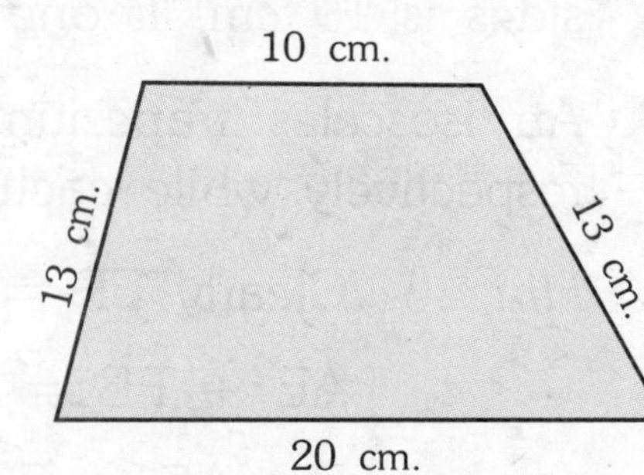

32. Given in front is a kite ABCD in which AC = 40 cm., AO = 28 cm. If DB = 24 cm. Find the area of the kite.

(*Hint* : The diagonals of a kite bisect at rt. ∠s)

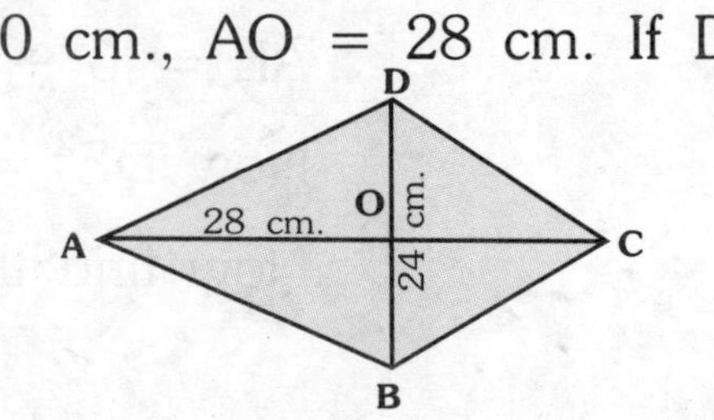

26 VOLUME AND SURFACE AREA

KNOW THESE TERMS :

1. **cuboid**—rectangular cube-shaped solid object
2. **volume**—total space occupied by a solid object
3. **vertex**—point where the three dimensions of a solid meet
4. **edge**—line along which two surfaces of a solid meet

VOLUME OF A CUBOID

A cuboid is a solid rectangle. Clearly—

(a) it has **six surfaces**—*bottom, top* and *four walls.*

(b) it has **eight vertices**—*four at the top* and *four at the bottom.*

(c) it has **twelve edges** in all.

(d) at **each vertex**, three dimensions—**length, breadth** and **height** meet to form it.

(e) **a** *cube* **is a cuboid with all its dimensions equal.**

We read about *cubes* and *cuboids* in the previous class. We also learnt how to calculate their volumes. The figures shown below show a *cuboid* and a *cube.*

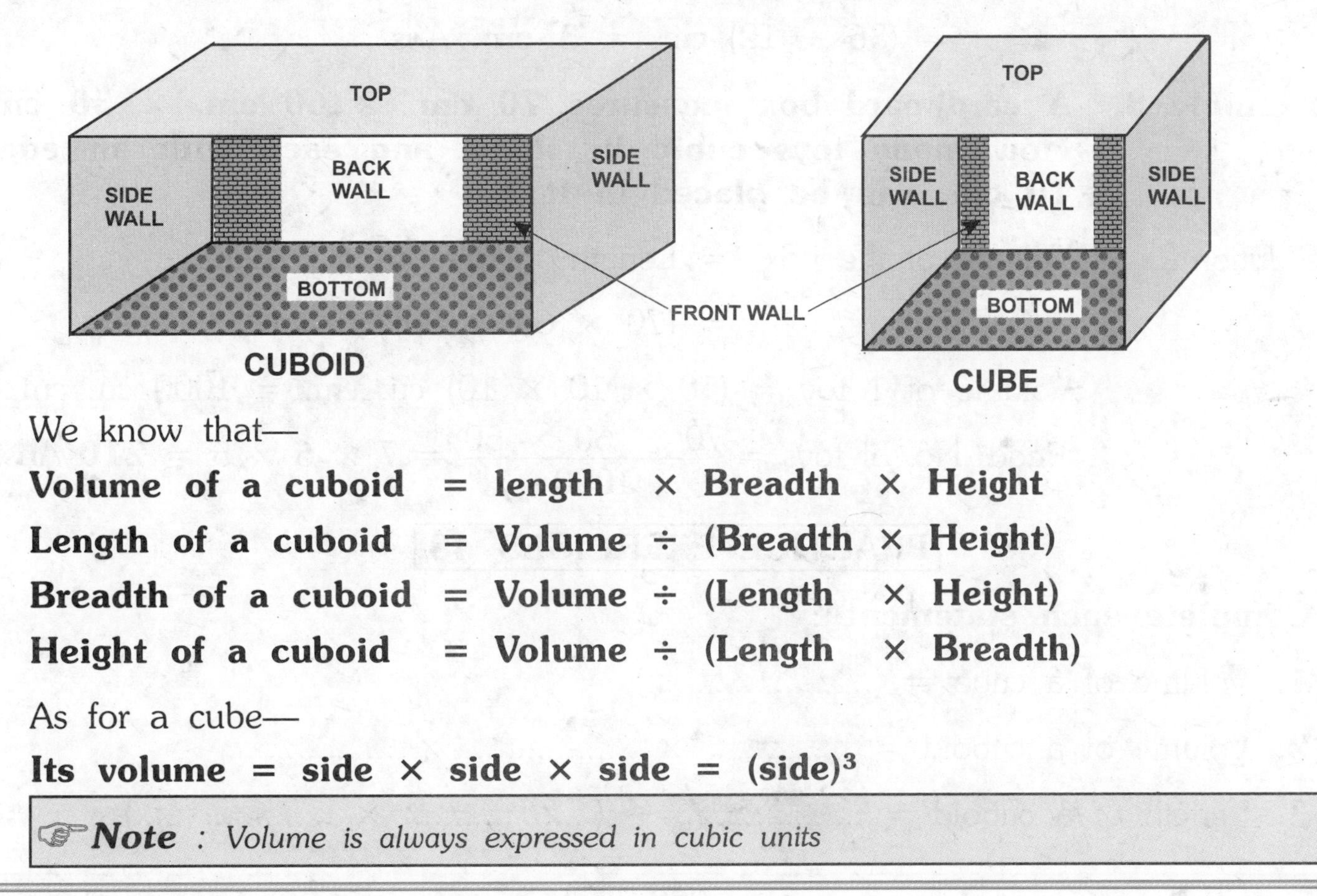

CUBOID

CUBE

We know that—

Volume of a cuboid = length × Breadth × Height

Length of a cuboid = Volume ÷ (Breadth × Height)

Breadth of a cuboid = Volume ÷ (Length × Height)

Height of a cuboid = Volume ÷ (Length × Breadth)

As for a cube—

Its volume = side × side × side = (side)^3

☞ **Note** : *Volume is always expressed in cubic units*

Let us solve some examples :

Example 1. Find the volume of a cuboid whose length = 10 cm., breadth = 8 cm. and height = 2·5 cm.

Solution : Length of the cuboid = 10 cm.

Breadth of the cuboid = 8 cm.

Height of the cuboid = 2·5 cm.

$\therefore$ Its volume = (10 × 8 × 2·5) cu. cm.

$= (10 \times 8 \times \frac{25}{10})$ cu. cm. = **200 cu. cm** *Ans.*

Example 2. A cuboid wooden block has a volume of 36 cu. cm. It is 4 cm. long and 3 cm. wide. How high is it ?

Solution : Volume of the wooden block = 36 cu. cm.

Length of the block = 4 cm.

Breadth of the block = 3 cm.

Height = Volume ÷ (Length × Breadth)

= 36 cu. cm. ÷ (4 × 3) sq. cm.

= (36 ÷ 12) cm. = **3 cm.** *Ans.*

Example 3. A cardboard box measures 70 cm. × 60 cm. × 50 cm. How many toys cubic in shape and each with an edge 10 cm. can be placed in it ?

Solution : Volume of the box = Length × Breadth × Height

= (70 × 60 × 50) cu. cm.

Volume of 1 toy = (10 × 10 × 10) cu. cm. = 1000 cu. cm.

$\therefore$ Reqd. No. of toys $= \frac{70 \times 60 \times 50}{1000} = 7 \times 6 \times 5 =$ **210** *Ans.*

PRACTICE EXERCISES 48

A. Complete each statement :

1. Volume of a cube = (......................)

2. Volume of a cuboid = ... × .... × ....

3. Length of a cuboid = ... ÷ (................. × ....)

4. Breadth of a cuboid = ... ÷ (.................. × ....)

5. Height of a cuboid = ... ÷ (.................. × ....)

B. 6. Find the volume of a wooden block whose length is 10 cm., breadth is 5 cm. and height is 3 cm.

7. How many cubes each with an edge of 5 cm. can be obtained from a bigger cube with an edge 20 cm. long ?

8. There are two cubes with edges 3 cm. and 6 cm. respectively. What is the ratio between their volumes ?

9. A rectangular block of ice is 30 cm. long 20 cm. wide and 10 cm. high. Find its weight if ice weighs $\frac{9}{10}$ of the weight of the same volume of water and 1 cm^3 of water weighs 1 gram.

10. A swimming pool is 150 m. long, 75 m wide and 10 m deep. How much water can it hold if it is full to the brim ?

11. A box is 54 cm. × 45 cm. × 30 cm. How many soap-cakes can be placed in it if each cake is 9 cm. × 5 cm. × 3 cm. ?

12. A chalk-box is cubical in shape and its edge is 12 cm. long. How many chalk-sticks can it hold if each stick needs 19·2 cm^3 of space ?

13. A water-tank is 30 m long, 15 m wide and 10 m high. How much water can it hold, If 100 cm^3 of water = 1 litre ?

14. A wooden block measures 80 cm. × 70 cm. × 60 cm. It was cut into 336 cubes. Find the edge of the cube.

15. The internal measurements of a box are 22 cm. × 17 cm. × 12 cm. If the thickness of the material of which it is made is 2 cm. How much material has been used to make it ?

16. Find the volume of a cube whose one face has an area of 81 cm^2.

17. A tank has its dimensions to be 30 m, 15 m and 10 m respectively. How much water can it hold ?

18. The length, breadth and height of a room are 5 m, 4·5 m and 3·5 m respectively. Find its volume and the cost of paving its floor at Rs. 10 per square metre.

19. A rectangular room is thrice as long as it is wide. It can contain 60 cubic metre of air. Find its length, breadth and the cost of plastering its floor at Rs 10 per square metre, if its height is 5 metres.

AREA OF FOUR WALLS

Observe the figures given below. On the left is the figure of a *box* that resembles a **room**. On the right is shown as if this *box* (room) has been opened up along a corner and spread out to take the shape of a rectangle (ABCD).

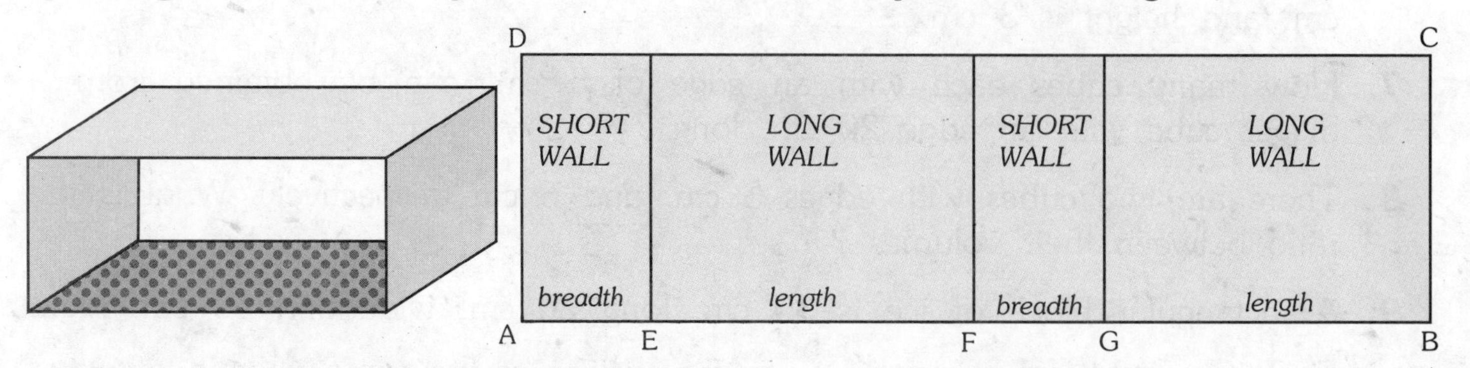

Clearly, if we want to find the surface-area of the walls of the box (room), we shall have to find the area of this rectangle. We can easily follow that—

1. AE is the **breadth** of the room.
2. EF is the **length** of the room.
3. FG is the **breadth** of the room.
4. GB is the **length** of the room.

So, AB, the **length** of the rectangle = 2 lengths + 2 breadths = **2 (*l* + *b*)**

BC, **the breadth** of the rectangle = **height** of the room

Area of the rectangle = AB × BC = **height × 2 × (*l* + *b*)**

∴ **Area of the four walls of a room = Height × 2 (length + Breadth)**

☞ *Remember that if walls are to be plastered, the areas of the doors and windows in it, if any, have to be* ***subtracted*** *from the total area of the walls.*

Let us now solve some examples :

Example 1. Find the area of the four walls of a class-room that is 11 m long, 8m wide and 4m high including all its windows and doors. Find the cost of white-washing it at Rs. 3 per square metre.

Solution : Length of the class-room = 11 m

Breadth of the class-room = 8 m

Height of the class-room = 4 m

Area of its four walls = 2 × (Length + Breadth) × Height

= 2 × (11 m + 8 m) × 4 sq. m

= 38 × 4 = **152 sq. m**

Cost of white-washing per sq. metre = Rs. 3

∴ Total cost of white-washing = Rs. 3 × 152 = **Rs. 456** *Ans.*

Example 2. Find the cost of plastering the walls and the bed of a swimming pool that is 5 metres long, 4 metres wide and 3 metres deep at the rate of Rs. 12 per square metre.

Solution : Length of the swimming pool = 5 m

Width of the swimming pool = 4 m

Depth of the swimming pool = 3 m

∴ area of its floor = Length × Breadth

= 5 m × 4 m = **20 sq. m.**

Area of the four-walls = Height × 2 (length + Breadth)

= 3 m × 2 × (5 m + 4 m)

= 6 m × 9 m = **54 sq. m.**

Total area to be plastered = (20 + 54) sq. m. = 74 sq. m.

Cost of plastering per square metre = Rs. 12

∴ Total cost of plastering = Rs. 12 × 74 = **Rs. 888** *Ans.*

SURFACE AREA OF A CUBOID

We learnt in the previous class that the **surface area of a cuboid**.

= 2 (length × breadth) + 2 (length × height) + 2 (breadth × height)

= **2 (*lb* + *lh* + *bh*)**

Example 3. Find the surface area of a cuboidal wooden box with dimensions 30 cm., 20 cm. and 15 cm. respectively. Find the cost of painting it at Rs. 4 per 100 sq. cm.

Solution : Length of the box = 30 cm.

Breadth of the box = 20 cm.

Height of the box = 15 cm.

∴ Its surface area = 2 ($lb + lh + bh$)

= 2 [(30 × 20) + (30 × 15) + (20 × 15)] sq. cm.

= 2 (600 + 450 + 300) sq. cm. = 2700 sq. cm.

Cost of painting per 100 sq. cm. = Rs. 4

∴ Total cost of painting = Rs. 4 × $\frac{2700}{100}$ = **Rs. 108** *Ans.*

PRACTICE EXERCISES 49

A. Complete each statement :

1. Area of the four walls = height × 2 × (................. + ...)

2. Surface area of a cuboid = 2 (............. + ... + ...)

B. 3. Find the surface-area of a cuboidal block of wood whose length is 10 cm, width 8 cm and height 5 cm.

4. A cuboidal tin is 50 cm × 40 cm × 30 cm. How much tin-sheet shall be needed to make 30 such tins. Find their cost at Rs. 10 per square metre.

5. Find the surface area of a cube that has an edge equal to 9 cm.

6. Find the total surface-area of a cuboid whose length is 6 cm. breadth is 5 cm. and height is 4 cm.

7. Find the surface area of a block that has its length and breadth in the ratio 3 : 2 if the area of one of its faces is 54 square m. and height is 2 m.

8. A room is 6 metres long, 5 metres broad and 4 metres high. It has one door 2 metres × 1·25 metres and two windows 1·25 metres × 1 metre. Find the cost of covering the walls of the room with a paper-strip 75 cm. wide at the rate of Rs. 2·50 per metre.

9. The volume of a cube is 729 cubic metres. Find its total surface area.

10. Find the ratio between the surface areas of a 6 m cube and of a cuboid 4 m × 3 m × 2·5 m.

11. A match-box is 5 cm × 3 cm × 2 cm. How many match-boxes can be contained in a box 60 cm × 40 cm × 30 cm. ?

12. A wall is 42 metres long and 4 metres high. Find the thickness of the wall if its total volume is 6·72 cubic metres.

13. The perimeter of a room is 144 metres and its height is 3·5 metres. Find the cost of plastering its walls at Rs. 15 per square metre.

14. The dimensions of a class-room are 8 m × 5 m × 3 m. How many desks can be placed in it if each desk requires 200 cm × 100 cm × 75 cm space ?

15. The volume of a cuboid is equal to the volume of a cube that has an edge 24 cm long. If the cuboid is 24 cm broad and 6 cm. high, what is its length ?

27 BAR GRAPHS

KNOW THESE TERMS :
1. **pictograph**—a pictorial symbol of an object used to make a graph
2. **bar**—a rectangle of uniform width drawn vertically/horizontally in a bar graph
3. **horizontal axis**—axis of a graph that is drawn from east to west
4. **vertical axis**—axis of a graph that is drawn from north to south

We learnt in the previous class how to draw bar graphs to show some given data. We know that—

1. We can show numerical data in two ways—through **pictographs** and through **bars**.
2. Bars are rectangles of uniform width.
3. Bars can be *vertical* or *horizontal*.
4. Representation of data through bars is called a **bar graph**.
5. Information can be easily understood from bar graphs.

Let us have some examples.

Example 1. The number of candidates for IAS Examination in six consecutive years was as shown in the following table. Construct a bar graph to show this data.

Year	*First year*	*Second year*	*Third year*	*4th year*	*Fifth year*	*Sixth year*
Number of candidates	80	110	140	160	180	210

Solution : Take the following steps to draw the graph :

Steps : 1. On a graph paper, draw two lines perpendicular to each other. They are called **vertical axis** and **horizontal axis**.

2. Along the *horizontal axis*, we mark years—I, II, III, IV, V, VI, at equal distances.

3. Along the vertical axis, we mark a scale to show the No. of candidates. The scale

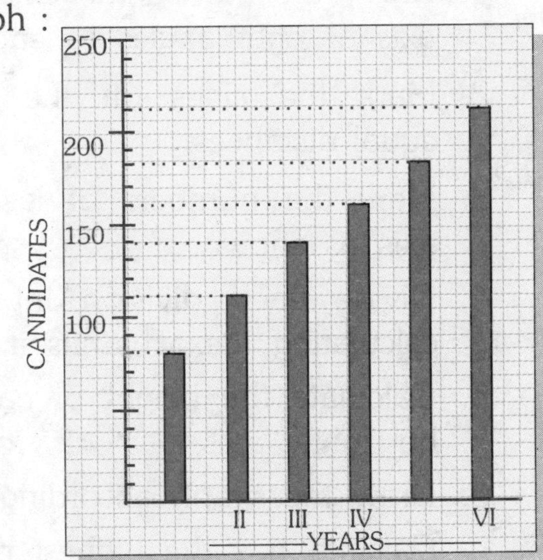

shows 50, 100, 150, 200, 250 marks at regular distances. Each division has marks to show the sub-divisions of the big division.

4. We calculate the heights according to the varying number of candidates and draw dotted lines parallel to the horizontal axis.
5. We draw six vertical graphs of equal width to reach the calculated heights marked by dotted lines.

Precautions :

1. Don't forget to mention what is shown on the *horizontal axis* and what on the *vertical axis.*
2. To make the bars attractive you can shade it or even colour it.
3. Bar graphs can be constructed on plain paper by choosing a suitable school.
4. Every mark on the horizontal axis and on the vertical axis should be supported by indicative terms (words or numbers).
5. If the calculation of heights happens to be in inexact numbers of units, use *observation* and *approximation* to draw the bar.

Example 2. The population of five major cities of India in 1991 was as given below :

Construct a bar graph to show the information given in the table. Also, write which city has the largest population and which the lowest.

City	*Population*
Bangalore	40 lakhs
Calcutta	100 lakhs
Chennai	55 lakhs
Delhi	90 lakhs
Mumbai	95 lakhs

Solution : Take the following steps to draw the graph :

1. Draw the *horizontal* axis and the *vertical axis* at right angles to each other.
2. Mark the cities on the horizontal axis at equal distances.
3. Mark the numbers of lakhs on the vertical axis as shown.
4. Divide each division into sub-divisions for calculating inexact units if any..

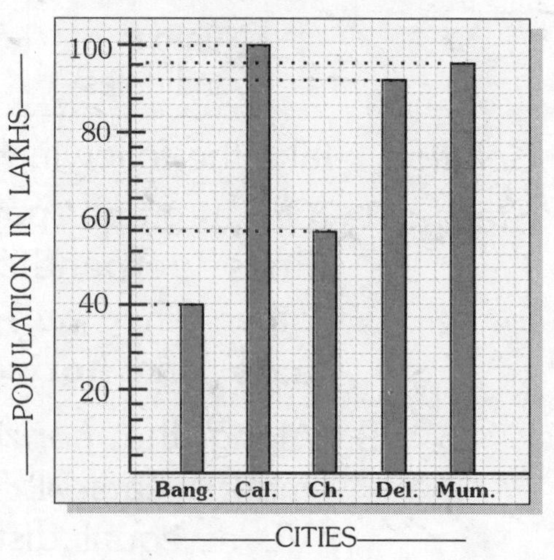

5. Calculate the height of each population and draw dotted lines parallel to the horizontal axis.
6. Draw the graph according to the dotted lines.

Calcutta has the highest population while Bangalore has the lowest.

PRACTICE EXERCISES 50

1. A gardener was to plant saplings for a royal garden. He worked for five consecutive weeks and did the planting as shown in the table given below.

Week	*I*	*II*	*III*	*IV*	*V*
No. of Saplings Planted	800	1000	1100	1200	1400

Construct a graph representing the above data. Write the steps also.

2. The Delhi Government spent the money in crore as shown in the table given below on education. It shows the expenditure for the six five-year plans.

Five-year Plan	*Expenditure in crores*
I	7 crores
II	14 crores
III	25 crores
IV	35 crores
V	55 crores
VI	90 crores

Construct a bar graph to show the data given above and write the steps.

3. A scooter factory was asked to produce 5000 scooters for export. IT employed its workers who worked for five consecutive weeks and prepared scooters as per the table given below :

Weeks	*I*	*II*	*III*	*IV*	*V*
No. of Scooters	800	1000	1000	1100	1100

Construct a bar-graph to show this data write the steps you take.

4. The expenditure of a school during a year on various items is shown in the table below :

Items	*Expenditure in Rupees*
Salaries	11 lakhs
Transport	4 lakhs
Boarding House	6 lakhs
Purchase	5 lakhs
Maintenance	3 lakhs
Miscellaneous	2 lakhs

Construct a bar-graph to represent the date given above. Also mention the steps.

MISCELLANEOUS EXERCISES V

A. Complete each statement :

1. A parallelogram is an .... rectangle.

2. A rhombus is an oblique ....

3. A trapezium has its two opposite sides parallel and ....

4. An isosceles trapezium has its .... sides equal to each other.

5. The diagonals of a .... and a .... intersect each other at right angles.

6. A cuboid has .... surfaces, ... vertices and .... edges.

7. A cube is a cuboid with all its dimensions ....

8. A pictograph is a pictorial symbol of an object used in drawing a ....

9. A bar is a .... of uniform width drawn vertically or .... in a bar graph.

10. A horizontal axis is drawn from .... to .... But a .... axis is drawn from south to north.

B. 11. PQRS is a parallelogram in which SL is drawn perpendicular to PQ. Its side PQ = 20 cm., the side QR = 13 cm. and the area of the parallelogram is 240 cm^2 Find the length of PL.

12. ABCD is a parallelogram in which DL is perpendicular to AB and DM is perpendicular to BC. If AB = 18 cm., BC = 12 cm. and DL 6·2 cm. find DM.

13. A wall is 9 metres long and 3 metres high. It has two equal windows each having its measurements and form as shown in the figure given in front. Find the cost of painting the remaining wall at Rs. 12 per square metre.

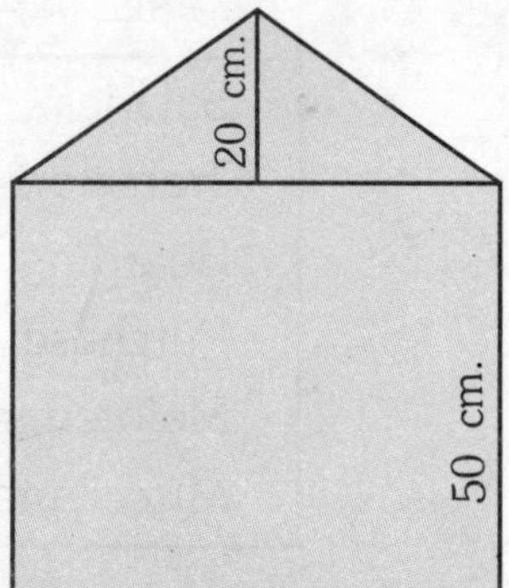

20 cm.
50 cm.
80 cm.

14. An isosceles trapezium has its parallel sides equal to 27 cm. and 19 cm. respectively. The measure of its non-parallel sides is 5 cm. Find its area.

15. The lengths of the parallel sides of an isosceles trapezium are 36 cm. and 20 cm. and its area is 168 sq. cm. Find the length of its non-parallel sides.

16. A card-board box measures 70 cm. × 60 cm. × 50 cm. How many toys of cubic shape and each with an edge 10 cm. can be placed in it ?

17. The internal measurements of a box are 22 cm. × 17 cm. × 12 cm. If the thickness of the material of which it is made is 2 cm., how much material has been used to make it ?

18. A rectangular room is thrice as long as it is wide. It can contain 60 cubic metres of air. Find its length, breadth and cost of plastering its floor and walls at Rs. 8 per square metre if its height is 5 metres.

19. The number of candidates for a competition in five successive years was as shown in the table given below. Construct a bar graph to represent this data :

Years	First	Second	Third	Fourth	Fifth
Candidates	90	120	130	150	170

MEMORABLE FACTS

1. Area of a parallelogram = Base × Height
2. Base of a parallelogram = Area ÷ Height
3. Height of a parallelogram = Area ÷ Base
4. Area of triangle = $\frac{1}{2}$ × Base × Height
5. Base of a triangle = 2 × Area ÷ Height
6. Height of triangle = 2 × Area ÷ Base
7. Area of a trapezium = $\frac{1}{2}$ × Height × (sum of the parallel sides)
8. Height of a trapezium = 2 × Area ÷ (sum of the parallel sides)
9. Area of a rhombus = $\frac{1}{2}$ × product of its diagonals
10. Volume of a cuboid = Length × Breadth × Height
11. Length of a cuboid = Volume ÷ (Breadth × Height)
12. Breadth of a cuboid = Volume ÷ (Length × Height)
13. Height of a cuboid = Volume ÷ (Length × Breadth)
14. Volume of a cube = $(\text{side})^3$
15. Area of the four walls of a room = Height × 2 × (Length + Breadth)

OBJECTIVE-TYPE TESTS

SET I

A. Answer yes or no :

1. A rational number resembles a fraction in form. ....

2. $\frac{-13}{-18}$ is a positive rational number. ....

3. $\frac{-3}{5}$ is also a positive rational number. ....

4. The standard form of $\frac{21}{35}$ is $\frac{3}{5}$ ....

5. $\frac{p}{-q}, \frac{-p}{q}, -\frac{p}{q}$ are various forms of the same quantity. ....

B. Tick the correct choice :

6. Out of the rational numbers $\frac{-5}{6}$ and $\frac{-7}{9}$, $\frac{-5}{6}$ is :

(a) equal to $\frac{-7}{9}$ (b) smaller than $\frac{-7}{9}$ (c) greater than $\frac{-7}{9}$

7. Out of the rational numbers $\frac{-3}{5}, \frac{7}{-10}$ and $\frac{-5}{6}$ the highest number is :

(a) $\frac{-3}{5}$ (b) $\frac{7}{-10}$ (c) $\frac{-5}{6}$

8. Every positive rational number bears a relation to zero as—

(a) smaller than it (b) equal to it (c) larger than it

9. The sum of $\frac{-3}{4}$ and $\frac{3}{4}$ is : (a) 0 (b) 1 (c) $\frac{3}{2}$

10. The sum of a rational number and 0 is : (a) 0 (b) 1 (c) rational number

C. Fill up each blank :

11. $\frac{-3}{4}$ is the .... inverse of the rational number $\frac{3}{4}$.

12. $\frac{1}{-3}$ is the .... inverse of the rational number – 3.

13. – 7 is a .... rational number than – 17.

14. On a number-line, we write 2 .... the 0 than 4.

15. On a number-line we write – 2 .... the 0 than – 7.

D. Write the correct name of the—

16. Numeral written above the line of division in a fraction : ....

17. Numeral written below the line of division of a fraction : ....

18. The product of a rational number and its reciprocal : ....

19. The number obtained by changing place of the numerator and the denominator of a rational number : ....

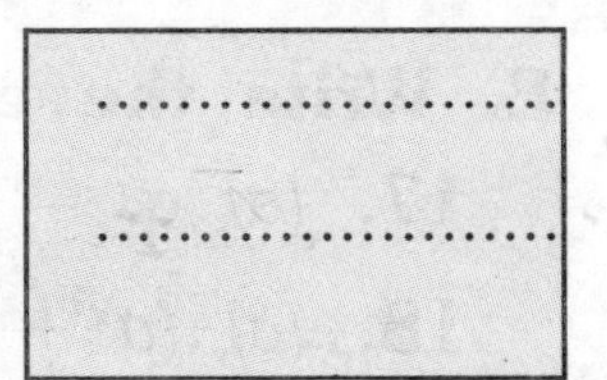

SET II

A. Answer :

1. Is there gain or loss, if SP is higher than CP ? ....
2. Is there gain or loss if CP is higher than SP ? ....
3. Is gain or loss calculated on SP or CP ? ....
4. Will there be a loss or gain if the SP of 10 eggs = CP of 11 eggs ? ....

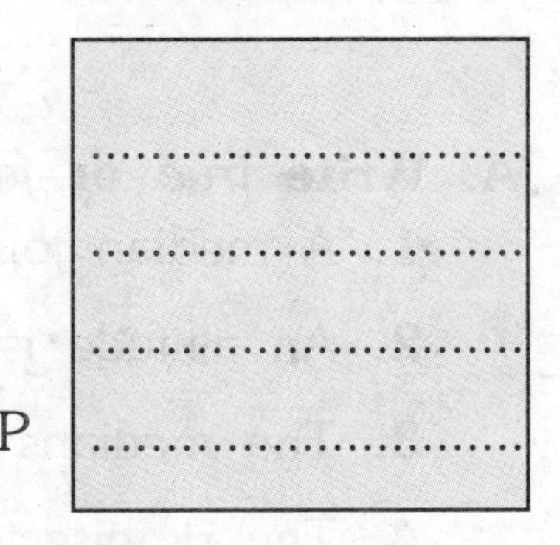

B. Tick the correct choice :

5. 0·3 expressed as a fraction is : *(a)* $\frac{3}{8}$ *(b)* $\frac{3}{10}$ *(c)* $\frac{3}{7}$

6. 0·4 expressed as a fraction is : *(a)* $\frac{4}{5}$ *(b)* $\frac{2}{5}$ *(c)* $\frac{3}{5}$

7. A rational number can be expressed as a terminating decimal if its denominator has no other prime factors than—

   (a) 3, 5 *(b)* 2, 3 *(c)* 2, 5

8. The rational number $\frac{26}{25}$ is equal to :

   (a) 10·4 *(b)* 1·04 *(c)* 0·4

C. What is each of the following called ?

9. The unknown quantity in a linear equation : ....
10. Transfer of a term from LHS to RHS of an equation : ....
11. Principal + Simple Interest : ....
12. An algebraic expression with one term only : ....

D. Write the technical term for each of the following :

13. The price written on an article. ....
14. The per cent reduction out of a marked price. ....
15. The price at which an article is sold. ....
16. Two discounts allowed one after the other on M.P. ....

E. Write the correct answer :

17. *(a)* $a^2 - b^2$ = ... *(b)* $5^2 - 4^2$ = ...

18. *(a)* $(a + b)^2$ = ... *(b)* $(3 + 4)^2$ = ...

19. *(a)* $(a - b)^2$ = ... *(b)* $(7 - 3)^2$ = ...

SET III

A. Write *true* or *false* :

1. A median joins a vertex with the mid-point of the opposite side. ....

2. An altitude is the perpendicular from a vertex to the opposite side. ....

3. The medians of a triangle are not concurrent. ....

4. The rt. bisectors of the sides of a triangle are concurrent. ....

B. Tick the correct choice :

5. The medians to the equal sides of an isosceles Δ are—
(a) equal *(b)* unequal *(c)* neither of the two

6. The medians of a Δ concur at the : *(a)* centroid *(b)* incentre *(c)* orthocentre

7. The orthocentre of a right angled triangle lies :
(a) in its interior *(b)* in its exterior *(c)* at the right vertex

C. 8. The quantity 0·025 in terms of per cent is :
(a) $\frac{1}{4}$ % *(b)* 2·5 % *(c)* 5·6 %

9. 16 men can reap a field in 30 days. 20 man reap the field in :
(a) 27 days *(b)* 25 days *(c)* 24 days

10. If each side of a cube is doubled, its volume becomes :
(a) 4 times *(b)* 6 times *(c)* 8 times

11. The area of a square with side x is equal to the area of a triangle with base x. The height of the triangle is : *(a)* $2x$ *(b)* x *(c)* $3x$

12. The axis of a bar graph drawn from west to east is called—
(a) vertical axis *(b)* horizontal axis *(c)* slanting axis

13. The small picture of an object used to draw a bar graph is called a—
(a) pictograph *(b)* autograph *(c)* photograph

14. The point where the bisectors of the angles of a triangle intersect is its—
(a) incentre *(b)* circumcentre *(c)* orthocentre

15. The area of the four walls of a room is : *(a)* $H \times 2(l + b)$ *(b)* $L \times B \times H$

SET IV

A. 1. $x\%$ of 64 = 24, so $x\%$ =

(a) $39\frac{1}{2}\%$ *(b)* 40% *(c)* $37\frac{1}{2}\%$

2. 7% of a number is less than its 11% by 18. The number is :

(a) 400 *(b)* 450 *(c)* 500

3. 30% of the total candidates failed a test. If the number of passed candidates is 336, the total number of cadidates was :

(a) 500 *(b)* 700 *(c)* 480

B. 4. The value of $\frac{6{\cdot}94 \times 6{\cdot}94 - 2{\cdot}06 \times 2{\cdot}06}{4{\cdot}88}$ is

(a) 4·88 *(b)* 9 *(c)* 8·96

5. The centroid of a Δ divides each of its medians in the ratio :

(a) 2 : 1 *(b)* 1 : 3 *(c)* 1 : 2

6. The orthocentre of a *rt.* triangle lies —

(a) in its interior *(b)* at the right vertex *(c)* in its exterior

7. The medians of an equilateral triangle are —

(a) unequal *(b)* equal *(c)* neither of the two

C. 8. A convex quadrilateral has each of its angles :

(a) equal to 180° *(b)* larger than 180° *(c)* smaller than 180°

9. The sum of the exterior angles of a quadrilateral with its sides produced in order is :

(a) 2*rt.*$\angle$s *(b)* 4*rt.*$\angle$s *(c)* 6*rt.*$\angle$s

10. $\angle D$ and $\angle C$ of the quadrilateral given in front are equal to 60° and 100° respectively. The bisectors of $\angle A$ and $\angle B$ meet in *O*. The value of $\angle AOB$ is

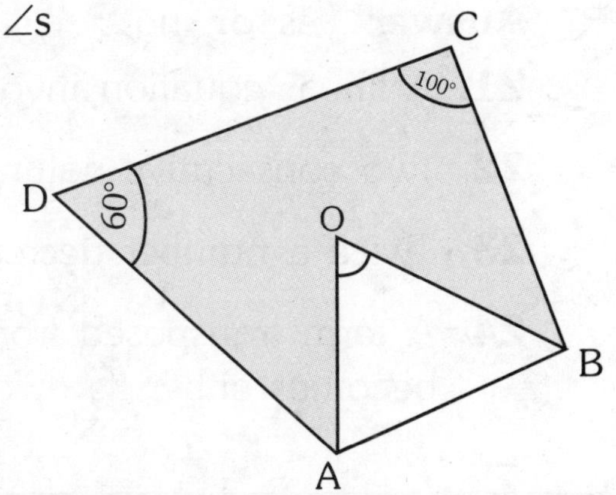

(a) 90° *(b)* 80° *(c)* 100°

11. A kite is a quarilateral with two pairs of equal adjacent sides but its opposite sides are :

(*a*) parallel (*b*) unequal (*c*) equal

12. An isosceles trapezium has its non-parallel sides

(*a*) unequal (*b*) equal (*c*) intersecting each other

D. 13. A kite is made up of two triangles with a common base. The triangles are —

(*a*) equilateral (*b*) isosceles (*c*) right-angled

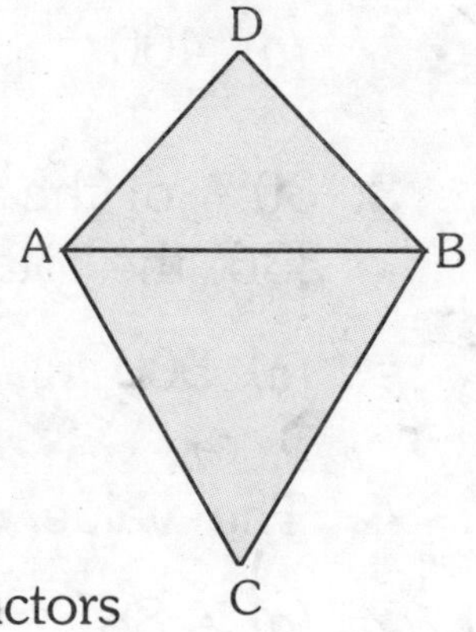

14. The sum of $0{\cdot}\overline{3}$ and $0{\cdot}\overline{6}$ is :

(*a*) $\frac{2}{3}$ (*b*) $\frac{1}{3}$ (*c*) 1

15. $(\frac{3}{4})^2$ and $(\frac{3}{4})^{-2}$ are mutually :

(*a*) opposite numbers (*b*) reciprocals (*c*) common factors

16. $2^{-9} \times 2^x = 2$. The value of x is :

(*a*) 9 (*b*) 8 (*c*) 10

E. 17. The usual form of $9{\cdot}3 \times 10^5$ is :

(*a*) 9300000 (*b*) 930000 (*c*) 93000

18. Quantities x^0 and 5^0 are :

(*a*) equal (*b*) unequal (*c*) opposite to each other

19. If $(x + \frac{1}{x}) = 3$, the value of $(x^2 + \frac{1}{x^2})$ is :

(*a*) 11 (*b*) 7 (*c*) 9

20. $x^4 - 1$ has :

(*a*) three factors (*b*) two factors (*c*) no factors

F. Answer *yes* **or** *no* **:**

21. A linear equation involves variables with the first degree exponents ....

22. Two consecutive natural numbers with their sum 63 are 31, 32. ....

23. Twice a number decreased by 3 equals 47. So, the number is 26. ....

24. A term transposed from one side of an equation to its other side becomes either its own additive inverse or reciprocal. ....

ANSWERS – I

REVISION EXERCISES (*Page 7*)

A. **1.** 1 **2.** 0 **3.** infinite number **4.** whole number **5.** 1000
6. None **7.** 1 **8.** 1000 **9.** 0 **10.** two
11. neither **12.** 2 **13.** 1 **14.** their product **15.** 1
16. p **17.** q **18.** –7 **19.** vinculum **20.** consequent

B. **21.** *(a) A* ***number*** *is mere an idea but a* ***numeral*** *is its writing symbol.*

(b) ***Face value*** *of a digit is equal to itself and it never changes.*

Place value *of a digit depends on its place in a numeral and it can change.*

22. *(a) A* ***minuend*** *is the quantity from which another quantity called* ***subtrahend*** *is subtracted.*

(b) A ***multiplicand*** *is the quantity which is multiplied by another quantity called* ***multiplier***

23. *(a) A* ***multiple*** *is a quantity that can be divided into smaller quantities called its* ***factors.***

(b) A ***prime number*** *has only one factor (1) except itself but a composite number s larger than 3 and has two or more factors.*

24. *(a)* ***H.C.F.*** *is the highest common factor of two or more quantities. But* ***L.C.M.*** *is the lowest common multiple of two or more quantities.*

(b) ***Co-primes*** *have only one common factor (1) while* ***twin primes*** *have a composite number in between them.*

(c) The ***consecutive predecessor*** *of a number is the number* ***less than it by only 1*** *while the consecutive successor of a number is the number* ***more than it by only 1.***

25. *(a) A* ***positive integer*** *is larger than 0 but a* ***negative integer*** *is less than 0.*

(b) A ***quotient*** *is the number got after dividing a larger number by another number.*

The larger number divided by another number is called ***dividend*** *while the dividing number is called* ***divisor.***

(c) A ***ratio*** *is the relation that one quantity has with another quantity of the same kind.*

A ***proportion*** *is formed when two ratios are said to be equivalent.*

(d) The first and the fourth terms of a proportion are called ***extremes***

The second and third terms of a proportion are called ***means.***

26. *(a) The last term of a proportion with four different terms is called the* ***fourth proportional.***

The last term of a proportion with three different terms is called the ***third proportional.***

The middling term of a three term proportion is called the ***mean proportional.***

(b) In ***direct variation,*** *both the quantities increase or decrease together but in an* ***indirect variation*** *they increase or decrease inversely (in the opposite way).*

27. *(a)* ***Numerator*** *is the term in a fraction written above its line of division.*

Denominator *is the term in a fraction written below its line of division.*

(b) A **term** is a quantity taken singly out of a series of quantities joined together by signs of + or – or both. Such a series is called an **expression**.

28. (a) **Principal** means the sum of money borrowed by a person from another.
Interest is the sum of money charged for the use of the principal from the borrower.
Amount is the sum of the principal and the interest.

(b) A **line** is a straight drawing with no end-points and made up of points placed in close proximity.
A **line-segment** is the part of a line cut off by any two points taken on it.

29. (a) **Interior** of a triangle is the part of its plane enclosed by its boundary.
Exterior of a triangle is the part of its plane lying out of its boundary.

(b) **Supplementary angles,** when added, amount to 180°.
Complementary angles, when added, amount to 90°.

30. (a) **Area** refers to the expanse of a surface contained within its boundaries (dimensions).
Perimeter is the total of the lengths of all the dimensions of a surface,

(b) A **rectangle** is a parallelogram with each of its angles = 90°
A **parallelogram** is a four -sided figure with its opposite sites parallel.

31. 7, 700 ; 693 **32.** 100002 **33.** 900 **34.** Ninety-four crore thirty-seven lakh twenty thousand six hundred and ninety-five ; Nine-hundred forty-three million, seven hundred twenty thousand, six hundred and ninety-five **35.** 782

36. (a)
```
  9 2 6
– 5 9 7
-------
  3 2 9
```
(b)
```
  6 4 7
+ 2 8 9
-------
  9 3 6
```
(c)
```
      9 8 3 7
×       3 0 8
-------------
    7 8 6 9 6
    0 0 0 0
2 9 5 1 1
-------------
3 0 2 9 7 9 6
```
(d)
```
715 ) 1 5 3 7 2 5 ( 215
      1 4 3 0
      -------
        1 0 7 2
          7 1 5
        -------
          3 5 7 5
          3 5 7 5
          -------
                0
```

37. 0·22 grams **38.** $x = 2{\cdot}5$ **39.** 15 **40.** 20

41. 14 days **42.** Rs. 1680 **43.** $3\frac{1}{3}\%$ **44.** $6\frac{1}{4}\%$ gain

45. 10% **46.** 240 days **47.** $-5x^2 - 11xy + y^2$

48. $-3x^2 - 18x - 3$ **49.** 91 **50.** $x = 2$ **51.** 41, 82

52. (a) addition, subtraction, multiplication, division
(b) simple brackets, curly brackets, square brackets, vinculum

53. 10 cm , 30 cm. **54.** (a) AC, BD, RS, PQ (b) DC, BD, AD and DRC, SOR
(c) D, R, C ; P, O, Q ; A, S, B ; R, O, S ; D, O, B ; A, O, C ; D, P, A ; C, Q, B

55. acute, right, obtuse, reflex

56. supplementary, adjacent, alternate, corresponding

57. obtuse-angled, right-angled, acute-angled

58. 90°, 60°, 30° **61.** Rs, 200 **62.** 20 m

63. Rs. 1350, Rs. 135 **64.** 9990 **65.** 10080

PRACTICE EXERCISES 1. *(Page 18)*

A. **1.** based on reasoning **2.** subtraction **3.** 0 **4.** whole numbers

5. subtraction **6.** integers **7.** division **8.** rational numbers

9. $\frac{0}{1}$ **10.** yes, yes

B. **11.** No **12.** yes **13.** yes **14.** No

15. yes **16.** No **17.** yes **18.** No

19. yes **20.** No **21.** yes **22.** No, $\frac{5}{1}$

C. **23.** 1, 2 **24.** 1, 2, 3 **25.** –2, –1, 0, 1, 2 **26.** 0 **27.** $\frac{3}{1}$

D. **28.** –15, 7, 5, –9, –8 **29.** 5, 7, 5, –2, 1 **30.** Positive $\frac{3}{7}, \frac{-10}{-11}, \frac{-8}{-7}$

E. **31.** *(a)* $\frac{15}{-18}$ *(b)* $\frac{-15}{18}$ *(c)* $\frac{-25}{30}$ **32.** $\frac{11}{13}$ **33.** $\frac{-7}{9}, \frac{9}{17}, \frac{4}{9}, \frac{-6}{1}$

34. *(a)* $\frac{2}{5}$ *(b)* $\frac{3}{5}$ *(c)* $\frac{-3}{2}$ *(d)* $\frac{-2}{3}$

F. **35.** *(a)* $\frac{-4}{7} = \frac{-28}{49}$ *(b)* $\frac{5}{-9} = \frac{-5}{9} = \frac{25}{-45}$

(c) $\frac{-9}{-11} = \frac{36}{44}$ *(d)* $\frac{-4}{-7} = \frac{8}{14} = \frac{-32}{-56}$

36. *(a)* 15 *(b)* 3 *(c)* 20 *(d)* $\frac{133}{5}$

G. **37.** T **38.** T **39.** T **40.** T **41.** T **42.** F

43. T **44.** T **45.** F **46.** F **47.** F **48.** T

49. *(a)* see page 11 *(b)* see page 11 **50.** *(a)* see page 9 *(unit page)* *(b)* see page 9

PRACTICE EXERCISES 2. *(Page 25)*

A. **1.** yes **2.** yes **3.** No **4.** yes **5.** yes **6.** yes

C. **13.** $\frac{7}{4}$ **14.** $\frac{-3}{4}$ **15.** $\frac{2}{5}$ **16.** $\frac{3}{7}$ **17.** 0

18. $\frac{2}{-11}$ **19.** $\frac{2}{-3}$ **20.** $\frac{4}{5}$ **21.** $\frac{-3}{-4}$

D. **22.** $\frac{8}{10}, \frac{12}{15}, \frac{16}{20}, \frac{20}{25}$ **23.** $\frac{-4}{6}, \frac{-6}{9}, \frac{-8}{12}, \frac{-10}{15}$

24. $\frac{10}{8}, \frac{15}{12}, \frac{20}{16}, \frac{25}{20}$ **25.** $\frac{6}{8}, \frac{9}{12}, \frac{12}{16}, \frac{15}{20}$

26. $\frac{-18}{14}, \frac{-27}{21}, \frac{-36}{28}, \frac{-45}{35}$ 27. $\frac{2}{6}, \frac{3}{9}, \frac{4}{12}, \frac{5}{15}$

E. 28. $\frac{3}{4}$ 29. $\frac{8}{11}$ 30. $\frac{4}{11}$

F. 31. $x = 12$ 32. $x = 33$ 33. $x = 18$ 34. $x = 6$

35. $x = 3$ 36. $x = 10$

G. 37. $\frac{-5}{6}, \frac{7}{-10}, \frac{-3}{5}$ 38. $\frac{-5}{2}, \frac{-7}{4}, \frac{1}{10}, \frac{3}{8}$ 39. $\frac{-6}{7}, \frac{-3}{4}, \frac{-5}{11}, \frac{1}{2}$

40. $\frac{17}{-30}, \frac{-11}{20}, \frac{7}{-15}, \frac{-3}{10}$ 41. $\frac{-3}{4}, \frac{-2}{3}, \frac{-1}{2}, \frac{4}{5}$ 42. $\frac{-5}{6}, \frac{-5}{8}, \frac{2}{7}, \frac{7}{2}$

H. 43. $\frac{53}{12}, \frac{25}{6}, \frac{-17}{4}$ 44. $\frac{-3}{5}, \frac{-7}{10}, \frac{-5}{6}$ 45. $\frac{7}{8}, \frac{3}{-10}, \frac{-4}{5}$

46. $1, 0, \frac{-1}{3}, \frac{-2}{5}, -1$ 47. $\frac{-5}{9}, \frac{-11}{18}, \frac{20}{-27}, \frac{-9}{10}$ 48. $5, -3, \frac{27}{-8}, \frac{-7}{2}, \frac{-15}{4}$

I. 49. $\frac{-2}{5}$ 50. $\frac{1}{4}$ 51. -1 52. $0, \frac{1}{2}$

PRACTICE EXERCISES 3 *(Page 29)*

A. 1. fractions 2. denominator 3. $\frac{p}{q} + \frac{r}{q} = \frac{p+r}{q}$ 4. denominators

5. $\frac{\text{Numerator of the I + Numerator of II}}{\text{Common Denominator}}$

B. 6. $\frac{1}{12}$ 7. $\frac{-7}{48}$ 8. $\frac{-19}{24}$ 9. $\frac{4}{7}$ 10. $\frac{-1}{4}$

11. $\frac{-2}{7}$ 12. $2\frac{1}{4}$ 13. $\frac{-9}{5}$ 14. $\frac{-1}{15}$ 15. $\frac{7}{18}$

16. $\frac{-23}{24}$ 17. $\frac{7}{12}$ 18. $\frac{-13}{35}$ 19. $-1\frac{1}{5}$ 20. $\frac{1}{6}$

C. 21. $\frac{-19}{36}$ 22. $1\frac{11}{72}$ 23. $\frac{13}{12}$ 24. $\frac{-25}{18}$

25. $\frac{-1}{12}$ 26. $\frac{29}{24}$

D. 27. $2\frac{1}{7}$ 28. $-5\frac{1}{20}$ 29. $-1\frac{7}{20}$ 30. $-3\frac{4}{7}$ 32. 0 33. $\frac{13}{20}$

PRACTICE EXERCISES 4 *(Page 34)*

A. 1. $\frac{5}{12}$ 2. $\frac{-4}{9}$ 3. $\frac{7}{11}$ 4. $\frac{-3}{8}$ 5. $\frac{10}{21}$ 6. $\frac{7}{8}$

7. $\frac{-5}{9}$ 8. $\frac{15}{7}$ 9. $\frac{8}{13}$ 10. $\frac{12}{13}$ 11. $\frac{-4}{11}$ 12. $\frac{7}{20}$

B. 13. $\frac{11}{56}$ 14. $\frac{-1}{12}$ 15. $\frac{23}{72}$ 16. $\frac{19}{12}$ 17. $\frac{-1}{4}$ 18. $\frac{-13}{33}$

C. 19. $\frac{-71}{60}$ 20. $\frac{-8}{7}$ 21. $\frac{9}{40}$ 22. $\frac{-49}{20}$

23. $\frac{-29}{360}$ 24. $\frac{37}{33}$ 25. $\frac{29}{54}$ 26. $\frac{73}{84}$

D. 27. $\frac{-17}{6}$ 28. $\frac{95}{72}$ 29. $\frac{2}{5}$ 30. $\frac{12}{7}$ 31. $\frac{-12}{7}$ 32. –3

E. 33. $\frac{5}{26}$ 34. $\frac{-6}{11}$ 35. $\frac{76}{23}$ 36. $\frac{-47}{20}$

F. 37. false 38. false 39. true 40. true

41. false 42. true 43. true

PRACTICE EXERCISES 5 *(Page 40)*

A. 1. 1 2. 0 3. $\frac{-1}{17}$ 4. 0, 1 5. 0

B. 6. No 7. yes 8. yes 9. yes 10. yes 11. yes 12. yes

C. 13. $\frac{2}{5}$ 14. $\frac{-7}{9}$ 15. $\frac{4}{75}$ 16. $\frac{-7}{27}$ 17. $\frac{1}{20}$ 18. $\frac{-5}{4}$

19. $\frac{-8}{35}$ 20. $\frac{-8}{15}$ 21. 0 22. $\frac{-52}{243}$ 23. $\frac{3}{16}$ 24. –1

D. 25. $\frac{55}{2704}$ 26. $16\frac{1}{3}$ 27. $\frac{2}{5}$ 28. $6\ \frac{321}{3240}$ 29. $3\frac{3}{4}$ 30. 0

31. $\frac{-13}{15}$ 32. $\frac{-1}{10}$

E. 33. true 34. true 35. true 36. true 37. true 38. true 39. true

F. 40. $\frac{289}{81}$ 41. $\frac{19}{-25}$ 42. $\frac{3}{8}$ 43. 4, 9, 3

G. 44. $\frac{a}{b} \times \frac{c}{d} = \frac{c}{d} \times \frac{a}{b}$ 45. Product of two rational numbers is a rational number.

46. $\frac{a}{b} \times (\frac{c}{d} \times \frac{e}{f}) = \frac{c}{d} (\frac{a}{b} \times \frac{e}{f}) = \frac{e}{f} (\frac{a}{b} \times \frac{c}{d})$

47. $\frac{a}{b} \times 1 = 1 \times \frac{a}{b} = \frac{a}{b}$ 48. $\frac{a}{b} \times \frac{b}{a} = 1$

49. $\frac{a}{b} \times (\frac{c}{d} + \frac{e}{f}) = (\frac{a}{b} \times \frac{c}{d}) + (\frac{a}{b} \times \frac{e}{f})$

50. *(a)* 1, 0 *(b)* $\frac{1}{x}$ *(c)* No

H. 51. 81 52. $\frac{1}{212}$ 54. $\frac{13}{30}$

PRACTICE EXERCISES 6 *(Page 44)*

A. 1. yes 2. No 3. yes 4. yes 5. yes

B. 6. $\frac{-4}{5}$ 7. $\frac{-4}{3}$ 8. $\frac{3}{4}$ 9. $\frac{-7}{10}$ 10. $\frac{-6}{5}$

11. $-3\frac{5}{33}$ 12. $\frac{5}{4}$ 13. $\frac{16}{15}$ 14. $\frac{2}{3}$ 15. $\frac{40}{63}$

16. $3\frac{1}{3}$ **17.** $\frac{54}{55}$ **18.** $\frac{7}{108}$ **19.** $\frac{1}{-14}$ **20.** $\frac{-16}{15}$

C. 21. $\frac{7}{8}$ **22.** $\frac{8}{507}$ **23.** $\frac{3}{4}$ **24.** unequal **25.** not equal

26. $\frac{1729}{501}$ **27.** 7 **28.** $\frac{-137}{201}$ **29.** 20 **30.** *(a)* $\frac{15}{22}$ *(b)* $\frac{3}{2}$ *(c)* $\frac{-7}{45}$ *(d)* $\frac{47}{45}$

PRACTICE EXERCISES 7 *(Page 50)*

A. **1.** see page 44 **2.** see page 45

B. **3.** yes **4.** yes **5.** yes **6.** yes

C. **7.** $\frac{5}{7}$ **8.** $\frac{7}{9}$ **9.** $\frac{12}{5}$ **10.** 0

11. $\frac{9}{13}$ **12.** $\frac{13}{8}$ **13.** $\frac{11}{8}$ **14.** $\frac{6}{13}$

D. **15.** $\frac{-1}{2}, \frac{1}{2}$ **16.** $\frac{-3}{4}, \frac{3}{4}$ **17.** $\frac{-5}{6}, \frac{5}{6}$

24. $\frac{5}{12}$ **25.** $\frac{3}{2}, \frac{13}{4}$ **26.** $\frac{1}{4}, \frac{7}{24}, \frac{15}{48}$ **27.** $\frac{17}{24}, \frac{35}{48}, \frac{71}{96}, \frac{143}{192}$

PRACTICE EXERCISES 8 *(Page 54)*

A. **1.** Dividing the numerator by the denominator

2. Terminating, Recurring **3.** see page 49 **4.** see page 49

B. **5.** 0·75 **6.** 3·75 **7.** 2·3 **8.** 0·52

9. 2·5488 **10.** 0·8 **11.** 1·25 **12.** 1·04

13. 3·4512 **14.** 0·48 **15.** 0·22 **16.** 0·6

17. $0{\cdot}8\overline{3}$ **18.** 1·4 **19.** 0·625 **20.** 0·45

C. **21.** $0{\cdot}41\overline{6}$ **22.** $0{\cdot}\overline{3}$ **23.** $0{\cdot}\overline{4}$ **24.** $0{\cdot}\overline{18}$

25. $0{\cdot}1428\overline{5}$ **26.** $0{\cdot}3\overline{5}$ **27.** $3{\cdot}\overline{428571}$ **28.** $2{\cdot}\overline{6}$

29. $3{\cdot}\overline{142857}$ **30.** $-0{\cdot}\overline{27}$ **31.** $2{\cdot}\overline{6}$ **32.** $-3{\cdot}1\overline{6}$

D. **33.** Terminating **34.** Non-terminating **35.** Non-terminating **36.** Terminating

37. Terminating **38.** Non-terminating **39.** Non-terminating **40.** Non-terminating

PRACTICE EXERCISES 9 *(Page 58)*

A. **1.** see page 53 **2.** see page 49 **3.** see page 53 **4.** see page 54 **5.** see page 55

B. **6.** $\frac{8}{9}$ **7.** $\frac{16}{99}$ **8.** $\frac{234}{999}$ **9.** $\frac{1}{3}$

10. $\frac{13}{99}$ **11.** $\frac{4}{9}$ **12.** $\frac{32}{99}$ **13.** $\frac{133}{999}$

C. **14.** $\frac{13}{45}$ **15.** $\frac{8}{45}$ **16.** $\frac{43}{11100}$ **17.** $\frac{233}{990}$ **18.** $\frac{229}{990}$ **19.** $\frac{244}{495}$

20. $\frac{69}{550}$ **21.** $\frac{83}{495}$ **22.** $\frac{59}{110}$ **23.** $\frac{37}{90}$ **24.** $\frac{139}{1100}$ **25.** $\frac{37}{990}$

D. **26.** $\frac{57}{9}$ **27.** $\frac{29}{99}$ **28.** $\frac{1}{3}$ **29.** $\frac{49}{99}$ **30.** $4\frac{82}{99}$

PRACTICE EXERCISES 10 (Page 62)

A. **1.** 3^4 **2.** 5 raised to the power 6 **3.** base **4.** index

5. –1 **6.** 1 **7.** $\frac{5}{1}$ **8.** $\frac{1}{5}$ **9.** $\frac{a^m}{b^m}$

B. **10.** $\frac{9}{25}$ **11.** $\frac{-64}{125}$ **12.** $\frac{1}{16}$ **13.** $\frac{32}{243}$ **14.** $\frac{216}{1331}$ **15.** $\frac{81}{4096}$

16. $\frac{4}{169}$ **17.** $\frac{1331}{-1728}$ **18.** $\frac{27}{64}$ **19.** $\frac{64}{729}$ **20.** $\frac{81}{2401}$ **21.** $\frac{-1024}{3125}$

D. **28.** $\left(\frac{2}{5}\right)^4$ **29.** $\left(\frac{-7}{8}\right)^3$ **30.** $\left(\frac{-3}{4}\right)^3$ **31.** $\left(\frac{1}{3}\right)^5$ **32.** $\left(\frac{-2}{5}\right)^3$

33. $\left(\frac{-1}{3}\right)^3$ **34.** $\left(\frac{7}{11}\right)^2$ **35.** $\left(\frac{7}{8}\right)^3$ **36.** $\frac{(5)^3}{(2)^9}$ **37.** $\left(-\frac{10}{9}\right)^3$

38. $\left(\frac{25}{49}\right)^2$ **39.** $\left(\frac{4}{5}\right)^5$ **40.** $\frac{p^3}{q^3}$

E. **41.** $\frac{1}{-5}$ **42.** $\frac{1}{(2)^3}$ **43.** $\frac{1}{(-5)^4}$ **44.** $\left(\frac{5}{2}\right)^4$

45. $\left(\frac{7}{-3}\right)^{11}$ **46.** $\left(\frac{9}{-5}\right)^m$ **47.** $\left(\frac{7}{4}\right)^4$ **48.** $\left(\frac{5}{-4}\right)^5$

F. **49.** $\frac{64}{6561}$ **50.** $\frac{81}{1250}$ **51.** $\frac{16}{105}$ **52.** $\frac{1}{8}$ **53.** $\frac{1}{24}$ **54.** $\frac{335}{729}$

PRACTICE EXERCISES 11 (Page 67)

A. **1.** a^{n+m} **2.** a^{n-m} **3.** a^{nm} **4.** $\frac{1}{a^m}$ **5.** 1 **6.** $\frac{1}{a^{n-m}}$

B. **7.** –243 **8.** –27 **9.** –1 **10.** $\frac{4096}{15625}$ **11.** $\frac{49}{36}$

12. $\frac{121}{81}$ **13.** 3 **14.** $\frac{64}{729}$ **15.** 1

C. **16.** $\frac{6}{7}$ **17.** $\frac{125}{64}$ **18.** 1 **19.** $\frac{7}{8}$ **20.** $\frac{25}{9}$

21. $\frac{17}{20}$ **22.** $\frac{9261}{8000}$ **23.** $\frac{(9)^6}{256}$ **24.** $\frac{9}{16}$ **25.** $\frac{729}{128}$

D. **26.** $\frac{15}{16}$ **27.** $\frac{32}{147}$ **28.** $\frac{81}{16}$ **29.** –64 **30.** 1

E. **31.** true **32.** true **33.** true **34.** true

35. $\frac{729}{128}$ **36.** $\frac{256}{81}$ **37.** $x = -2$ **38.** $\frac{2}{3}$ **39.** $\frac{4}{5}$

40. $\frac{27}{32}$ **41.** $\frac{81}{32}$ **42.** true **43.** 1 **44.** –1

PRACTICE EXERCISES 12 (Page 70)

A. **1.** $2{\cdot}5 \times 10^0$ **2.** $1{\cdot}5 \times 10$ **3.** positive **4.** negative

B. **5.** $1{\cdot}5 \times 10^4$ **6.** $2{\cdot}59 \times 10^5$ **7.** $3{\cdot}2 \times 10^{-1}$

8. $2{\cdot}79 \times 10$ **9.** $2{\cdot}3 \times 10^{-3}$ **10.** $1{\cdot}3 \times 10^4$

C. **11.** $2{\cdot}9 \times 10^{-3}$ **12.** $7{\cdot}3 \times 10^{-6}$ **13.** $9{\cdot}2 \times 10^{-4}$

14. $3{\cdot}7 \times 10^{-5}$ **15.** $7{\cdot}4 \times 10^{-6}$ **16.** $2{\cdot}9 \times 10^{-5}$

D. **17.** 3×10^8 **18.** $3{\cdot}3 \times 10^4$ **19.** $9{\cdot}4605 \times 10^{15}$

20. $3{\cdot}844 \times 10^8$ **21.** 1.5×10^{-8}cm

E. **22.** 598000000 **23.** 0·0000041 **24.** 0·00000098

25. 1060000000 **26.** 7030000 **27.** 0·0000073

28. $1{\cdot}8 \times 10^4$ **29.** 289000 **30.** 930000

31. $2{\cdot}7 \times 10^8$ seconds **32.** $8{\cdot}0 \times 10^{-3}$cm **33.** 50×10 hours

34. 30 minutes **35.** $1{\cdot}5 \times 10^{-8}$ cm.

MISCELLANEOUS EXERCISES I (Page 72)

A. **1.** yes **2.** No **3.** No **4.** yes **5.** yes

6. yes **7.** No **8.** yes **9.** No **10.** yes

11. yes **12.** yes **13.** yes **14.** yes

C. **16.** $1\frac{17}{26}$ **17.** $-1\frac{1}{32}$ **18.** $12\frac{16}{43}$ **19.** $\frac{2}{9}$ **20.** $12{\cdot}\overline{29}$

21. $3\frac{1}{24}$ **22.** 1 **23.** $\frac{7}{2}, \frac{5}{8}, \frac{7}{20}, \frac{9}{40}, 0, \frac{-3}{4}, \frac{-3}{7},$

24. $\frac{41}{8}, \frac{21}{20}, \frac{47}{64},$ **25.** (a) 380 (b) 131·4

D. **26.** (a) 1 (b) $a^3\ b^{-3}$ **27.** 1 **28.** 1 **29.** $(p\ )^{x+y+z}$

30. $x = 6$ **31.** $\frac{1}{3}$ **32.** $x = -1$

F. **33.** $\frac{125}{216}$ **34.** $\frac{2197}{216}$ **35.** $-11\frac{1}{3}$ **36.** $\frac{-97}{78}$ **37.** 0

38. $\frac{5}{-8}$ is the larger **39.** $\frac{19}{132}, \frac{129}{264}$

G. **40.** order **41.** negative form **42.** reciprocal **43.** $\frac{-95}{72}$

H. **45.** b, a **46.** p, q **47.** $\frac{19}{25}$ **48.** 4, 9, $\frac{3}{-7}$ **49.** $\frac{8}{3}$

50. (a) $8{\cdot}46 \times 10^3$ (b) 1×10^{-5} (c) $3{\cdot}72 \times 10^3$

PRACTICE EXERCISES 13 *(Page 78)*

A. **1.** see page 74 **2.** see page 74 **3.** yes

B. **4.** No **5.** yes **6.** yes **7.** No

C. **8.**

Metres	6	2	3	9	12	15
Rupees	24	8	12	36	48	60

9. 1·5 kg. **10.** Rs. 208 **11.** 450 men

12. 8 hours **13.** 16 cartons **14.** Rs. 100 **15.** Rs. 1920 **16.** Rs. 675

17. 20 m. **18.** 6 m. **19.** 45 metres **20.** 27 cartons

21. 1710 litres **22.** Rs. 18 **23.** $2\frac{1}{12}$ hrs. **24.** 99 HP.

D. **25.** No. **26.** No. **27.** No. **28.** yes

PRACTICE EXERCISES 14 *(Page 82)*

A. **1.** yes **2.** No

B. **3.** 100, 250, 5, 2500 **4.** 2, 12, 4, 24

C. **5.** Rs. $78\frac{2}{5}$, Rs. $65\frac{1}{3}$, Rs. 49, Rs. $43\frac{5}{9}$ **6.** 60 days

7. 120 men **8.** 24 days **9.** 24 minutes **10.** 5 ladies

11. 2·5 kg. **12.** 36 days **13.** 10 days **14.** 120 men **15.** $3\frac{3}{4}$ hours

PRACTICE EXERCISES 15 (Page 85)

A. **1.** Rs. 52·50 **2.** 21 labourers **3.** 4 days **4.** 45 days

B. **5.** 300 sq. m. **6.** 45 km. **7.** 60 men **8.** 56 pages

9. 1000 men **10.** Rs. 9 **11.** $5\frac{1}{4}$ hrs. **12.** 9 days

PRACTICE EXERCISES 16 (Page 90)

A. **1.** less **2.** more **3.** less **4.** more

B. **5.** $\frac{5}{14}$ of the work **6.** 4 days **7.** 24 days **8.** $4\frac{4}{9}$ days **9.** 24 days

10. 6 days **11.** 60 days **12.** 30 days **13.** 10 days ; A = 30 days ; B = 20 days C = 60 days

14. $12\frac{4}{5}$ days **15.** $2\frac{2}{3}$ hours **16.** 12 hrs. **17.** 48 hrs.

18. A = 75 days, B = 50 days **19.** *(a)* 12 hrs. *(b)* 12 hrs. **20.** 30 days

21. A = Rs. 5, B = Rs. 3, C = Re. 1

22. A = 50 days, B = 50 days **23.** at 9 : 36 a.m.

PRACTICE EXERCISES 17 *(Page 94)*

A. **1.** Time × Speed **2.** Distance ÷ Speed **3.** Distance ÷ Time

B. **4.** 10 m/sec. **5.** 105 m/sec **6.** 125 m/sec **7.** 320 m/sec

C. **8.** 54 km./hr. **9.** 90 km./hr. **10.** 18 km./hr. **11.** 720 km./hr.

D. **12.** 3 km. **13.** 1740 km. **14.** 9 km./hr. **15.** 9 seconds

16. 17 km. **17.** 16·5 km./hr. **18.** 6 km. **19.** 150 metres

20. 1 hr. 40 min. **21.** 2 km. **22.** *(a)* 18 sec. *(b)* 54 sec.

23. 54. seconds **24.** 7 : 39 a.m. **25.** 60 km./hr. **26.** *(a)* 12·5 km./hr. *(b)* 1 hr. 12 min. *(c)* 1 hr. 48 min. *(d)* 2 hrs. 52 min 48 sec.

PRACTICE EXERCISES 18 *(page 98)*

A. **1.** sum **2.** difference

B. **3.** 36 sec. **4.** 10 min 12 sec. **5.** 360 metres **6.** 385 metres

7. at 10 : 45 a.m. **8.** at 12 : 30 p.m. **9.** 12 seconds **10.** 1 min.

11. at 2 : 00 a.m. in the night **12.** 80 metres

PRACTICE EXERCISES 19. *(Page 101)*

A. **1.** *x* out of a hundred, i.e. $\frac{x}{100}$

B. **2.** 200 **3.** 10,000 **4.** 500 **5.** 200

C. **6.** $\frac{17}{25}$ **7.** 7 : 50 **8.** ·06 **9.** $\frac{3}{1000}$

D. **10.** 40% **11.** 93·75% **12.** 18% **13.** 100·3% **14.** $2\frac{1}{12}\%$

E. **15.** Rs. 7500 **16.** 400 grams, 360 grams, 240 grams **17.** Rs. 85737·50 **18.** 20%

19. $16\frac{2}{3}\%$ **20.** $33\frac{1}{3}\%$ **21.** 91·6% **22.** Rs. 2·50

23. 23·64 ml ; 0·99 ml ; 5·16 ml ; 0·21 ml

24. Rs. 800 **25.** 63·5% **26.** $46\frac{2}{3}\%$ **27.** 40500, 31500

PRACTICE EXERCISES 20. *(Page 106)*

A. **1.** Income tax is the tax that a citizen has to pay to the government according to his/her income.

2. see page 102 **3.** see page 103

B. **4.** Rs. 1100 **5.** Rs. 6000 **6.** Rs. 35000

C. **7.** Rs. 6000 **8.** Rs. 630·50 **9.** Rs. 200 **10.** Rs. 308

11. Rs. 600 **12.** Rs. 600 **13.** 8% **14.** Rs. 240

15. 40% **16.** Rs. 6423·90 **17.** 12·6% **18.** $16\frac{2}{3}\%$

19. Rs. 20 **20.** Rs. 1256·85 **21.** 28%

PRACTICE EXERCISES 21. *(Page 112)*

A. **1.** SP – CP **2.** CP – SP **3.** gain × 100 **4.** loss × 100 **5.** gain%

6. loss% **7.** gain% **8.** loss% **9.** SP > CP **10.** CP > SP

B. **11.** 10% **12.** Rs. 9350 **13.** $12\frac{1}{2}\%$ **14.** $18\frac{1}{3}\%$ loss **15.** Rs. 75900

16. Rs. 731 17. Rs. 690 18. Rs. 3360 19. 50% 20. Rs. 62.50
21. 4% 22. 4% 23. Rs. 55 each 24. Rs. 1056 25. Rs. 250
26. 1% loss 27. Wheat = Rs. 6·87 per kg. ; Rice = Rs. 8·75 per kg. ; $1\frac{11}{25}$% loss
28. Rs. 1350 ; 35% 29. 25% 30. Rs. 7000 31. 25%
32. Rs. 15 33. Rs. 750 34. $3\frac{1}{8}$% 35. Rs. 7·20 36. Rs. 375
37. $\frac{5}{6}$% loss 38. Rs. 6·026 39. Rs. 1035 40. $8\frac{1}{3}$% gain

PRACTICE EXERCISES 22 *(Page 119)*

A. 1. $\frac{P \times \text{rate} \times \text{time}}{100}$ 2. $T = \frac{S.I. \times 100}{P \times T}$ 3. $P = \frac{S.I. \times 100}{R \times T}$
4. $R = \frac{S.I. \times 100}{P \times T}$ 5. A= P + S.I. 6. S.I. = A – P

B. 7. Rs. 711·25 8. Rs. 516 9. Rs. 972 10. Rs. 90 11. Rs $\frac{xyz}{100}$

C. 12. Rs. 800 13. Rs 7300 14. Rs. 900 15. Rs 3600 16. Rs. 9540

D. 17. $3\frac{1}{2}$ years 18. $4\frac{1}{2}$ years 19. $4\frac{1}{6}$ years 20. 2 years

E. 21. 14% 22. 10% 23. $12\frac{1}{2}$ % 24. $13\frac{1}{3}$%
25. 4%

F. 26. Rs. 800 27. P=Rs. 2600, R=12%
28. Rs. 4000, Rs. 2000 29. Rs. 1400 30. Rs. 2400, 10%
31. Rs. 8000, Rs. 4000 32. Rs. 1200, Rs. 550 33. 16%
34. 10% 35. Rs 1050 36. 9% 37. 8%

MISCELLANEOUS EXERCISES II *(Page 121)*

A. 1. yes 2. no 3. no 4. yes 5. no 6. yes 7. yes, yes
8. yes 9. yes 10. no

B. Answers not required for Question 11.

C. 12. (i) 1 (ii) $a^{2(xy+yz+zx)}$ 13. 45 kg. 14. 25 days
15. 21 men 16. $3\frac{3}{7}$ hours 17. A=30 days, B=20 days, C=60 days
18. 12 hours 19. 6 km 20. $14\frac{2}{3}$ seconds 21. 20% 22. $28\frac{4}{7}$%
23. 0.18m^3 24. 25% 25. $16\frac{2}{3}$ % 26. Rs. 760 27. Rs. 240
28. Rs. 1240 and Rs. 1360

ANSWERS – II

PRACTICE EXERCISES 23 *(Page 126)*

A. **1.** $3a^4b^2c$ **2.** $180x^4y^2z^2$ **3.** $\frac{-1}{2}p^3qr$ **4.** $12x^3y^2z^2$

5. $-8a^4b^4c^4$ **6.** $-3x^4y^5z^5$ **7.** $\frac{1}{10}x^2y^2z^2$ **8.** $3x^4y^4z^4$

B. **9.** $2\frac{2}{3}x^5y^4z^7$, 10368 **10.** $2x^9y^9$, 1024 **11.** $-2x^3y^4z^3$, -162

12. $\frac{-8}{7}x^4y^4$, $-18\frac{2}{7}$ **13.** $\frac{2}{5}a^3b^3c^3$, 400 **14.** $x^4y^4z^3$, $\frac{1}{82944}$ **C.** **16.** $-224x^{14}a^7$

D. **17.** No. **18.** No

PRACTICE EXERCISES 24 *(Page 128)*

A. **1.** $15x^2 + 4xy - 35y^2$ **2.** $6x^4 + 11x^2y^2 + 3y^4$ **3.** $x^3 - \frac{5x^2y}{4} - \frac{4xy^2}{5} + y^3$

4. $28l^2 + 23lm - 15m^2$ **5.** $3m^3 + 7m^2n + 2mn^2$ **6.** $6a^2 + 13ab + 6b^2$

7. $2a^2 - ab - 15b^2$ **8.** $6x^5 - 7x^4 + 2x^3$ **9.** $\frac{3x^4y}{5} - x^2y^3 - x^3y^2 + \frac{5xy^4}{3}$

B. **10.** $10x^3 - 27x^2 + 36x - 27$ **11.** $4x^3 - 4x^2 - 7x + 12$

12. $3x^3 + 19x^2 - 38x + 16$ **13.** $9x^4 - x^3 - 21x^2 + 4x - 60$

14. $5x^4 - 17x^3 + 14x^2 - 35x + 49$ **15.** $x^3 + y^3$

C. **16.** $2x^4 - 9x^3 - 47x^2 + 68x - 32$ **17.** $x^4 - 9x^3 + 25x^2 - 17x - 24$

18. $6x^4 + 9x^3 - 28x^2 + 41x - 28$ **19.** $2x^2 - 3y^2 + xy + 7x + 23y - 30$

20. $5x^4 - 16x^3 + 37x^2 - 65x + 42$

D. **21.** $24x^3 + 38x^2 - 37x - 60$

22. $a^2b + ab^2 + a^2c + ac^2 + b^2c + bc^2 + 2abc$

23. $-4x^2 + 21x - 31$ **24.** $-12x^2 + 31x - 16$

E. **25.** -18 **26.** 7 **27.** 689

PRACTICE EXERCISES 25 (Page 134)

A. **1.** $x^2 + y^2 + 2xy$ **2.** $x^2 + y^2 - 2xy$ **3.** $(x + y)(x - y)$

B. **4.** $4x^2 + 9y^2 + 6xy$ **5.** $\frac{9x^2}{4} + 36y^2 - 9xy$ **6.** $(x + y)(x - y)$

7. $a^2 + \frac{1}{a^2} + 2$ **8.** $a^2 + \frac{1}{a^2} - 2$ **9.** $(a + \frac{1}{a})(a - \frac{1}{a})$

10. $\frac{x^2}{4} + y^2 + xy$ **11.** $\frac{x^2}{4} + y^2 - xy$ **12.** $(\frac{x}{2} + \frac{y}{3})(\frac{x}{2} - \frac{y}{3})$

13. $16a^2 + 9b^2 + 24ab$ **14.** $9x^2 + 49y^2 - 42xy$ **15.** $(2a + 5b)(2a - 5b)$

16. 11664 **17.** 8464 **18.** 1200

C. **19.** $9x^2 + 16y^2 + 24xy$ **20.** $4p^2 + 25q^2 - 20pq$ **21.** $9c^2 + 16d^2 + 24cd$

22. $25m^2 + 36n^2 - 60mn$ **23.** $\frac{a^2}{25} + \frac{b^2}{4} + \frac{ab}{5}$ **24.** $m^2 + \frac{1}{m^2} - 2$

25. $m^2 - \frac{1}{m^2}$ **26.** $x^2 - 25$ **27.** $\frac{x^2}{y^2} - \frac{y^2}{x^2}$

28. $\frac{9x^2}{16} - \frac{4y^2}{9}$ **29.** $9x^2 - 4y^2$ **30.** $z^2 - \frac{1}{z^2}$

D. **31.** 7396 **32.** 324 **33.** 4900

34. 3025 **35.** 400 **36.** 23

37. 527 **38.** 79, 6239 **39.** 27, 727

40. 11, 119 **41.** $440\frac{440}{441}$ **42.** $a \times \sqrt{a^2 + 4}$

E. **43.** 6400 **44.** 9831 **45.** 2451

46. 1480 **47.** 2000 **48.** 289

49. 64 + *(Read × in place of +)*

PRACTICE EXERCISES 26 (Page 137)

A. **1.** see page 133 **2.** see page 133 **3.** see page 133

4. see page 134 **5.** see page 134

B. **6.** $2 \times x \times x \times y$ **7.** $3 \times x \times x \times y$ **8.** $5 \times x \times y \times y$

9. $2 \times 3 \times a \times a \times a \times b \times b \times b \times b \times b$ **10.** $7 \times x \times x \times y \times y$

11. $-5 \times 3 \times 2 \times m \times m \times n \times n \times n$ **12.** $3 \times 5 \times y \times y \times y \times y \times z \times z \times z$

13. $2 \times 7 \times a \times a \times b \times b \times b \times b$

14. $-2 \times 2 \times 2 \times 2 \times a \times a \times a \times b \times b \times c \times c \times c$

15. $11 \times 5 \times 2 \times m \times m \times n \times n$ **16.** $-5 \times 5 \times l \times l \times l \times m \times m \times m$

17. $-3 \times 2 \times 2 \times y \times y \times y \times y \times z \times z \times z$

C. **18.** $5(x + 3)$ **19.** $n(2n - 3)$ **20.** $5xy(x + y)$

21. $2x^2(3 - 4xy)$ **22.** $2x^3(x^2 + 6)$ **23.** $2a(2a^2 - 1)$

24. $7m^3(2m^4 - 1)$ **25.** $2xyz(-7xy - 4z)$ **26.** $5m^4(3m^2 - 1)$

D. 27. $x(9x - 1 - y^2)$ **28.** $(a + b)(c + a)$ **29.** $(a + b)(x^2 + y^2)$

30. $(m + 7)(m + 7)$ **31.** $(a + b)(m + n)$ **32.** $(p + q)(x + y)$

33. $(a + b)(x^2 + y^2)$ **34.** $(x + y)(4 - a)$ **35.** $(a - b^2)(a^2 + 1)$ **36.** $(1 - m)(n^2 - lm)$

E. 37. $(2x + 3y)(2x - 3y)$ **38.** $(4a + 3b)(4a - 3b)$

39. $(4m - n)\ 2m + n)$ **40.** $8x^2(2xy + 1)(2xy - 1)$ **41.** $(2x + 3)(2x - 3)$

42. $(5a + 4b)(5a - 4b)$ **43.** $(6x + a - b)(6x - a + b)$ **44.** $(x + y)(x - y)(x^2 + y^2)$

45. $(x^2 + 1)(x^2 + 1)$ **46.** $(2m - 1)^2$ **47.** $(x + y + z)(x - y - z)$

48. $(a^2 + 4)(a + 2)(a - 2)$ **49.** $(a - b + 3)(a - b - 3)$ **50.** $(2x + 3y + 5)(2x + 3y - 5)$

PRACTICE EXERCISES 27 *(Page 140)*

5. $x = 6$ **6.** $x = 5$ **7.** $x = -2$ **8.** $x = 4$

9. $x = \frac{3}{2}$ **10.** $x = \frac{11}{10}$ **11.** $x = 19\frac{1}{2}$

12. $x = \frac{9}{20}$ **13.** $x = 2\frac{3}{7}$ **14.** $x = -9$ **15.** $y = \frac{21}{20}$

16. $x = 8$ **17.** $x = 5$ **18.** $x = 6$ **19.** $y = \frac{-9}{20}$

20. $x = 3\frac{1}{5}$ **21.** $x = 38$ **22.** $x = 1\frac{1}{8}$ **23.** $x = -9$

24. $x = 1{\cdot}5$ **25.** $x = -5\frac{3}{7}$ **26.** $x = -1$ **27.** $x = 4$

PRACTICE EXERCISES 28 *(Page 144)*

1. $(x - 7)$ yrs ; $(x + 9)$ yrs. **2.** $x - y$ **3.** $10b + a$ **4.** 15, 45

5. 9*m* ; 23*m* ; 23*m* **6.** 2 **7.** Amita = 10 yrs, Anita = 7 yrs

8. $\frac{9}{5}$ **9.** Sohan = 10 yrs, his father = 30 years

10. 12 **11.** 33, 36 **12.** 33*m* ; 38*m* 13. chair = Rs. 60 ; table = Rs. 80

14. 42 15. 26 **16.** 36 **17.** 720 **18.** Length 15 metres, Breadth 10 metres

19. Renu = 32 years, brother = 8 years **20.** 30 kg.

PRACTICE EXERCISES 29 *(Page 150)*

A. 1. three **2.** three **3.** three **4.** six **5.** three **6.** its interior

7. boundary **8.** interior and the triangle itself 9. its exterior

B. 12. (a) A figure having three angles

(b) Δ's interior along with Δ itself

(c) A meeting-point of two lines that form an angle
(d) The part of the plane marked by points in which all the points are enclosed by Δ
(e) The part of the plane marked by points in which all the points are not enclosed by Δ
(f) The sides of Δ mark its boundary

13. ΔPOS, ΔQOR, ΔSOR, ΔPOQ, ΔSQR, ΔPQS, ΔPQR, ΔRSP
14. Isosceles, equilateral, scalene **15.** acute, obtuse, right
16. (a) interior (b) on (c) exterior (d) triangular region

MISCELLANEOUS EXERCISES III *(Page 145)*

A. **1.** yes **2.** no **3.** yes **4.** no **5.** no

B. **6.** $\frac{1}{5}x^5y^6z^2$ **7.** $-\frac{5}{3}x^4y^3 + \frac{4}{3}x^3y^4$ **8.** $\frac{15}{2}x^2y^5 + 2x^3y^4$

9. $a^4 - 24a$ **10.** $-12x^2 + 55x - 50$ **11.** $4x^4 + 3x^2y^2 - 10y^4$

12. $9m^2 + 16n^2 - 24mn$ **13.** $y^2 + z^2 - 2yz$ **14.** $z^2 + \frac{1}{z^2} - 2$

15. $x^2 - 196$ **16.** $x^4 - y^2z^2$ **17.** $\frac{x^2}{9} - \frac{y^2}{25}$

18. 6384 **19.** $(a + b)x^2 + y^2$ **20.** $2(x - 3y)(2x - 6y - 3)$

21. $y = -1\frac{1}{20}$ **22.** $y = 2$ **23.** 32, 36

PRACTICE EXERCISES 30 *(Page 153)*

A. **1.** 180° **2.** 90° **3.** 180° **4.** No **5.** Yes **6.** No **7.** Yes

B. **8.** 60° **9.** *(a)* Yes *(b)* No *(c)* Yes *(d)* Yes *(e)* Yes *(f)* No

10. ∠BAL = 20°, ∠ACL = 20°, ∠CAL = 70° **11.** 72°, 72°, 36° **12.** 30°, 30°

13. right-angled, 90°, 45°, 45° **14.** obtuse-angled, 120°, 30°, 30° **15.** 45°, 60°, 75°

16. ∠B= 30°, ∠1= 30°, ∠2= 110° **17.** 360° **18.** 360° **19.** 540° **20.** 720°

PRACTICE EXERCISE 31 *(Page 156)*

A. **1.** *(a)* It is formed when one side of a triangle is produced
(b) It is formed outside the triangle as an adjacent supplementary angle.
2. *(a)* It is called interior adjacent angle **3.** angles other than the interior adjacent angle

B. **4.** *(a)* 180° *(b)* ∠A + ∠B *(c)* adjacent interior angle *(d)* interior opposite angles
5. *(a)* ∠x *(b)* ∠y *(c)* ∠ACB *(d)* ∠ABC *(e)* ∠A, ∠ABC
(f) ∠A, ∠BCA *(g)* ∠A+∠ABC *(h)* ∠A + ∠BCA
6. ∠c = 45°, ∠x = 120°, ∠y = 135°, ∠z = 105°, ∠A + ∠B + ∠C = 180°, ∠x + ∠y + ∠z = 4rt ∠s
7. *(a)* ∠x = ∠B + ∠C *(b)* ∠y= ∠A + ∠B *(c)* ∠z = ∠A+ ∠C
(d) ∠z = 360°– (∠x + ∠y) *(e)* ∠y= 360° – (∠y + ∠z) *(f)* ∠y = 360° – (∠x + ∠z)

PRACTICE EXERCISE 32 *(Page 158)*

A. **1.** *(a)* No *(b)* Yes *(c)* Yes *(d* Yes

2. (a) $AB < (BC + CA)$ (b) $(AB + BC) > CA$ (c) $(AC + BC) > AB$ (d) $(AB + AC) > BC$

3. (a) false (b) true (c) false (d true (e) false

4. (a) $(PA + PB) > AB$ (b) $AB < (AQ + BQ)$ 5. AD

PRACTICE EXERCISE 33 *(Page 160)*

A. 1. 40°, 40° 2. 66°, 66° 3. 60° 4. $\angle a = 110°$, $\angle b = 110°$ 5. equilateral

6. (a) $\angle$s opposite to equal sides (b) *corresponding* $\angle$s (c) corresponding angles (d) equals of equal angles (e) $\angle 1 = \angle 2$ (f) *equals subtracted from equals*

7. $\angle Q > \angle R$; yes ; the larger side has the larger angle opposite to it.

8. $\angle C = 80°$; $AC > BC$; It is opposite to the larger angle ; The same as above.

9. (a) yes (angles opposite to equal sides) (b) yes (angles opposite to equal sides) (c) yes (sum of equal angles) (d) No, $\because \angle 1 \neq \angle 3$ and $\angle 2 \neq \angle 4$

PRACTICE EXERCISE 34 *(Page 165)*

A 1. Wheel, any coin, ball 2. H, M, A 3. isosceles and equilateral

4. square, rectangle and circle

B. 5. Its bisector 6. along its rt. bisector 7. (a) yes (b) yes (c) yes

8. (a) Yes (b) two 9. (a) yes (b) no 10. yes, common chord

11. three 12. 8 metres 13. 1·5 metres 14. *Read three right triangles*

PRACTICE EXERCISE 35 *(Page 168)*

A. 1. vertices 2. pass, concurrent 3. centroid 4. (a) interior (b) *interior*

5. centroid 6. (a) No (b) No (c) *yes* 7. (a) *yes* (b) *yes* (c) *yes* 9. Yes

PRACTICE EXERCISE 36 *(Page 169)*

A. 1. vertices, opposite 2. orthocentre 3. one 4. outside

5. (a) yes (b) yes (c) *yes* (d) yes 6. yes ; R is the orthocentre

8. they can 9. (a) yes (b) yes (c) yes

PRACTICE EXERCISE 37 *(Page 172)*

A. 1. perpendicular bisector 2. equal 3. rt $\angle$s 4. concurrent

5. circumcentre 6. equidistant 7. circum-radius

B. 8. they are equal 9. read the hint 10. yes 11. yes

PRACTICE EXERCISE 38 *(Page 174)*

A. 1. line segment, equal 2. in-centre 3. equidistant, sides 4. interior

B. 6. (a) yes (b) yes (c) yes 7. all three are yes 8. follow the hint.

PRACTICE EXERCISE 39 *(Page 179)*

A. 1. four cases 2. SSS 3. SAS 4. ASA 5. hyp. side

A. 6. SAS 7. SSS 8. ASA 9. Hypotenuse, side

10. Draw the besector of the angle contained by the equal sides. Then prove Δ**s** $\cong$ by SAS

11. do as in Q 10 12. Prove the Δ**s** $\cong$ by SSS 13. Use the hypotenuise , side case of $\cong$ cys

14. Prove the Δs $\cong$ by SAS method 15. Follow the hint and prove Δs $\cong$ ASA method

16. Follow the hint 17. Prove the *rt* Δ**s** $\cong$ 18. Follow the hint

PRACTICE EXERCISE 40 *(Page 183)*

A. 1. four, four 2. two, intersect 3. four, non-collinear 4. vertex

5. arm 6. common 7. arm

B. 8. four, P, Q, R, S 9. four; PQ, QR, RS, PS 10. four, $\angle P$, $\angle Q$, $\angle R$, $\angle S$

11. two, PR, SQ 12. four; $\angle P$, $\angle Q$; $\angle Q$, $\angle R$; $\angle R$, $\angle S$; $\angle S$, $\angle P$,

13. four PQ, QR, RS; RS, PS; PS, PQ 14. two; PQ, RS; QR, PS

15. two; $\angle P$,$\angle R$ and $\angle Q$, $\angle S$

C. 16. see page 179 17. see page 179 18. see page 179 19. see page 180

20. see page 180 21. see page 181 22. see page 179

23. line-segment joining its opposite vertices 24. four triangles 25. 4*rt* $\angle$s

PRACTICE EXERCISES 41 *(Page 188)*

A. 1. yes 2. yes 3. yes 4. yes 5. No 6. No 7. yes

B. 8. square, rhombus 9. rectangle, square 10. square, rhombus, rectangle, parallelogram

11. trapezium

C. 12. trapezium 13. 100° each 14. 45°, 75°, 105°, 135° 15. 85°, 85°

16. 90° 17. 70°, 70°, 70° 18. $\angle C = 140°$, $\angle D = 120°$

19. Its two non-parallel sides are equal in length 20. 4rt $\angle$s

PRACTICE EXERCISES 42 *(Page 193)*

A. 1. 100°, 80°, 100° 2. each angle = 90°, rectangle 3. 60°, 120°, 60°, 120° 4. 18 cm.

5. 8 cm., 6 cm. 6. 10 cm., 15 cm. 7. Draw the diagonal and prove the Δs $\cong$ by sss method

8. No ; because diagonals of a parallelogram bisect each other.

9. $\angle A$ and $\angle C$ are opposite $\angle$s of the parallelogram which are equal

$\angle 1$, $\angle 3$ are *halves of equal angles* In Δs ADF, BCE

$\angle 2$, $\angle 4$ are *halves of equal angles* AD = BC *(opp. sides)*

$\angle 1$, $\angle 5$ are *corresponding angles* $\angle B = \angle D$ *(opp. $\angle$s)*

$\angle 3$, $\angle 5$ are *alternate angles* $\angle 2 = \angle 5$ *(Both = $\angle 1$)*

$\therefore$ Δs are $\cong$ $\therefore$ AF = CE

$\angle 5 = \angle 4$ as both are equal to $\angle 3$, $\therefore$ BE = BC

10. rhombus, kite **11.** *(a)* yes ; more than one case *(b)* yes, each diagonal bisects the angles it passed through *(c)* yes

12. *(a)* No *(b)* yes *(c)* yes *(d)* No

PRACTICE EXERCISES 43 *(Page 196)*

A. **1.** yes **2.** yes **3.** No **4.** No **5.** yes **6.** yes **7.** yes

B. **8.** square or rectangle **9.** Follow the hint **10.** 60°, 120°, 60°, 120°

11. *(a)* Diagonals of parallelogram bisect each other *(b)* alternate $\angle$s *(c)* vert. opp. $\angle$s *(d)* ASA ; yes *o* bisects *xy* **14.** 60°, 120°, 60°, 120° **16.** Its sides are 4 cm., 6 cm.

PRACTICE EXERCISES 44 *(Page 201)*

A. **1.** boundry **2.** circumference **3.** line-segment **4.** centre
5. arc **6.** chord **7.** boundary **8.** interior plane

B. **9.** 5 cm. **10.** 3·5 cm. **11.** By folding into four quadrants **12.** yes

13. By marking the boundary of the coin on paper **14.** exterior **15.** concentric circles

16. The interior of the circle and the circle itself together make its circular region

18. APB, AQB **19.** $1\frac{22}{7}$ **20.** Either of them = 90°, so they are equal

21. right **22.** obtuse **23.** acute **24.** O^{ce} is $\frac{22}{7}$ times the diameter

PRACTICES EXERCISES 45 *(Page 208)*

All questions are constructions to be drawn

MISCELLANEOUS EXERCISES IV *(Page 209)*

A. **1.** six **2.** no **3.** only one **4.** 180° **5.** 4rt. $\angle$s **6.** Triangular Region
7. Quadrilateral Region **8.** Circular Region

B. **9.** Triangle with all its sides of different lengths **10.** see page 183 **11.** see page 184

12. triangle with two of its' sides equal **13.** a trapezium with its non-parallel sides equal

14. see page 197

C. **15.** Prove it by drawing a line through the vertex parallel to the base

16. Divide it into two Δs by joining a diagonal **17.** 120° **18.** 8 cm.

19. 3 metres **20.** $\angle ABD = \angle ACD$ as they are sums of equal angles

D. **21.** A convex quadrilateral has each of its angles smaller than 180°. But a concave quadrilateral has each of its angles larger than 180°.

22. a rhombus has none of its angles = 90° but a square has each of its ∠s = 90

23. An ordinary trapezium has its non-parallel sides unequal but an isosceles trapezium has them to be equal.

E. **24.** yes **25.** yes **26.** yes **27.** yes

F. **28, 29, 30** are all constructions

PRACTICE EXERCISES 46 *(Page 214)*

A. **1.** Base × Height **2.** Area ÷ Height **3.** Area ÷ Base

B. **4.** 540 sq. cm. **5.** 44·8 sq. cm. **6.** 200 metres
7. 0·29 m **8.** Rs. 3937·50 **9.** 9 cm **10.** 5·85 cm. **11.** 20 cm.
12. 4 cm. **13.** Rs. 507 **14.** 2·6 cm., 4·26 cm. **15.** 4 cm.

PRACTICE EXERCISES 47 *(Page 218)*

A. **1.** $\frac{1}{2}$ × Base × Height **2.** 2 × Area ÷ Height **3.** 2 × Area ÷ Base
4. $\frac{1}{2}$ × Height (sum of the parallel sides) **5.** 2 × Area ÷ Base

B. **6.** 14 sq. cm. **7.** 50 sq. cm. **8.** 200 metres **9.** 108·5 sq. cm.
10. 180 m **11.** 152·88 sq. cm. **12.** 260 sq. cm. **13.** 48 sq. cm.
14. 768 sq. cm. **15.** 200 sq. cm. **16.** 24 sq. cm. **17.** 390 sq. cm.
18. 23 cm. **19.** 88 sq. cm. **20.** 24 cm.

C. **21.** 288 sq. cm. **22.** 400 sq. cm. **23.** 2·25 sq. cm. **24.** 40 sq. cm.
25. 20 sq. cm. **26.** 17·5 sq. cm. **27.** Rs. 15750 **28.** 8·2 metres
29. 32 cm, 48 cm. **30.** 10 cm. **31.** 180 sq. cm. **32.** 488 sq. cm.

PRACTICE EXERCISES 48 *(Page 222)*

A. **1.** $(\text{side})^3$ **2.** Length × Breadth × Height **3.** Area ÷ (Breadth × Height)
4. Area ÷ (Length × Height) **5.** Area ÷ (Length × Breadth)

B. **6.** 150 cu. cm. **7.** 64 cubes **8.** 1 : 8 **9.** 5·4 kg. **10.** 112500 cu. m.
11. 540 soap-cakes **12.** 90 chalk-sticks **13.** 45000000 litres **14.** 10 cm.
15. 1876 cu. cm. **16.** 729 cu. cm. **17.** 4500 cu. m. **18.** 78.75 cu. m., Rs. 225
19. 2m, 6m ; Rs. 120

PRACTICE EXERCISES 49 *(Page 226)*

A. **1.** Height × 2 (Length + Breadth) **2.** 2 ($lb + bh + lh$)

B. **3.** 340 sq. cm. **4.** 28·2 sq. metres, Rs. 282 **5.** 486 sq. cm. **6.** 148 sq. cm.
7. 168 sq. m. **8.** Rs. $276\frac{2}{3}$ **9.** 486 sq. m. **10.** 216 : 59
11. 2400 matchboxes **12.** 0·04 m **13.** Rs. 7560 **14.** 80 desks **15.** 96 cm.

MISCELLANEOUS EXERCISES V *(Page 230)*

A. **1.** oblique **2.** square **3.** unequal **4.** non-parallel **5.** rhombus and square
6. six, eight, twelve **7.** equal **8.** graph
9. rectangle, horizontally **10.** west to east, vertical

B. **11.** 5 cm. **12.** 9·3 cm. **13.** Rs. 312·48 **14.** 69 sq. cm. **15.** 10 cm.
16. 210 toys **17.** 4248 cu. cm. **18.** Rs. 736

OBJECTIVE TESTS

SET I

A. **1.** yes **2.** yes **3.** No **4.** yes **5.** yes

B. **6.** *(b)* **7.** $\frac{-3}{5}$ **8.** *(c)* **9.** *(a)* **10.** *(c)*

C. **11.** additive **12.** multiplicative **13.** larger **14.** nearer **15.** nearer

D. **16.** numerator **17.** denominator **18.** unity **19.** reciprocal

SET II

A. **1.** gain **2.** loss **3.** CP **4.** gain

B. **5.** *(b)* **6.** *(b)* **7.** *(c)* **8.** *(b)*

C. **9.** variable **10.** transposition **11.** amount **12.** monomial

D. **13.** marked price **14.** discount **15.** selling price **16.** successive discounts

E. **17.** *(a)* $(a + b)(a - b)$ *(b)* 9 **18.** *(a)* $(a + b)(a + b)$ *(b)* 49
19. *(a)* $(a - b)(a - b)$ *(b)* 16

SET III

A. **1.** true **2.** true **3.** false **4.** true

B. **5.** equal **6.** centroid **7.** at the right vertex

C. **8.** 2·5% **9.** 24 days **10.** 8 times **11.** $2x$
12. horizontal axis **13.** pictograph **14.** in-centre **15.** $H \times 2(l + b)$

SET IV

A. **1.** *(c)* **2.** *(b)* **3.** *(c)*

B. **4.** *(b)* **5.** *(c)* **6.** *(b)* **7.** *(b)*

C. **8.** *(c)* **9.** *(b)* **10.** *(b* **11.** *(b)* **12.** *(b)*

D. **13.** *(b)* **14.** *(c)* **15.** *(b)* **16.** *(c)*

E. **17.** *(b)* **18.** *(a)* **19.** *(b)* **20.** *(a)*

B. **21.** yes **22.** yes **23.** no **24.** yes